THE CONTRA COSTA COUNTY
BREEDING BIRD ATLAS

BREEDING BIRD ATLAS
OF
CONTRA
COSTA
COUNTY

STEVEN A. GLOVER

EDITED BY HELLER STANTON
ILLUSTRATED BY DANA GARDNER
BOOK DESIGN BY ELLIS MYERS
MAPS BY RUSTY SCALF

MOUNT DIABLO AUDUBON SOCIETY

Library of Congress Cataloging-in-Publication Data:
Glover, Steven A., 1968-
Editor: Stanton, Heller, 1967-
The Contra Costa County Breeding Bird Atlas
        p. cm.
Includes bibliographic references and index (p.)
1. Birds – California – Contra Costa County. 2. Bird populations – California – Contra Costa County – geographical distribution. 3. Contra Costa County (California) – Natural history. I. Title.

ISBN: 978-0-615-30194-5

Printed in the United States of America, using soy-based inks and recycled paper, by Alonzo Printing Company, Inc., Hayward, California, certified as a Green Business by the Alameda County Green Business Program.

Published 2009 by:
Mount Diablo Audubon Society
P.O. Box 53
Walnut Creek, CA 94596

To my mom and my sister,
for everything,

To Misty,
my friend forever, for putting up with this project for so long,

To Ashley, Morgan, and Sydney,
the greatest nieces on the planet,

To Luke Cole,
Perhaps the smartest person I have ever known, but more importantly also the most compassionate.
I miss you, my friend.

and,

To Pennie, Courtney, and Cooper,
for providing me with an amazing future. I will be there soon.

PEREGRINE FALCON

CONTENTS

ILLUSTRATIONS

* All illustrations are by Dana Gardner. All are original for this publication except for the three marked. Those first appeared in *At Home in the Big Woods*, by Nancy Overcott, Taxon Media 2002.

LIST OF TABLES

INTRODUCTION

This atlas, both in terms of its founding and its publishing, was long overdue. Fieldwork for most of the Bay Area atlas projects had already been completed before this one was even founded, and several of them had already been published. After years of encouragement, primarily from George Finger and Bob Richmond, the Contra Costa County Breeding Bird Atlas was finally founded in late 1997, with fieldwork commencing in the spring of 1998. That fieldwork was complete in the summer of 2002. The published atlas that you now hold in your hands should have been available years ago. The volunteers who patiently gave up their valuable time deserved to see the results of their efforts far sooner and for this I can offer no excuses. I will never be able to thank them properly for their efforts but I deeply hope that this book can come close to matching the high standards achieved during the fieldwork.

That the native habitats of Contra Costa County are being developed at breakneck pace is beyond doubt. It is up to the individual to decide for himself the merits of recent land-planning. The fact that this book exists at all is a clear indication of how most of those involved with this atlas feel. And yet, if forced to summarize the purpose of this project, it seems most fitting, if a bit clichéd, to say that at its core it is designed to speak for the birds and for the habitats, some deeply imperiled, upon which they depend.

We can only hope that this book is read by more than just the choir. Numerous consulting firms, many of which have done significant amounts of work in Contra Costa County, contributed to the publishing of this atlas. We fervently hope that it is utilized by the numerous agencies which are responsible for planning decisions.

In hindsight, it is unfortunate in many ways that a cooperative, statewide atlas was never attempted, as numerous other states have done. The result of this is a plethora of single county atlases, nearly all of which are aimed at coastal counties with significant populations of birders. There are no atlas projects in sight for any of the Sierra counties, for example, and the Central Valley has hardly been touched. Each atlas, in a very real sense, is an island rather than a united whole which can provide a "big picture." Although it is certainly true that this published work offers a far higher level of detail for Contra Costa County than a statewide effort could, it stands as a piece of a puzzle that has yet to be united. Clearly what is called for is the kind of statewide cooperative effort for which county-obsessed California has never been known. A Central Valley-wide atlas project, if the will exists, would be a magnificent start. At some point perhaps there will be enough gaps filled in that a serious student of California bird status and distribution will be able to attempt a summary of completed atlas projects.

To use yet another cliché, this atlas is a mere snapshot in time. It was conducted during a random five-year period that is a mere blink of the eye in comparison with the history of the local avifauna. And yet, it was also conducted during a period of time that, even without the benefit of hindsight, was almost certainly one of the bellwether moments for the county, its open spaces, and its wildlife. The pace of development has been ratcheted up to a daredevil pace, with little obvious foresight or restraint.

Ideally, at some point in the future, another group of atlasers will take it upon themselves to found a new atlas project and the mountain of data produced during 1998 and 2002 will provide a priceless baseline for comparing the present Contra Costa County with a new, almost certainly more crowded one. The results, at least for some of the more vulnerable species, may prove disheartening. But there is room for optimism. The sky hasn't fallen yet and there is reason to believe that most species are more resilient to human-induced changes to the landscape than often given credit for, for despite the presence of well over one million human beings only a few breeding species have been lost.

This atlas is our humble gift to our bird neighbors, friends really.

Steve Glover
December 2008

ACKNOWLEDGEMENTS

Funding

The initial outlay for topographic maps and the printing of atlas forms was generously paid for by the Mt. Diablo Audubon Society, with additional contributions from two anonymous and generous donors.

The costs of publishing were covered through two sources. Fundraising birding trips to the Salton Sea, Arizona, Texas, and North Carolina, led by the author, raised about $13,000. Thank you to the following participants (those who braved each of the trips is marked with an *) for their camaraderie and generous donations: Alan Abel, Cheryl Abel, Judi Cooper*, Jerry Daniel, Theresa Daniel, Connie Diernisse, Bob Dunn*, Bingham Gibbs*, Larry Gibbs*, Joel Goldman, Barbara Hakala, Joyce Hansen*, Judy Johnstone, Eugenia Larson, Gary Larson, Bob Lewis, Hanno Lewis, Jean Lucken, Sara Matthews, Kathy Robertson, Maury Stern, and Lila Witt.

An unexpected suggestion for fundraising came from Malcolm Sproul, an employee at LSA Associates, Inc. and one of our more effective atlasers. Malcolm proposed asking local biological consulting firms for donations. He took it upon himself to send letters to numerous Northern California firms and was able to raise $6,000 donations from the following firms: Contra Costa County Community Development Department and John Kopchick, EDAW and Mark Winsor, Environmental Collaborative and Jim Martin, ESA and Tom Roberts, H. T. Harvey & Associates and Ron Duke, Ibis Environmental, Inc. and Sue Orloff, Jones & Stokes and Dan Airola, Live Oak Associates and Rick Hopkins, Monk & Associates and Geoff Monk, Swaim Biological Consulting and Karen Swaim, Sycamore Associates and Marylee Guinon, Wetlands Research Associates and Mike Josselyn, Zander Associates and Mike Zander, and Zentner & Zentner and John Zentner.

Cooperating Agencies

Audubon Canyon Ranch, California Department of Fish and Game, California State Parks Department, Contra Costa Water District, East Bay Municipal Utilities District, East Bay Regional Parks District, Lindsay Wildlife Museum, Mount Diablo Audubon Society, Naval Weapons Station Concord, PRBO Conservation Science, Save Mount Diablo.

Thank Yous

Not enough can be said for the efforts of the following generous souls, all of whom were crucial to the completion of the atlas and all of whom were volunteers in every sense of the word. To single out any of them is impossible, so they appear here in alphabetical order.

Steve Bobzien of the East Bay Regional Parks District alerted us to several significant nest records we would have otherwise missed.

William Bousman promptly answered numerous inquiries about nest records in the Bay Area. His knowledge of historical Bay Area bird records is unmatched. Additionally, many of the historical breeding records from the Western Foundation of Vertebrate Zoology which appear in the text are due to his research and generosity.

Betty Burridge, editor of the Sonoma County Breeding Bird Atlas, graciously offered encouragement and advice on the publishing of an atlas book.

Bill Chilson of the Contra Costa Water District provided valuable information about nesting birds at Los Vaqueros Reservoir.

Carla Cicero at the Museum of Vertebrate Zoology kindly provided assistance with tracking down nest records.

Rene Corado at the Western Foundation of Vertebrate Zoology provided important nest records.

Jeff Davis critically reviewed much of the text and willingly shared his incredible knowledge of all things ornithological (and botanical) whenever he was asked. His help has greatly improved this atlas and I cannot possibly thank him enough for his help.

George Finger provided enormous encouragement before, during and after the atlas project. It was he who perennially championed the idea of an atlas and, with Marjorie Plant, tirelessly atlased on Mt. Diablo.

Dana Gardner, world-famous bird artist whose work can be found in numerous books, including field guides to Costa Rica, Peru and Wallacea, generously created original artwork at scandalously low prices, a great coup for the atlas.

Dr. William Gilbert reviewed the Orange-crowned and Wilson's Warbler accounts and has improved them immensely.

Roger Hartwell of the East Bay Municipal Utilities District provided a veritable treasure trove of data involving waterfowl, raptor and owl nesting on watershed lands.

Scott Hein, a crack atlaser, graciously set up an email list-serve through his company, Diablo Analytical, Inc. This list-serve allowed the prompt and inexpensive distribution of atlas newsletters to atlasers with email access, saving the atlas project the costs of printing and shipping. It also provided a venue for the sharing of recent sightings, questions, and comments.

Joel Herr stepped in when he was needed most and volunteered to create, free of charge, a computer program to accommodate the atlas data and represent it in the form of colorful maps that were available for public viewing on his website. His generous efforts were crucial to the success of the atlas. Readers are encouraged to visit his website: www.flyingemu.com

John Kelly of the Audubon Canyon Ranch graciously provided data on nesting herons and egrets.

Mark Lagarde of H. T. Harvey and Associates, with great patience, created the beautiful plant communities map.

Ellis Myers graciously undertook the effort of putting the atlas together for publication. The fact that the book you hold now is so attractive is due completely to the professionalism and attention to detail of Ellis.

Frances Oliver was constantly supportive of the writing of the atlas, offering many insightful comments about the species accounts; her honest critiques were crucial in giving direction to my ramblings.

Audrey Riddlebarger generously took on the task of retrieving records of injured birds from the Lindsay Wildlife Museum.

Don Roberson, just as the atlas project was about to kickoff, kindly agreed to present his slide show based upon the Monterey County breeding bird atlas. Additionally, Don and his wife, Rita Carratello, went above and beyond by commuting from Pacific Grove to work on two blocks. His *Atlas of the Breeding Birds of Monterey County*, written with Chris Tenney, proved extremely valuable in the writing of this atlas.

Mike Rogers kindly and timely searched the North American Birds notebooks for information pertaining to ducks, herons, and egrets. He also reviewed the drafts of numerous species.

Fred Safier proofread the entire atlas, saving us a great deal of embarassment.

Rusty Scalf created the beautiful maps that are the centerpiece of this published atlas.

Jim Schnitzen shared a bounty of unpublished information on the Bushtit, in addition to likely spending more hours in the field than any member of the atlas team.

W. David Shuford, author of the stellar *Marin County Breeding Bird Atlas*, timely replied to many, many emails and provided finished species accounts for California Bird Species of Special Concern. The Marin atlas, the first California atlas to be published and the one by which all future ones will be judged, was hugely influential on this one.

Malcolm Sproul, in addition to his atlasing efforts, solicited funding from various northern California consulting firms which helped fund the publishing of the atlas. Perhaps more importantly, his regular phone calls helped push along my plodding efforts at writing the species accounts.

Heller Stanton, with much appreciated humor, took on the ominous and very lengthy task of editing my haphazard scribblings. However this atlas turned out, it is far better thanks to her.

Denise Wight, besides working in several atlas blocks, kindly reviewed several sections of this book.

— ⁓ —

In addition, the following promptly replied to various online queries: *Ted Beedy, Amanda Castaneda, Laura Collins, Jeff Davis, Bruce Deuel, Meredith Elliot, Andrew Engelis, Jr., Kevin Enns-Rempel, Gil Ewing, Jim Gain, Corinne Louise Greenberg, Steve Hampton, John Harris, Waldo Holt, Tim Manolis, Mary Beth Metcalf, Joe Morlan, Ed Pandolfino, Mark Rauzon, Jim Roethe, Jim Snowden, John Sterling, Larry Turnstall, Bud Widdowson, Brian Williams,* and *David Yee* answered online queries about specific species.

Finally, the board of the Mt. Diablo Audubon Society, ably led by *Mike Williams* and later *Jimm Edgar*, underwrote the early administrative costs of the atlas project.

Incidental Reports

The following individuals submitted incidental reports:

Steve Bobzien, Ore Camhi, Judi Cooper, Joe DiDonato, Joan Giacosa, Barbara Hakala, Hugh Harvey, Rosita Harvey, Roger Hartwell, Debbie Hebert, Kevin Hintsa, Ron Lindeman, Dee Mitchell, Mark Rauzon, Jean Richmond, Greta Savage, Jeff Seay, Bessie Smyth, Charlotte Spencer, Rudi Thomas, Jim Tietz, Susan Watson

CONTRA COSTA COUNTY BREEDING BIRD ATLAS PARTICIPANTS

Cheryl Abel
Jane Bettencourt
Kathryn Blake
Ann Blandin
Ellen Blustein
Jeanne Bonner
Barbara Brandriff
Bob Brandriff
Gloria Cannon
Rita Carratello
Bethi Carver
Jerry Daniel
Connie Diernisse
Sharyn Fernandez
George Finger
Mary Foley
Lillian Fujii
Dorthy Furseth
Bingham Gibbs
Steven Glover
Helen Green
George Griffeth
Steve Hayashi
Jill Hedgecock

Claudia Hein
Scott Hein
Joel Herr
Janet Jamerson
Alan Kaplan
Debbie Kirshen
Kris Koundakjian
Ted Koundakjian
Michael Larkin
Janet Larkin
Robin Leong
Bob Lewis
Don Lewis
Kay Loughman
Jean Lucken
John Luther
Pat MacEachern
Paul MacEachern
Jennifer Matkin
Susanne Methvin
Sara Mathews
Marty Morrow
Marjorie Plant
David Rice

Bob Richmond
Don Roberson
Steve Rottenborn
Fred Safier
Rusty Scalf
Don Schmoldt
Jim Schnitzen
Tina Scruggs
Dick Spight
Malcolm Sproul
Maury Stern
Lynn Strandberg
Emilie Strauss
Joel Summerhill
Kirk Swenson
Barbara Vaughn
Linda Wallace
Sally Walters
Nancy Wenninger
Peter White
Denise Wight
Uzelle Williams
Teri Wills

Factors Influencing Bird Distribution

The Topography and Biogeography of Contra Costa County

Almost every Californian has seen Monte Diablo. It is the great central landmark of the state. Whether we are walking in the streets of San Francisco, or sailing on any of our bays and navigable rivers, or riding on any of the roads in the Sacramento and San Joaquin Valleys, or standing on the elevated ridges of the mining districts before us—in lonely boldness, and at almost every turn, we see Monte del Diablo.   ❧ *J. M. Hutchings 1860*

In California's exceptional topography—with its crowd gathering glacial excavations, its high Sierran hanging wall, its itinerant Salinian coast—nothing seems more singular to me than the Great Central Valley. It is far more plainer than the plainest of plains. With respect to its surroundings, it arrived first. At its edges are mountains that were set up around it like portable screens.   ❧ *John McPhee 1993*

Contra Costa County is, by California standards, a rather small county. At only 798 square miles it is just the 48th largest in the state out of a total of 58. Alameda County is just slightly larger at 825 square miles. Despite its small size, its population of 1,044,201 in 2006 ranks it 8th in California. The population density in 2005 was 1,277 people per square mile, also the 8th highest in California.

The county was once significantly larger but in 1853 Alameda County was carved out of portions of Contra Costa and Santa Clara counties. Areas formerly within the confines of Contra Costa County include Oakland, Berkeley, San Leandro, Hayward, Union City, Dublin, Pleasanton and Livermore, as well as at least a portion of Mines Rd. south of Livermore (Marschner 2000).

The name "Contra Costa" means "opposite coast" in Spanish, a reference to its position across the bay from San Francisco. It lies nestled between San Francisco and San Pablo bays to the west, San Pablo Bay, the Carquinez Strait and the Sacramento River/San Joaquin River Delta to the north, Alameda County to the south, and the great Central Valley to the east.

The most notable landscape feature of the East Bay is, of course, San Francisco Bay. More precisely, it is the San Francisco Bay estuary, encompassing San Francisco, San Pablo, and Suisun bays as well as the confluence of the Sacramento and San Joaquin rivers. The general area of this confluence is known as the Delta. San Francisco Bay, at just 10,000 years old, is the product of today's high sea levels and is ephemeral. It has come and gone several times. Runoff from 40% of California (from the Cascade Range and Klamath Mountains to the north and the Tehachapi Mountains to the south, the Sierra Nevada to the east and the Coast Ranges to the west) passes through this estuary. Diversion of freshwater for municipal drinking water and agriculture has resulted in a 40% decrease over the inflow of 1850 (Sloan 2006).

The topography of the upland portion of the county is dominated by two arms of the Coast Range. The Berkeley Hills, modest and more densely forested, runs northwest to southeast from Crockett south into Alameda County while the Diablo Range, more dramatic and chaparral-cloaked, runs parallel from Antioch south through Alameda County.

The Berkeley Hills are generally rounded and of lower elevation than the Diablo Range. None of the ridgetops are taller than 1900 feet in elevation. Several low passes allow brisk winds and summer fogs to penetrate the interior, most notably near Orinda at the Caldecott Tunnel, substantially affecting the vegetation and corresponding avifauna. Numerous small streams drain from the Berkeley Hills, although none of them are large and most of them only flow seasonally. The most significant is Wildcat Creek, which flows from Tilden Park southwest to Richmond, where it ends in a rather significant marsh.

The Diablo Range is the wilder, more rugged counterpart to the Berkeley Hills. The Contra Costa County portion is crowned by Mt. Diablo which rises to a height of 3849 feet. It is clad mostly in blue oak and valley oak woodlands, as well as mixed and chamise chaparral, although both the northern extremity around Concord and Pittsburg and the southern extremity north of Livermore are nearly pure perennial grasslands. Due to low rainfall, the numerous streams which flow out of the Diablo Range are almost completely dry during the summer. Marsh Creek, at 34.57 miles in length, is the longest creek in the county (*Contra Costa County Watershed Atlas*). It flows from the vicinity of Morgan Territory Regional Preserve southeast of Mt. Diablo and empties into "Big Break" at Oakley.

West of the Berkeley Hills is a narrow, gently sloping plain barely higher than sea level. This plain is alluvial, the result of thousands of years of erosion in the Berkeley Hills (Sloan 2006). The plain stretches northeast to about Crockett where it abruptly ends, replaced by smooth, low-lying hills and a rather steep cliff that drops dramatically to the Carquinez Strait. The strait itself is a narrow passage of bedrock, carved by the Sacramento River system, allowing runoff to reach San Pablo and San Francisco bays. At Martinez the land once again drops back down to sea level, forming yet another plain, this one both wider and longer than that at Richmond and still covered with extensive marshes. It stretches from the shores of Suisun Bay at the north to the northern extreme of the Diablo Range to the south. Eastward it essentially becomes the Delta and Great Central Valley, though where that might actually begin depends on who you ask.

East of the Berkeley Hills and west of the Diablo Range is a pair of north-south trending valleys. Ygnacio Valley, the northern of the two, runs from near Martinez south to Walnut Creek, while the San Ramon Valley stretches from Walnut Creek south to, and past, the county line at San Ramon. Each of the valleys is rather narrow, just a mile or two wide at most points. Walnut Creek runs north through the Ygnacio Valley before emptying into the Carquinez Strait. Conversely, San Ramon Creek runs south through the San Ramon Valley, eventually feeding into Alameda Creek in Alameda County. A significant portion of the county's population is centered in this portion of the county.

The eastern flank of the Diablo Range is covered primarily in blue oak savannah woodlands and open grassland; however, it is rapidly being usurped by housing. The boundary between the Coast Range and the Central Valley is ill-defined as the slope is gradual and the grasslands of each region blend into one another almost seamlessly.

The Central Valley portion of the county, once lightly inhabited and primarily agricultural in focus, has become increasingly urbanized during the past decade. Cities such as Oakley and Brentwood have gone from sleepy hamlets to bustling suburbs almost overnight. The sandy grasslands, so favored by the Burrowing Owl, are disappearing at a reckless pace.

The far eastern portion of the county, including Bethel Island, Jersey Island, and Holland Tract, is below sea level and hospitable only because of an expensive and aging levee system. This area still has significant acreage of pasturelands and, locally, rice fields, which flood in winter, providing habitat for wintering waterfowl.

Although there are no large permanent rivers or streams in the county, numerous large reservoirs were constructed during the 20th century. These reservoirs provide suitable habitat for numerous waterbirds in winter, as well as for the Osprey and Bald Eagle, but offer precious little in the way of permanent emergent vegetation to support nesting waterfowl. Four of these reservoirs, Upper San Leandro, San Pablo, Briones and Lafayette, are in the watershed lands of the Berkeley Hills. Los Vaqueros Reservoir is west of Brentwood on the eastern flanks of the Diablo Range and Clifton Court Forebay is in the Central Valley near Byron. A few smaller reservoirs, most notably Marsh Creek Reservoir, also dot the countryside.

Climate

We have not yet fulfilled the age-old dream of controlling the weather, but in the Bay Region we come close: we can change the weather around us by moving a short distance. Probably no comparable area on earth displays as many varieties of weather simultaneously as the region around San Francisco Bay.
ı► Harold Gilliam (2002)

Contra Costa County, as well as much of the lowlands of California, enjoys what is known as a Mediterranean climate, much like that found in the eastern Mediterranean but in a mere handful of additional regions. This generally means that summers are dry and hot while winters are cool and wet. Well over 95% of precipitation falls between October and April (particularly November through March). The obvious result of this pattern is moist, green hills in winter and parched brown hills throughout the summer.

For a more thorough discussion of Bay Area weather patterns, the reader is referred to Shuford (1993).

Temperatures

Winter temperatures are generally quite mild, particularly west of the Berkeley Hills. There the cool waters of the Pacific Ocean and San Francisco Bay combine to moderate the temperature, resulting in a relatively constant average throughout the year. The average winter low at Richmond is 42° F while slightly inland at Moraga it is just 35° F (*Contra Costa County Watershed Atlas*). Because winter storms are usually accompanied by warm air masses, decades may pass between significant snowfalls in the lowlands. Mt. Diablo, the highest point in the county at 3849 ft., generally receives a dusting or two each winter, although occurrence and amounts are erratic from year to year.

Average summer high temperatures vary far more dramatically. The average daily high on the Bay plain at Richmond and Hercules is just 70° F. At Walnut Creek and Martinez, just east of the Berkeley Hills, the average high soars to 87° F. In East County, where the influence of the Pacific Ocean is at its weakest, the average high at Byron is a steamy 92° F (*Contra Costa County Watershed Atlas*).

Rainfall

As stated above, the vast majority of Contra Costa County's precipitation falls during the winter months. The amount of precipitation, however, varies greatly from site to site and from year to year. The annual average at Richmond is 22 inches. Slightly inland in the Berkeley Hills, the average jumps to 33.5 in. at Tilden Regional Park. On the east side of the Berkeley Hills, at Orinda, the average is still 33 in. despite being on the leeward side of the hills. At Walnut Creek, less than ten miles from Orinda, the average plummets to just 21 inches. Just to the east, the upslope of Mt. Diablo wrings out additional rainfall, with an average of 28 inches. East of the crest of the Diablo Range, rainfall averages drop dramatically. Brentwood, little over 10 mi. east of Mt. Diablo, receives a scant 12.5 inches in an average year (*Contra Costa County Watershed Atlas*).

Rainfall totals vary dramatically from year to year. The average annual rainfall at Orinda from 1937 to 2007 was 32.17 inches. The lowest annual total during that time period was 13.31 inches in the winter of 1976–1977, the first of two years of extreme drought in the region. The highest annual totals were in the winters of 1982–1983 and 1983–1984, consecutive years of El Niño conditions which brought rain in biblical proportions to California. Those winters saw rainfall totals of 57.24 in. and 59.08 in., respectively (Data courtesy Roger Hartwell and EBMUD).

Rainfall totals during the atlas were significantly higher than average. Orinda, with an average annual rainfall of 32.17 in. from 1937 through 2007, received an average annual rainfall of 38.27 in. during the years of the atlas project. The winter of 1998–1999, which was wrapping up as the second year of fieldwork began, brought a whopping 56.49 in. of rain to Orinda, the third highest total on record behind only the aforementioned El Niño years (Data courtesy of Roger Hartwell and EBMUD).

THE PLANT COMMUNITIES OF CONTRA COSTA COUNTY

The following plant communities are based on those described for California by Mayer and Laudenslayer, Jr. (1988). Of 39 tree or shrub dominated habitats within the state, 17 are included here, a fairly remarkable number for a county of such small size. As with any such classification scheme, the following is a broad simplification of actual habitats and is based upon the dominant species found there. Each of the habitats below may blend with several others and take on myriad forms. For example blue oak woodlands may mix with coastal oak and riparian woodlands, various types of chaparral, and grasslands. These conglomerations generally result in a larger number of breeding bird species than might be expected from a more homogeneous plant community.

Tree Dominated Habitats

Redwood

The native redwood community in Contra Costa County is restricted to a small, relict population in the western Berkeley Hills around the headwaters of Redwood Creek and just to the east along San Leandro Creek. Redwoods have been planted throughout the settled portions of the county, even in arid East County, but nowhere do these plantings amount to a forest.

In Contra Costa County, redwoods inhabit deep canyon bottoms within the reach of persistent summer fog, where temperatures remain relatively stable. The canopy can reach heights of well over 100 feet, even in second-growth stands as exist in Contra Costa County (Mayer and Laudenslayer, Jr. 1988).

Local redwood forests feature a mostly barren understory, typical of second-growth stands. Where there is an understory, usually in drainages, California bay may occupy the subcanopy and California huckleberry and sword fern typically form the shrub and herb layers.

The redwood forests of Contra Costa County are not extensive and their corresponding avifauna is not diverse. However, Northern Saw-whet Owl, Pacific-slope Flycatcher, Brown Creeper, and Winter Wren may be more common in such forests than anywhere else in the county. The only known breeding site for Hermit Thrush is in the redwood forest around Redwood Peak in Redwood Regional Park.

Monterey Pine (Closed-Cone Pine-Cypress)

In Contra Costa County the closed-cone pine-cypress community is represented only by stands of introduced Monterey pine in residential neighborhoods, with extensive forest-like stands at scattered sites in the Berkeley Hills. Monterey pine stands in Contra Costa County tend to be dense and may include an overstory of coast live oak and madrone and an impenetrable understory of Himalayan blackberry. The most prominent of these stands, around Inspiration Point near Tilden Regional Park, may host a wider variety of breeding passerines than any other site in the county.

Just a single species, Pygmy Nuthatch, is known to breed only in Monterey pine stands, but numerous other species are more common in this habitat than anywhere else. These include Hairy Woodpecker, Red-breasted Nuthatch and perhaps Band-tailed Pigeon. Other representative species include Northern Saw-whet Owl, Olive-sided Flycatcher, Western Wood-Pewee, Violet-green Swallow, MacGillivray's Warbler and Purple Finch.

Blue Oak Woodland (includes Blue Oak-Gray Pine Woodland)

Blue oak woodland occurs throughout much of the Coast Range where it is particularly well represented in the Diablo Range. On Mt. Diablo itself, gray pine co-occurs with blue oak, but it is less numerous and is absent below 500 feet in elevation (Ertter and Bowerman 2002). Blue oak woodland occupies hilltops and gently sloping hillsides, predominantly those with southern exposure.

In many areas, particularly below 1000 ft. elevation, blue oak woodland forms a savannah, with typical grassland species occupying open areas between trees. At higher elevations on Mt. Diablo, gray pine and interior live oak may join the association, often in combination with an understory of California bay, toyon, poison oak, hop tree and California coffeeberry (Errter and Bowerman 2002).

The breeding avifauna of blue oak woodlands is not diverse. The most characteristic species is White-breasted Nuthatch. Other representative species of this habitat include Acorn Woodpecker, Nuttall's Woodpecker, Oak Titmouse, Western Bluebird, Bullock's Oriole, Lesser Goldfinch and, locally, Chipping Sparrow.

Valley Oak Woodland

Valley oak woodland is scarce in Contra Costa County. Given its tendency to occur mainly in valley bottoms, which have long been subjected to development, this habitat type was likely far more extensive historically than it is today. Where it does occur, mostly in the eastern Diablo Range, it is typically degraded.

The structure of this habitat ranges from open, savanna-like woodlands on upland sites to dense, nearly closed-canopy forests in valley soils along drainages. The shrub layer follows a similar pattern. It may be insignificant in upland situations featuring open stands. Where there is a partial shrub layer, poison oak typically predominates. In lowland settings, particularly along drainages, the shrub layer is usually more substantial and generally includes poison oak, blackberry and blue elderberry (Mayer and Laudenslayer, Jr. 1988). The canopy along drainages may also include California sycamore, live oaks, and blue oak.

Well developed valley oak woodlands tend to be birdy, particularly since they often occur adjacent to open habitats, thus forming an "edge" habitat. Typical breeding species include Acorn, Nuttall's, and Downy woodpeckers, Ash-throated Flycatcher, Oak Titmouse, White-breasted Nuthatch, Western Bluebird, Orange-crowned Warbler, Black-headed Grosbeak, and Lesser Goldfinch.

Coastal Oak Woodland

The structure and composition of coastal oak woodland in Contra Costa County are highly variable, as they are throughout California. Factors shaping these woodlands include elevation, slope, soil, precipitation, moisture availability, and air temperature (Mayer and Laudenslayer, Jr. 1988).

The overstory is composed of deciduous and evergreen hardwoods, mostly oaks which may range in height from 15 to 70 ft tall. The trees are dense and form a closed canopy in mesic sites but often form open stands in drier areas. The understory is equally variable and can include shrubs from adjacent chaparral, sometimes creating an impenetrable understory. More often scattered shrubs grow under and between trees (Mayer and Laudenslayer, Jr. 1988).

In Contra Costa County, coastal oak woodland is usually dominated by coast live oak, which may be the only overstory species at some locations. In wetter areas, particularly in the Berkeley Hills, other trees such as California bay and madrone may be common. At drier sites, coast live oaks may mix with valley and blue oaks as well as gray pines. The understory at dense sites typically includes various species of shade tolerant shrubs as well as herbaceous plants such as ferns. In drier sites with more widely spaced oaks, the understory may be almost completely composed of grassland species (Mayer and Laudenslayer, Jr. 1988).

The bird diversity of Contra Costa County's coastal oak woodlands tends to be high. Typical species include Cooper's Hawk, Pacific-slope Flycatcher, Western Wood-Pewee, Hutton's Vireo, Warbling Vireo, Steller's Jay, Chestnut-backed Chickadee, Brown Creeper, American Robin, Dark-eyed Junco, Black-headed Grosbeak, and Purple Finch.

Eucalyptus

Thickets of introduced eucalyptus have been planted throughout Contra Costa County. The species most often present is blue gum eucalyptus (*Eucalyptus globulus*), which can be found in virtually monotypic forests as well as linear windbreaks. Partially due to high amounts of litter deposition, a true understory is usually absent with the exception of eucalyptus saplings and poison oak.

The widespread planting of eucalyptus windbreaks, particularly in East County, has provided nest sites for numerous species in places where suitable nest sites tend to be scarce.

True eucalyptus forest is rare in Contra Costa County. Where it does occur, such as at Pt. Pinole Regional Shoreline, the avifauna is greatly impoverished compared with that of native woodlands. Individual trees or small clumps in open country may host Anna's Hummingbird, Western Kingbird, Western Scrub-Jay, Yellow-billed Magpie, and American Crow. Red-tailed, Red-shouldered and Swainson's hawks are also fond of eucalyptus. In addition, several of the heronries in the county occur in eucalyptus.

Montane Riparian

Montane riparian habitat occurs exclusively around ponds, streams and rivers where the water table remains at or very near the surface. This habitat takes on a myriad of forms but generally occurs as a narrow, often dense grove with trees that may reach heights of nearly 100 feet. The understory is generally sparse (Mayer and Laudenslayer, Jr. 1988).

The most common trees of montane riparian settings include big-leaf maple, white alder, western sycamore, Fremont cottonwood, California bay and various species of willow. The shrubby understory often includes Himalayan blackberry and poison oak.

In Contra Costa County this habitat may be best developed along the Marsh Creek drainage in the foothills east of Mt. Diablo. Dominant trees there include Fremont cottonwood, live oaks, big-leaf maple and willows. Western sycamore is also present.

On the north side of Mt. Diablo there are permanent streams in Donner and Mitchell canyons. Canopy trees there include white alder, Fremont cottonwood, big-leaf maple, coast live oak, western sycamore, and willows. Species present in the understory often include toyon, blue elderberry, common snowberry, and poison oak (Ertter and Bowerman 2002).

Montane riparian habitats in Contra Costa County are often bordered by coastal oak woodland as well as various types of chaparral and grasslands, each of which contributes to a high number of breeding bird species. Typical species include Red-shouldered and Cooper's hawks, Western Screech-Owl, Acorn and Nuttall's woodpeckers, Western Wood-Pewee, Pacific-slope Flycatcher, Ash-throated Flycatcher, Warbling Vireo, Chestnut-backed Chickadee, House Wren, Orange-crowned Warbler, and Black-headed Grosbeak.

Valley Foothill Riparian

Valley foothill riparian habitat is usually associated with low-velocity stream flows, flood plains, and gentle topography (Mayer and Laudenslayer, Jr. 1988). This habitat is scarce in Contra Costa County. It is prominent only along the Marsh Creek drainage on the western edge of the Central Valley around Brentwood. Even there, however, the habitat is less diverse botanically than elsewhere on the valley floor. Copses of Fremont cottonwood and willows continue to exist in low-lying areas around Jersey and Bethel islands and on Holland Tract.

Mature riparian forests may attain a canopy of nearly 100 feet with a canopy cover of 20 to 80 percent. There is typically a subcanopy tree layer and an understory shrub layer. California grape, which often provides ground cover and festoons trees in this habitat, is mostly absent from the county (Mayer and Laudenslayer, Jr. 1988).

On the Central Valley floor along Marsh Creek, the dominant tree species are Fremont cottonwood and valley oak. Western sycamore is also present. Willows, blackberry and blue elderberry make up the understory. This habitat stretches only from about Marsh Creek Reservoir downstream to about Balfour Road. Even at its best, this corridor is narrow and hemmed in by agriculture and, increasingly, housing. Downstream from Balfour Road vegetation becomes sparse and is increasingly composed of ornamental plantings.

Perhaps due to a lack of botanical diversity, the number of breeding species is modest. Representative species include California Quail, Red-tailed and Red-shouldered hawks, Black-chinned Hummingbird, Nuttall's and Downy woodpeckers, Oak Titmouse, White-breasted Nuthatch and, locally, Blue Grosbeak.

Shrub Dominated Habitats
Mixed Chaparral

The distinction between mixed chaparral and chamise chaparral (see below) is subtle. In general, mixed chaparral is floristically more diverse. Although chamise is often present it does not form the pure stands typical of south-facing exposures at lower elevations. Instead it occurs, at least on average, on north-facing slopes at higher elevations.In Contra Costa County this habitat is nearly exclusive to Mt. Diablo.

The composition of these associations is highly variable and depends upon precipitation, aspect, soil type and fire history. Some sites feature almost pure stands of certain dominant species while others may feature a diverse array of species. The most common shrubs tend to be ceanothus and manzanita, but chamise, toyon, poison oak and numerous others may also be common. Gray and Coulter pines may also be present (Mayer and Laudenslayer, Jr. 1988).

Typical bird species of mixed chaparral include California Quail, Anna's Hummingbird, Ash-throated Flycatcher, Blue-gray Gnatcatcher, Wrentit, Orange-crowned Warbler, California Thrasher and Spotted Towhee.

Chamise Chaparral

Chamise Chaparral occurs in the Coast Range, locally in the Berkeley Hills and commonly in the Diablo Range. The purest stands occur at relatively low elevations in rocky soils on steep south-facing slopes. At certain spots on Mt. Diablo, black sage may be as common as chamise (Errter and Bowerman 2002). At higher elevations the chamise is often mixed with other shrubs such as ceanothus and manzanita but chamise always maintains dominance. The shrub canopy often overlaps, forming an impenetrable canopy. Chamise chaparral is usually single layered, lacking herbaceous ground cover or overstory trees (Mayer and Laudenslayer, Jr. 1988).

Chamise chaparral in Contra Costa County often plays host to numerous species such as Common Poorwill, Anna's Hummingbird, Blue-gray Gnatcatcher, Wrentit, California Thrasher, Spotted Towhee and Lazuli Bunting. The most sought-after species, however, are two uncommon ones: Black-chinned Sparrow and Sage Sparrow.

Coastal Scrub

Coastal scrub typically features low to moderate-sized shrubs that often form a completely closed canopy. This habitat occurs widely in Contra Costa County in a variety of settings, mostly at lower elevations.

Northern coastal scrub in Contra Costa County is nearly always dominated by an overstory of the aggressive coyote brush but may also include various other shrubs such as Himalayan blackberry and poison oak. This habitat is particularly common west of the Interstate-680 corridor.

In some areas, this habitat is dominated by California sagebrush, black sage and California buckwheat. On Mt. Diablo, California sagebrush occurs mainly on the margins of the chaparral, particularly on steep, south-facing hillsides, but occasionally on north-facing slopes (Errter and Bowerman 2002).

Bird species typical of coastal scrub include Anna's and Allen's hummingbirds, Bewick's Wren, Wrentit, California Towhee, Lazuli Bunting and, in West County, White-crowned Sparrow. Rufous-crowned Sparrow is virtually restricted to this habitat.

Herbaceous Dominated Habitats
Annual and Perennial Grassland

The Annual Grassland community is an open grassland primarily composed of annual plant species, many of which also occur in the understory of valley oak woodland. The structure of this community is heavily influenced by weather patterns and livestock grazing (Mayer and Laudenslayer, Jr. 1988). This habitat dominates the dry rolling hills of Contra Costa County and is particularly extensive north and south of Mt. Diablo.

This habitat was apparently formerly dominated by native perennial bunch grasses but species present now overwhelmingly tend to be introduced annual grasses such as wild oats (*Avena* spp.), bromes (*Bromus* spp.), and filarees (*Erodium* spp.).

Perennial Grasslands do exist in remnant patches, particularly on Mt. Diablo. The four most common perennial grasses there are purple needlegrass, big squirreltail, one-sided bluegrass and California melic. Although patchily distributed, these perennial grasses are still fairly common and widespread but are vastly overwhelmed by alien annual species throughout much of their range in the county (Errter and Bowerman 2002).

Characteristic bird species of Contra Costa County's grasslands include Northern Harrier, Burrowing Owl, Loggerhead Shrike, Horned Lark, Western Meadowlark and, locally, Grasshopper and Savannah sparrows.

Fresh Emergent Wetland

Fresh Emergent Wetland is characterized by erect hydrophytes which are frequently flooded. Water may be standing or slow-moving. The size of this community varies from small clumps to vast acreages. The acreage of such habitats has decreased dramatically in the past century due to drainage, primarily for agriculture (Mayer and Laudenslayer, Jr. 1988).

Cattail and bulrush commonly ring freshwater reservoirs, ponds and even sewage treatment facilities, wherever water levels remain relatively consistent. In the Delta, where the vast majority of Contra Costa County's freshwater wetlands occur, dominant species include bulrush, cattail and common reed (Evens *et al.* 1991).

Many of the bird species thought to be declining in Contra Costa County nest in fresh emergent wetlands, including American Bittern, Virginia Rail, Common Moorhen, and Tricolored Blackbird. Numerous ducks nest almost exclusively in such situations. Other species typical of this habitat include Marsh Wren, Common Yellowthroat and Song Sparrow. Several species that typically nest in other habitat types also depend on these marshes, most notably the herons.

Saline Emergent Wetland

Saline Emergent Wetlands may be characterized as salt or brackish marshes with the component plants most often occurring in patches or as a sequence of overlapping species along an elevational gradient.

Fresh Emergent Wetlands in the San Pablo Bay area (Richmond) are dominated by pickleweed, California cord grass, saltgrass, seaside arrow-grass, marsh jaumea, alkali heath and gumplant (Evens *et al.* 1991). In Suisun Bay (from Martinez east to Pittsburg) the plant communties are a "diverse mosaic" of bulrushes, saltgrass, rushes, seaside arrow-grass, pickleweed, marsh jaumea and gumplant (Evens *et al.* 1991).

This imperiled habitat plays host to several endangered, threatened or imperiled species, most notably Black and Clapper rails, the "San Francisco" Common Yellowthroat, and the "Alameda", "Samuel's", and "Suisun" Song Sparrows.

Pasture

Pastures are composed of perennial grasses and legumes that usually provide complete canopy closure. The height of the vegetation varies by season and number of livestock present. Old or poorly drained pastures may have weeds over two feet in height. Prevalent species in northern California are said to include ryegrasses, tall fescue, Dallis grass, white clover, strawberry clover and trefoils (Mayer and Laudenslayer, Jr. 1988).

Although pasture habitat was likely once more widespread in Contra Costa County, particularly along the Bay plain around Richmond and along the Interstate-680 corridor, it is now essentially restricted to the low-lying Delta portion of the county.

Breeding bird diversity is low in the county's pasturelands, but this habitat is important for breeding Northern Harriers, Loggerhead Shrikes, and Western Meadowlarks.

Methods Employed in the Atlas Project

The Grid System

The blocks utilized for the Contra Costa County Breeding Bird Atlas were based upon the Universal Transverse Mercator grid system (UTM). The boundaries of these grids are noted with small blue "tick" marks on the margins of the standard United States Geological Survey maps. These five kilometer by five kilometer squares are standard throughout the world in both size and shape, allowing easy data comparison and a perfect mesh with other atlas projects. With the exception of Marin County, the first California County to undertake an atlas project, the UTM grid system has been used for all California atlas projects.

Data was collected from a total of 96 blocks. Of these, 76 of the blocks fall completely within the boundaries of Contra Costa County, or very nearly so, although numerous blocks along the western and northern shorelines feature significant amounts of open water. The remaining 20 blocks share territory with San Francisco, Marin, Solano, Sacramento, San Joaquin or Alameda counties. No atlasing work was done outside the confines of Contra Costa County, although a few birds were more than likely outside of the county proper. The most conspicuous example of this is a heronry on West Island, Sacramento County, which was viewed from the Contra Costa County shoreline. Other atlas projects have attempted to atlas entire blocks, even if the percentage represented by their home county was small. Because of water boundaries to the west and north, as well as already completed atlases for Alameda, Marin, San Francisco and Sacramento counties, we opted not to do so. Because we restricted our attentions exclusively to Contra Costa County, a few partial blocks, particularly in the eastern third of the county, had just a handful of breeding species present. The Solano County Breeding Bird Atlas, begun in 2005, will fill in many of the gaps to the north far more thoroughly than we could have done; a much-needed atlas project in development-happy San Joaquin County would leave Contra Costa County completely surrounded by atlased counties and alleviate this minor shortcoming.

Time Frame

The atlas project was completed over the five breeding seasons from 1998–2002. Atlasers were instructed to visit their assigned blocks as much as possible during the breeding season, particularly from April through July, when nearly all species are present and engaged in some form of nesting duties. Atlasers were, however, encouraged to visit their blocks on occasion both before and after these dates to catch early and late nesters. In practice, eager atlasers sometimes spent significant amounts of time in the field in February and March and then appeared to "burnout" by summer. The database thins considerably by July and there are relatively few records for August.

Because there was a clear concentration of effort from April through June, the nesting chronologies constructed in the individual species accounts should be viewed skeptically. This is especially true of certain permanent residents which are known to nest early, including Red-tailed Hawk, Great Horned Owl, Anna's Hummingbird, Bushtit and Chestnut-backed Chickadee.

Adequacy of Coverage

Nearly all atlas projects ever attempted have struggled with the concept of when to declare a block sufficiently covered. Because of diminishing returns, it is generally prudent to move an atlaser to a new block after a year or two. After all, the value of remaining in a block for an extra year to upgrade a handful of species from "probable" to "confirmed" is minor in comparison with the need for unoccupied blocks to receive coverage. This is a thorny issue because atlasers tend to make blocks their own. In a sense, they have come to be *the* expert on the breeding birds of that block and they dearly want to wring out every possible confirmation.

Different atlas projects have devised a wide array of formulas for declaring a block complete. Most commonly, the goal is to achieve a certain percentage (*i.e.* 50%) of confirmations. If 100 species are found in the block, then 50 must be confirmed.

This atlas project was very fortunate, in the sense that the county is small and the number of volunteers reasonably high. The Monterey County atlas team, for example, faced the daunting task of atlasing 385 blocks with a core atlas crew of only 20 (Roberson and Tenney 1993). In Contra Costa County we were confronted with just 96 blocks and we had a core of closer to 50 atlasers. This put us in the fortunate position of being able to let atlasers stay in favored blocks longer than was truly necessary. In fact, very few atlasers were asked to move to different blocks, although a few blocks could certainly have benefited from additional coverage.

Despite the small size of Contra Costa County, it proved very difficult to get atlasers to cover blocks in the far eastern portion of the county. Most of the atlas crew lived in either the Berkeley area or along the Interstate-680 corridor and, not surprisingly, most favored atlasing close to home. This left most of the Central Valley blocks to the author. Although each block was covered, and most reached the 50% confirmation threshold, some species must certainly have been missed.

The discrepancy in the amount of time devoted to individual blocks, particularly when comparing East County blocks to those elsewhere, is extreme in some cases (see Appendix E). Block 575-195, for example, was scoured for a whopping 469.5 hours. In comparison, many East County blocks received less than ten hours of atlasing. Despite the relatively low number of hours devoted to East County, each block was covered thoroughly and few species are likely to have been missed. Most of the eastern ⅓ of the county is either urban or agricultural, making detection and confirmation of nesting species relatively simple and certainly less problematic than in the woodlands elsewhere in the county. Although the percentage of detected species which were confirmed is, on average, slightly higher in West County than in East County, the difference isn't profound (see Appendix E).

There were few access difficulties encountered during the execution of the atlas. We had access to at least a portion of each of the blocks. Public roads bisect virtually the entire county and most of the roadless areas are comprised of public parklands or watersheds. This is a fortunate contrast to some of the blocks in southeastern Alameda County, for example, where the better part of a day must be spent just hiking to the block.

The Atlas Database

Atlas data was taken from field cards and incidental observation forms at the end of each season and entered into Joel Herr's "BBA List" computer program. Data was also later added from a handful of additional sources, primarily from the files of the Lindsay Wildlife Museum, but also from data provided by the East Bay Regional Parks District, East Bay Municipal Utility District and the Santa Cruz Predatory Bird Research Group.

After the completion of fieldwork, the data was copied onto Excel files and reviewed. The vast majority of records stand as submitted but a small percentage were removed. Most such removals pertained to birds reported as "possible" or "probable" but which likely represented wintering birds or spring migrants. The improper use of the "observed" code was widespread; all records not pertaining to colonial nesting species or wide-ranging foragers (*i.e.* herons, raptors, terns, *etc.*) were removed. In a handful of cases it was concluded that either the reported species was misidentified or the interpretation of the evidence was incorrect. In most instances, educated guesses were conservatively made. It is therefore conceivable that a small number of records were removed from the database that were, in fact, submitted correctly. This would most often apply to neotropical migrants such as flycatchers, warblers and the Western Tanager.

The current database weighs in at well over 17,500 records, a rather massive benchmark of breeding records for comparison by future researchers and, conceivably, by a future atlas team. The atlas database, as well as the complete set of completed atlas forms, will be available to interested researchers.

Table 1: BREEDING CRITERIA CODES

Standardized breeding codes used in this atlas. Codes are ranked from lowest to highest desirability.

DESIGNATION	CODE	EVIDENCE
OBSERVED	O	Species (male or female) observed in a block during its breeding season, but no evidence of breeding. Not in suitable nesting habitat. Includes wide-ranging species such as vultures or raptors, or a colonial nesting species not at the nesting colony.
POSSIBLE	√	Species (male or female) observed in suitable nesting habitat during its breeding season.
	X	Singing male present in suitable habitat during its breeding season.
PROBABLE	P	Pair observed in suitable habitat during its breeding season.
	S	Permanent territory assumed through song at same location on at least two occasions seven or more days apart.
	T	Permanent territory presumed through defense of territory (chasing individuals of same species).
	C	Courtship behavior or copulation.
	N	Visiting probable nest-site.
	A	Agitated behavior or anxiety calls from adult.
	B	Nest building by wrens or excavation of holes by woodpeckers.
CONFIRMED	CN	Carrying nest material, such as sticks.
	NB	Nest building at the actual nest-site.
	PE	Physiological evidence of breeding (*i.e.* highly vascularized, edematous incubation (brood) patch or egg in oviduct based on bird in hand. To be used by bird banders on local birds during the nesting season.
	DD	Distraction display or injury feigning. Used nests or eggshells found. *Caution:* these must be carefully identified.
	PY	Precocial young. Flightless young of precocial species restricted to the natal area by dependence of adults or limited mobility.
	FL	Recently fledged young (either precocial or altricial). Incapable of sustained flight, restricted to natal area by dependence on adults or limited mobility.
	ON	Occupied nest: adults entering or leaving a nest site in circumstances indicating an occupied nest. To be used for nests which are too high (tops of trees) or enclosed (*i.e.* chimneys) for the contents to be seen.
	CF	Carrying food: adult carrying food for the young.
	NE	Nest with egg (s).*
	FY	Adult feeding recently fledged young.
	FS	Adult carrying fecal sac.
	NY	Nest with young.*

*Presence of cowbird eggs or young is confirmation of both cowbird and host species.

Atlas Shortcomings

No perfect atlas project has ever been conducted and this one was certainly no exception. The finished product is the result of the best efforts of a group of amateur field ornithologists. All of the shortcomings noted here could have been avoided, although they appear typical for atlas projects.

The probable code proved, well, problematic. Atlasers tended to cite the first date on which they saw a pair of a given species, no matter how early in the season. Therefore a pair of harriers seen in February and seen in May simply goes on the block report as a pair seen in February. In actuality, the May report is far more useful because it is in the heart of the breeding season; the February report may simply pertain to wintering birds. In theory, atlasers should have omitted a February record if the birds were not seen again on subsequent trips but this was clearly not always the case.

The bane of all atlas projects, the rails and particularly the owls received scant attention by most atlasers. Access difficulties and reticence to bird at night left owl coverage to a handful of observers primarily restricted to public roads. Although the ranges outlined on the maps are likely representative for some common species such as Virginia Rail, Great Horned and Barn owls, at least broadly, other species such as Northern Saw-whet Owl and Common Poorwill clearly suffered.

Although atlas maps are valuable for giving a visual guide to the range of a given species, they offer no clues as to the prevalence of a species within that range. A technique known as "abundance codes" was designed to alleviate this shortcoming. Each atlaser was asked, at the end of the season, to make an educated guess as to the number of breeding pairs in their block for each species. This was not to be an exact count, but rather a categorization based upon orders of magnitude. The choices were one pair, 2–10 pairs, 11–100 pairs, 101–1000 pairs and 1001–10000 pairs. With this data we would have been able to calculate population estimates for each species, something that would have been particularly valuable for species already thought to be declining. Unfortunately, many atlasers seemed confused or intimidated by the abundance codes. By the end of the second year it became apparent that too few atlasers were submitting sound data to make this category useful and the decision was made to abandon it.

RESULTS

Number of Breeding Species

During the atlas project, breeding evidence was collected for 161 species. For 149 of these, confirmed breeding was established. Of the remaining twelve species, six have never been confirmed breeding in the county: Common Merganser, Black Rail, Virginia Rail, Northern Pygmy-Owl, Lesser Nighthawk, and Pileated Woodpecker. A seventh species, Indigo Bunting, is thought to have bred during the atlas project as part of a hybrid pair. The two rails, Northern Pygmy-Owl and Lesser Nighthawk almost certainly breed annually. The other five species were confirmed breeding prior to the atlas project: American Bittern, Northern Shoveler, Short-eared Owl, Common Poorwill, and Black-throated Gray Warbler; all but the shoveler and possibly the owl may breed annually. Two species, the Bald Eagle and Black Skimmer, were confirmed subsequent to atlas work. Two additional species (Greater Roadrunner and Yellow-headed Blackbird) historically bred in the county, although neither has been confirmed in over a half century. Finally, the Mute Swan is assumed to have bred on the Concord Naval Weapons Station during the atlas project and the Rose-breasted Grosbeak bred once, prior to the atlas, as part of a hybrid pair.

In historical times, Contra Costa County is known to have hosted 167 species of breeding birds, with confirmations for 161 species (two of which involved hybrid pairs). Approximately 144 of these species are thought to breed every year. Of the remaining twenty-three species which are known, or thought, to have bred at one time or another, two have apparently been extirpated (Greater Roadrunner and Yellow-headed Blackbird), a few likely breed with regularity but not necessarily every year (Pelagic Cormorant, Short-eared Owl, Long-eared Owl and Black-throated Gray Warbler), some may breed only irruptively or extralimitally (Cedar Waxwing, Pine Siskin), and a handful of others are simply very rare breeders (Green-winged Teal, Blue-winged Teal, Northern Shoveler, Western Grebe, Clark's Grebe, Bald Eagle, Osprey, Spotted Sandpiper and California Gull). At least two species, Pileated Woodpecker and Northern Pygmy-Owl, may well breed each year but their status awaits clarification. The Common Merganser is included based almost solely on a single bird found in mid-June during the atlas project. The Yellow Warbler was confirmed during the atlas project for the first time in decades but it is unclear if the species will reestablish itself. Finally, the Indigo Bunting and the Rose-breasted Grosbeak have each bred as part of hybrid pairs.

New Species

Because Contra Costa County has enjoyed at least some birding coverage for over a century (particularly from the late 1960s onward), the membership of the breeding avifauna is reasonably well known. Nevertheless, no less than six species were confirmed breeding for the first time during the atlas project: Green-winged Teal, Blue-winged Teal, Western Grebe, Clark's Grebe, California Gull, and Great-tailed Grackle. Additionally, three species were confirmed for which there may have been historical breeding records but which we were unable to track down: Long-eared Owl, Cedar Waxwing and Pine Siskin. A male Indigo Bunting, a species expanding its range in the west, apparently hybridized with a female Lazuli Bunting at Piper Slough, Bethel Island in 1998. At least three other species almost certainly nest but have yet to be confirmed: Northern Pygmy-Owl, Lesser Nighthawk and Pileated Woodpecker. Each of these species is currently, and historically, a peripheral member of the county's avifauna. Each is rare and local; some probably don't breed each year. Two additional species, the Bald Eagle and Black Skimmer, were confirmed nesting in 2006.

Other Atlas Highlights

Several species which had previously been confirmed nesting in the county were nonetheless noteworthy for differing reasons. The Swainson's Hawk was found to be more common than formerly believed in East County, as well as more tolerant of human disturbance. The Least Tern colonized a second breeding site, this time at Pt. Isabel near Richmond. The Common Raven, nearly unknown as a nester in the county before the atlas, was found to be fairly common and widespread, particularly in East County, a trend noted throughout the Bay Area. A Hermit Thrush nest at Redwood Regional Park in 1998 was the first for the county since Milton Siebert first confirmed the species in 1941! Likewise, two Yellow Warbler nests in 2001 could conceivably have been the first since 1931! A confirmation of nesting Savannah Sparrows at Oakley was exceptionally far inland. Finally, the Lawrence's Goldfinch was more common in the Berkeley Hills than in the arid Diablo Range, the exact opposite of what has come to be expected.

Questions Left Unanswered

Despite thousands of hours of fieldwork, the true breeding status of several species remains unresolved. This is particularly true, as might be expected, for nocturnal species such as owls and nightjars as well as for the rails. Is the Sora truly absent from the county during the breeding season or was coverage lacking? How common is the Clapper Rail, a species of whose habitats we were only barely able to sample the fringes? Just how common (or rare) is the Northern Pygmy-Owl and the Long-eared Owl in Contra Costa County? What is the exact status of the Anna's and Black-chinned hummingbird in East County? Further from our realm of expertise, what is the status of the Song Sparrow in the Pittsburg/Antioch shoreline and which subspecies are present where?

Table 2:

RANKING OF SPECIES BASED UPON TOTAL NUMBER OF BLOCKS IN WHICH DETECTED

Species ranked by number of blocks in which they were found to be confirmed, probable or possible. Another option for sorting this data, purely by confirmation, was discarded due to the obviously huge discrepancy in confirmation rates between species. Even so, a quick glance at the list reveals the fact that the species found in the most blocks are both common and conspicuous and thus more easily detectable.

Species	Total blocks	Confirmed	Probable	Possible
Red-winged Blackbird	94	81	10	3
House Finch	91	85	5	1
European Starling	90	88	1	1
Mourning Dove	90	68	20	2
Brewer's Blackbird	87	78	8	1
Mallard	87	56	26	5
Western Scrub-Jay	87	82	2	3
American Kestrel	86	52	23	11
American Crow	85	45	19	21
Barn Swallow	85	74	7	4
Cliff Swallow	85	68	4	11
Black Phoebe	83	71	8	4
Bushtit	83	76	6	1
Red-tailed Hawk	83	54	18	11
Northern Mockingbird	82	66	8	8
Killdeer	81	45	23	13
House Sparrow	80	68	8	4
American Robin	79	68	6	5
Western Meadowlark	79	38	26	15
Rock Pigeon	78	37	31	10
Anna's Hummingbird	76	60	1	15
Bullock's Oriole	75	54	12	9
Brown-headed Cowbird	74	19	34	21
Nuttall's Woodpecker	73	54	11	8
Western Kingbird	72	56	9	7
Song Sparrow	71	45	15	11
California Towhee	70	60	10	0
Spotted Towhee	69	51	13	5
Barn Owl	68	46	4	18
Lesser Goldfinch	66	48	13	5
California Quail	65	35	21	9
Common Raven	61	26	23	12
American Goldfinch	59	26	13	20
Downy Woodpecker	59	33	13	13
Bewick's Wren	58	41	9	8
Oak Titmouse	58	51	3	4
Red-shouldered Hawk	58	29	10	19
Northern Rough-winged swallow	54	27	18	9
White-tailed Kite	54	25	11	18
Black-headed Grosbeak	53	27	13	13
Great Horned Owl	53	35	10	8
Chestnut-backed Chickadee	51	48	2	1
Dark-eyed Junco	51	44	4	3
Loggerhead Shrike	51	40	4	7
Western Bluebird	50	48	1	1
Ash-throated Flycatcher	48	38	7	3
Steller's Jay	48	35	9	4
Violet-green Swallow	46	31	11	4
White-breasted Nuthatch	46	34	8	4
Allen's Hummingbird	45	18	4	23
Orange-crowned Warbler	44	30	6	8
Acorn Woodpecker	43	28	8	7

Belted Kingfisher	43	8	11	24
Lazuli Bunting	42	19	13	10
Pacific-slope Flycatcher	42	22	11	9
Canada Goose	41	24	14	3
Wrentit	41	21	14	6
Warbling Vireo	40	22	9	9
Hutton's Vireo	38	28	6	4
Western Wood-Pewee	38	19	11	8
Cooper's Hawk	37	16	8	13
Hooded Oriole	37	24	3	10
Northern Flicker	36	9	18	9
Purple Finch	36	12	11	13
Tree Swallow	36	21	8	7
Western Screech-Owl	36	21	9	6
Green Heron	35	12	8	15
Northern Harrier	35	9	11	15
American Coot	33	21	8	4
White-throated Swift	32	16	7	9
California Thrasher	31	6	15	10
Rufous-crowned Sparrow	30	17	6	7
Blue-gray Gnatcatcher	28	21	3	4
Band-tailed Pigeon	27	8	10	9
Cassin's Vireo	27	12	3	12
Hairy Woodpecker	27	15	5	7
Ring-necked Pheasant	27	4	7	16
Common Yellowthroat	26	10	7	9
Brown Creeper	25	21	0	4
Horned Lark	24	8	9	7
Wilson's Warbler	24	10	8	6
Lawrence's Goldfinch	23	12	9	2
Western Tanager	23	4	9	10
Pied-billed Grebe	22	16	6	0
Grasshopper Sparrow	21	10	6	5
Chipping Sparrow	20	5	9	6
Gadwall	20	8	9	3
Black-necked Stilt	19	9	8	2
Sharp-shinned Hawk	18	3	2	13
Marsh Wren	17	10	4	3
Savannah Sparrow	17	5	3	9
Red-breasted Nuthatch	16	8	1	7
Western Gull	16	8	2	3
White-crowned Sparrow	16	6	5	5
Wild Turkey	16	8	2	6
Blue Grosbeak	14	5	3	6
Olive-sided Flycatcher	14	2	3	9
Swainson's Hawk	14	9	3	2
American Avocet	13	8	5	0
Burrowing Owl	13	8	0	5
Rock Wren	13	4	3	6
Turkey Vulture	13	7	6	0
Wood Duck	12	8	4	0
Cinnamon Teal	11	5	3	3
Swainson's Thrush	11	3	4	4
Common Moorhen	10	5	2	3
Common Poorwill	10	0	2	8
Golden Eagle	10	6	4	0
Ruddy Duck	10	2	5	3
Black-chinned Hummingbird	8	2	0	6
Canyon Wren	7	2	2	3
Phainopepla	7	4	0	3
Sage Sparrow	7	6	1	0
Yellow-billed Magpie	7	5	0	2
American Bittern	6	0	2	4
Black Rail	6	0	3	3
Black-throated Gray Warbler	6	1	0	5
Great Blue Heron	6	5	1	0
Northern Pygmy-Owl	6	0	0	6
Northern Saw-whet Owl	6	5	1	0
Tricolored Blackbird	6	6	0	0
Virginia Rail	6	0	2	4
Yellow Warbler	6	2	1	3
Northern Pintail	5	3	2	0
Prairie Falcon	5	2	1	2
Winter Wren	5	3	1	1
MacGillivray's Warbler	4	2	2	0
Pelagic Cormorant	4	1	3	0
Pygmy Nuthatch	4	3	1	0
Say's Phoebe	4	2	0	2
Black Oystercatcher	3	3	0	0
Black-chinned Sparrow	3	1	1	1
Blue-winged Teal	3	1	1	1
Great Egret	3	3	0	0
Long-eared Owl	3	1	0	2
Northern Shoveler	2	0	2	0
Spotted Sandpiper	2	1	1	0
Yellow-breasted Chat	3	1	2	0
Black-crowned Night-Heron	2	2	0	0
Clapper Rail	2	1	0	1
Double-crested Cormorant	2	1	1	0
Indigo Bunting	2	0	1	1
Least Tern	2	2	0	0
Lesser Nighthawk	2	0	2	0
Peregrine Falcon	2	2	0	0
Short-eared Owl	2	0	0	2
Snowy Egret	2	1	1	0
Western Grebe	2	1	1	0
California Gull	1	1	0	0
Caspian Tern	1	1	0	0
Cedar Waxwing	1	1	0	0
Clark's Grebe	1	1	0	0
Common Merganser	1	0	0	1
Great-tailed Grackle	1	1	0	0
Green-winged Teal	1	1	0	0
Hermit Thrush	1	1	0	0
Osprey	1	1	0	0
Pileated Woodpecker	1	0	0	1
Pine Siskin	1	1	0	0

Identification of Breeding Bird Species of Special Concern

FEDERAL ENDANGERED

California Clapper Rail

California Least Tern

STATE THREATENED

Swainson's Hawk

Black Rail

CALIFORNIA BIRD SPECIES OF SPECIAL CONCERN

The California Bird Species of Special Concern list is an attempt "To meet California's pressing environmental challenges, and provide a means for allocating financial and staff resources, the California Department of Fish and Game (CDFG) has initiated a process to determine and set conservation priorities for native birds..." (Shuford and Gardali 2008).

A species, subspecies, or population has been identified as a "Bird Species of Special Concern" in California if it meets one of 5 criteria, reprinted here because it is so important:

(1) may meet the state definition of threatened or endangered but have not formally been listed.

(2) are extirpated from the state totally or in their primary seasonal or breeding role and were never listed as state threatened or endangered.

(3) are listed as federally, but not state, threatened or endangered.

(4) are experiencing, or formerly experienced, serious population declines or range retractions that if continued, or resumed, could qualify them for state threatened or endangered status.

(5) have naturally small populations exhibiting high susceptibility to risk from any factor(s) that if realized could lead to declines that would qualify them for state threatened or endangered status.

Hence, SSC generally share one or more of the following characteristics:

(1) show marked population declines or range retractions (population estimates are unavailable for the vast majority of taxa),

(2) occur in small, isolated populations or in fragmented habitat and are threatened by further isolation and population reduction,

(3) depend on habitat(s) that historically or recently has declined substantially in size (infers population viability of a taxon is influenced by trends in suitable habitats),

(4) occur only in or adjacent to areas where habitat is being converted to land uses incompatible with the species survival, and

(5) occur largely on public lands for which current management practices are inconsistent with the species' persistence.

Two earlier incarnations of the special concern list have previously been published. A landmark publication was the 1978 paper *Bird Species of Special Concern in California* by J. V. Remsen, Jr. It was followed by a revised list in 1991 by the California Department of Fish and Game. The birds on the two lists are generally similar, although the 1991 list includes additional species, including several local races of the Song Sparrow. Species on the first two versions of the list but not included on the 2007 list include Double-crested Cormorant, Osprey, Sharp-shinned Hawk, Cooper's Hawk, Golden Eagle, Prairie Falcon, California Gull, "California" Horned Lark, and "Bell's" Sage Sparrow. Several of these species, particularly Double-crested Cormorant and Osprey, have undergone population surges in recent years, while a few others are likely more stable than once thought.

Table 3: CALIFORNIA BIRD SPECIES OF SPECIAL CONCERN

First Priority

Tricolored Blackbird

Second Priority

Burrowing Owl
Olive-sided Flycatcher
Loggerhead Shrike (mainland populations)
Yellow Warbler
Grasshopper Sparrow
Alameda Song Sparrow *(Melospiza melodia pusillula)*

Third Priority

Northern Harrier
Black Skimmer
Long-eared Owl
Short-eared Owl
San Francisco Common Yellowthroat *(Geothlypis trichas sinuosa)*
Yellow-breasted Chat
Bryant's Savannah Sparrow *(Passerculus sandwichensis alaudinus)*
Song Sparrow ("Modesto"population)/ subspecies not recognized by Patten (2001)
Suisun Song Sparrow *(Melospiza melodia maxillaris)*
Samuel's Song Sparrow *(Melospiza melodia samuelis)*
Yellow-headed Blackbird

AUDUBON'S WATCHLIST 2002

The Audubon WatchList 2002 (Table 4) was created with the intention of identifying at-risk species before populations can shrink to such low levels that massive amounts of money and manpower are required to avoid their extinction. The list below is not the complete list but includes only the species which breed, or have bred, in Contra Costa County. Note that while several species on the list also appear on the list of California Bird Species of Special Concern, several others might, at first glance, be cause for surprise. Many of the species are listed here because of their limited ranges. For example, species such as Nuttall's Woodpecker, Oak Titmouse, Wrentit, and California Thrasher breed commonly in California but have limited ranges outside of the state. The Yellow-billed Magpie is a true California endemic, and has never been reliably recorded outside of the state. "Red List" species are thought to be declining rapidly and/or have very small populations or limited ranges. They also face major conservation threats and area typically of global concern. "Yellow List" species are either declining or are rare. They are generally species of national concern.

Table 4: AUDUBON'S WATCHLIST 2002

The numbers following the species listed below represent an estimate of the total population.

Red List Species

Black Rail
Nuttall's Woodpecker 100–200,000
Lawrence's Goldfinch <200,000

Yellow List Species

Swainson's Hawk
Black Oystercatcher 8,900
Band-tailed Pigeon
Short-eared Owl
White-throated Swift
Allen's Hummingbird
Olive-sided Flycatcher

Yellow-billed Magpie 25–50,000
Oak Titmouse
Wrentit
California Thrasher
Black-chinned Sparrow
Tricolored Blackbird

PRELIMINARY LIST OF CONTRA COSTA COUNTY SPECIES OF CONCERN

This list, based on the example set forth in Shuford (1993), includes additional species not found on the published lists discussed above but which nonetheless face significant obstacles to their long-term survival in Contra Costa County. The species here have not been chosen in a particularly scientific fashion, but have been selected either because the species has shown clear-cut declines in recent decades or is vulnerable because the number of breeding sites is small.

Wood Duck — tiny population dependent upon freshwater ponds; population possibly not self-sustaining.

Northern Pintail — known to nest at a small number of freshwater sites.

Ruddy Duck — known to breed at a small number of freshwater sites.

Double-crested Cormorant — known to breed at a single site.

Pelagic Cormorant — known to breed at a single site that is vulnerable to disturbance.

American Bittern — very small breeding population found only in freshwater marshes.

Great Blue Heron — known to nest at only a handful of sites; vulnerable to nest disturbance.

Great Egret — known to nest at only a handful of sites; vulnerable to disturbance at nest sites.

Snowy Egret — known to nest sporadically at only one site.

Black-crowned Night-Heron — known to nest at only a handful of sites; vulnerable to disturbance at nest sites.

Osprey — possibly just one nesting pair in the county.

Northern Harrier — vulnerable to recent widespread conversion of grasslands to housing.

Swainson's Hawk — although increasing in recent years, still vulnerable to habitat destruction.

Peregrine Falcon — vulnerable to nest site disturbance.

Prairie Falcon — tiny population subject to nest site disturbance.

Golden Eagle — very small population threatened by habitat fragmentation and nest site disturbance.

Black Rail — modest population threatened by habitat destruction.

Clapper Rail — small population threatened by habitat destruction.

Common Moorhen — small population reliant upon a dwindling number of freshwater ponds and sloughs.

Black Oystercatcher — tiny population vulnerable to nest site disturbance and oil pollution.

Spotted Sandpiper — known to nest at only two sites.

Caspian Tern — nests at only a single colony that is vulnerable to disturbance and the potential of a catastrophic oil spill.

Least Tern — just a single long-term nest colony.

Burrowing Owl — rapidly declining species; deeply vulnerable to urban development.

Short-eared Owl — possibly extirpated as a breeder; remaining grassland breeding habitat disappearing rapidly.

Lesser Nighthawk — only a handful of pairs suspected of breeding in imperiled Central Valley habitats.

Belted Kingfisher — nest sites limited by an inherent lack of dirt bank nest sites, this aggravated by stream channelization.

Olive-sided Flycatcher — tiny breeding population.

Loggerhead Shrike — breeding population declining due to rapid destruction of open habitats in East County.

Horned Lark — localized breeding population vulnerable to destruction of grassland nest sites.

Yellow-billed Magpie — known to nest at a handful of sites in East County.

Hermit Thrush — known to nest only around Redwood Peak.

Yellow Warbler — just two breeding pairs detected during the atlas.

Yellow-breasted Chat — perhaps as few as ten breeding pairs in the county, none of which are in protected areas.

Song Sparrow — local subspecies with limited ranges are vulnerable to habitat destruction.

White-crowned Sparrow — subject to severe loss of habitat in their limited local range; a prime target for cowbirds.

Tricolored Blackbird — colonies vulnerable to habitat destruction.

A Comparison of the Number of Breeding Bird Species in 1927 and 2008

Although the attention of the birding community tends to focus on imperiled species, there can be little doubt that the number of breeding species in Contra Costa County has increased significantly since the 1927 publication of *Directory to the Bird-Life of the San Francisco Bay Region*. A minimum of 38 species have commenced nesting during that time, many of them part of well-documented range extensions.

Extensive research by William Bousman has revealed that the list of breeding birds in Contra Costa County discovered by 1927 numbered just 86 species. That this is the third lowest total for the nine-county Bay Area is strong evidence for the idea that the county was lightly visited by early ornithologists and egg collectors. Of these 86 species there is direct evidence of confirmation (*i.e.* egg sets) for only about 30 species. The rest are assumed by Bousman to have bred based upon comments found in Grinnell and Wythe (1927). For example, the California Acorn-storing Woodpecker is cited as a common resident in each of the bay counties except San Francisco. The 86 species represents just 50% of the species known by Bousman to have nested in the Bay region by 1927.

As of 2007, Bousman (2007) had found evidence for 220 nesting species in the Bay region, including four species which he considered extirpated since 1927 (Fulvous Whistling-Duck, Yellow-billed Cuckoo, Lesser Nighthawk, and Willow Flycatcher), and one which was already extirpated by 1927 (California Condor) for a historical total of 220. By this time 161 species had been confirmed breeding and 6 more species were assumed breeding in Contra Costa County. The total of confirmed and probable breeders in Contra Costa County is 167, or 76% of the species known to have bred in the Bay region as a whole, far higher than the 50% calculated for 1927.

HOW MANY SPECIES WERE TRULY BREEDING BY 1927?

It is impossible to determine exactly how many species truly began to nest in the county after 1927 and how many were already nesting but were never confirmed. Additional species may well have been confirmed nesting but the documentation has either been lost or is housed in sources of which we are unaware. Certainly more than 86 species were nesting in the county in 1927.

Species known or assumed to nest in Contra Costa County by 1927, based on Bousman (2007).

California Quail	Burrowing Owl	Warbling Vireo
Great Blue Heron	Common Poorwill	Steller's Jay
Turkey Vulture	White-throated Swift	Western Scrub-Jay
White-tailed Kite	Anna's Hummingbird	American Crow
Red-shouldered Hawk	Allen's Hummingbird	Horned Lark
Red-tailed Hawk	Acorn Woodpecker	N. Rough-winged Swallow
Swainson's Hawk	Nuttall's Woodpecker	Bank Swallow
Golden Eagle	Downy Woodpecker	Barn Swallow
American Kestrel	Hairy Woodpecker	Cliff Swallow
Peregrine Falcon	Northern Flicker	Oak Titmouse
Prairie Falcon	Olive-sided Flycatcher	Bushtit
American Coot	Western Wood-Pewee	White-breasted Nuthatch
Killdeer	Pacific-slope Flycatcher	Canyon Wren
Rock Pigeon	Black Phoebe	Bewick's Wren
Mourning Dove	Ash-throated Flycatcher	House Wren
Greater Roadrunner	Western Kingbird	Blue-gray Gnatcatcher
Barn Owl	Loggerhead Shrike	Western Bluebird
Western Screech-Owl	Cassin's Vireo	Swainson's Thrush
Great Horned Owl	Hutton's Vireo	American Robin

Wrentit	Rufous-crowned Sparrow	Yellow-headed Blackbird
California Thrasher	Chipping Sparrow	Brewer's Blackbird
Orange-crowned Warbler	Lark Sparrow	Bullock's Oriole
Yellow Warbler	Sage Sparrow	Purple Finch
MacGillivray's Warbler	Savannah Sparrow	House Finch
Common Yellowthroat	Song Sparrow	Lesser Goldfinch
Wilson's Warbler	Black-headed Grosbeak	Lawrence's Goldfinch
Yellow-breasted Chat	Lazuli Bunting	American Goldfinch
Spotted Towhee	Red-winged Blackbird	House Sparrow
California Towhee	Western Meadowlark	

In addition to the 86 species identified by Bousman (2007) as having bred by 1927, the following 26 species likely did as well:

Mallard	Virginia Rail	Marsh Wren
Cinnamon Teal	American Avocet	Hermit Thrush
Ruddy Duck	Northern Saw-whet Owl	Phainopepla
Pied-billed Grebe	Lesser Nighthawk	Black-chinned Sparrow
American Bittern	Black-chinned Hummingbird	Grasshopper Sparrow
Sharp-shinned Hawk	Belted Kingfisher	White-crowned Sparrow
Cooper's Hawk	Tree Swallow	Blue Grosbeak
Black Rail	Violet-green Swallow	Tricolored Blackbird
Clapper Rail	Rock Wren	

This brings the likely pre-1927 total to 112.

Based solely upon the judgments of the author, the following 17 may very well have bred in Contra Costa County before 1927:

Wood Duck	Great Egret	Long-eared Owl
Gadwall	Snowy Egret	Short-eared Owl
Northern Shoveler	Green Heron	Brown Creeper
Northern Pintail	Black-crowned Night-Heron	Black-throated Gray Warbler
Green-winged Teal	Black-necked Stilt	Western Tanager
Ring-necked Pheasant	Northern Pygmy-Owl	

This brings the confirmed, probable and possible pre-1927 total to 129 species.

This new total of 129 species represents 78% of the species which have been confirmed breeding or are assumed to do so in the known history of Contra Costa County. This leaves an additional 38 species which very likely began to breed after 1927. Range extensions have been well-documented for most of these species and many others are conspicuous species which would not likely have been overlooked.

Mute Swan	Spotted Sandpiper	Pygmy Nuthatch
Canada Goose	California Gull	Winter Wren
Blue-winged Teal	Western Gull	Northern Mockingbird
Wild Turkey	Least Tern	European Starling
Western Grebe	Caspian Tern	Cedar Waxwing
Clark's Grebe	Black Skimmer	Dark-eyed Junco
Double-crested Cormorant	Band-tailed Pigeon	Rose-breasted Grosbeak
Pelagic Cormorant	Pileated Woodpecker	Indigo Bunting
Osprey	Say's Phoebe	Great-tailed Grackle
Bald Eagle	Yellow-billed Magpie	Brown-headed Cowbird
Northern Harrier	Common Raven	Hooded Oriole
Common Moorhen	Chestnut-backed Chickadee	Pine Siskin
Black Oystercatcher	Red-breasted Nuthatch	

CONTENT OF SPECIES ACCOUNTS

Interpreting the Atlas Maps

Each species which was known to breed, or suspected of breeding in Contra Costa County during the atlas field work of 1998–2002 is represented by a map. Additional species which bred prior to 1998 are treated in Appendix A and species which nested after 2002 are treated in Appendix B but maps are included for neither group. Each map features a basic map of Contra Costa County with an overlain grid. The grid contains 107 blocks which are either fully or partially within the boundaries of Contra Costa County. Eleven periphery blocks, primarily in East County, either included a tiny portion of Contra Costa County and/or was not visited during the project. Data were collected in 96 blocks. The bold dotted line marks the boundary of Contra Costa County. Unbroken lines within the county represent major freeways (see map inside front cover). Shaded areas on the map represent state and regional parks while hatched areas represent military land. Three symbols are used to represent three levels of evidence within individual blocks—empty circles represent possible nesting, half-filled circles represent probable nesting, and filled circles represent confirmed nesting.

Reading the Species Accounts

As with all atlas projects the focal point is, and should be, the maps. However, as Dave Shuford said so eloquently in his classic *The Marin County Breeding Bird Atlas* (1993), "…they are lifeless abstractions without an understanding of the intricate web of niche requirements that each species must meet for survival, and without their survival there is no atlas or map." Although this atlas book has neither the space, nor Shuford's expertise, to match the published Marin atlas, the accounts published here are an attempt to not only establish which species are found in which five-square-kilometer block, but also in which habitats they occur, whether or not their status and distribution has changed since record keeping began, when they breed, and whether their populations appear threatened.

Each account begins with some brief opening comments. In select cases, we have chosen to use quotations from William Leon Dawson's 1923 multi-volume masterpiece *The Birds of California*. Possibly due to its scarcity, the work is almost forgotten by most modern California birders. This is a shame because although the tone of the book may sound quaint to modern ears, there are many fascinating insights into the birds of California that have rarely, if ever, appeared elsewhere.

The second section, entitled "Current status and distribution," is an attempt to summarize as succinctly as possible in a couple of paragraphs where in the county each bird is found and in which habitat types. Numerous geographical phrases are repeated throughout the text. "West County" and "Bay plain" are used interchangeably and refer to the relatively flat terrain between San Francisco and San Pablo bays to the west and the Berkeley Hills to the east. This includes the flat portions of Richmond, El Cerrito, Pinole, San Pablo, Rodeo and Hercules. "Coast Range" is a term that encompasses both the Berkeley Hills to the west and the Diablo Range to the east; the latter two terms are frequently used, as numerous species are far more common and widespread in one more than the other. The label "Interstate-680 corridor" is a convenient dividing line that runs north to south, neatly bisecting the county. Though the line is actually a freeway and is somewhat arbitrary, there are clear average differences between the floras and the corresponding avifaunas of each side. The terms "Central Valley" and "East County" refer to the Contra Costa County portion of California's Great Central Valley, and is essentially everything flat that is east of the Diablo Range. On a few occasions we refer to the "Delta," a low-lying sub-region of the Central Valley itself, represented in Contra Costa County around northern Antioch, north and east of Brentwood, east of Knightsen and east of Bryon.

Descriptions of habitats are necessarily vague, more so in some accounts than others. This is mainly due to the fact that neither the author, nor the vast majority of the members of the atlas team, has any training whatsoever in botany. In some accounts we have chosen to utilize habitat descriptions found in papers specifically written about the local avifauna (see Black Rail for example). On numerous occasions we have appropriated habitat descriptions from Shuford (1993) as they appear particularly precise and are written about a county very close by. Habitat types are based upon Mayer and Laudenslayer, Jr. (1988).

In "Historical occurrence" we discuss any obvious changes which may have occurred during historical times. An attempt has been made to cite first county sightings and first known nest records, if any could be tracked down. This section is often a mere sentence for common species that have likely been common throughout historical times and for which little information has been published. Species like Western Scrub-Jay and Oak Titmouse are two good examples of this. Other accounts, particularly for those species that have colonized the county during historical times, may be much longer (see Chestnut-backed Chickadee for a particularly lengthy example). In some cases, egg sets collected from the county (most now in the possession of the Museum of Vertebrate Zoology and the Western Foundation of Vertebrate Zoology) are cited to document the earliest known nest records for the county.

In "Breeding and natural history," our goal was to make as much sense as possible of the mountain of data collected by the atlas team by constructing nesting chronologies for each species. For some common and conspicuous nesting birds, the atlas data appeared sufficient to establish a reasonable chronology. For other species, however, particularly those species which nest either sporadically or in very tiny numbers, we have fleshed out our data with additional data from published sources. Typically this was data from atlases already published for northern California (Marin, San Mateo, Sonoma, Napa, San Mateo and Humboldt counties) but occasionally was culled from scientific papers or from the *Birds of North America* series. *The San Mateo County Breeding Bird Atlas* (Sequoia Audubon Society 2001) was particularly helpful in this regard, as that atlas chose to publish its entire database in the atlas. It is unfortunate that the Santa Clara County Atlas was published as the writing of this atlas was nearly complete as much of the information contained there would have proven useful.

Information regarding other aspects of breeding and natural history are minimal, if for no other reason than the fact that both Shuford (1993) and Roberson and Tenney (1993) have already filled this need admirably. For instance, the dietary needs of the Gadwall, while fascinating, is covered in depth by Shuford and need not be repeated in every atlas.

Finally, the "Conservation" section is intended to identify threats to the well-being of a particular species, either locally or throughout its range. Here we cite if a species is included in any "watch-lists," including species which are Federally Endangered, State Threatened, or appear on California Bird Species of Special Concern lists, the most recent of which was released in 2008 (Shuford and Gardali).

Abbreviations

(Gull) = *The Gull*, the newsletter of the Golden Gate Audubon Society

(Quail) = *The Quail*, the newsletter of the Mt. Diablo Audubon Society

(Kite) = *The Kite Call*, the newsletter of the Ohlone Audubon Society

(AFN) = *Audubon Field Notes* January 1947–October 1970

(AB) = *American Birds* February 1971–Spring 1994

(FN) = *Field Notes* Summer 1994–Winter 1988

(NAB) = *North American Birds* Spring 1999–present

(MVZ) = Museum of Vertebrate Zoology, University of California, Berkeley

(WFVZ) = Western Foundation of Vertebrate Zoology, Camarillo, California

(EBMUD) = East Bay Municipal Utilities District

(EBRPD) = East Bay Regional Parks District

Mt. = Mountain

Rd. = Road

Res. = Reservoir

CBC = Christmas Bird Count

Other explanations

Bay Area: The Bay Area is generally considered to include the nine counties contiguous with the San Francisco Bay estuary but excluding Sacramento and San Joaquin counties to the east. Clockwise from the northwest, these counties are Sonoma, Napa, Solano, Contra Costa, Alameda, Santa Clara, San Mateo, San Francisco, and Marin.

Bay region: This term is used interchangeably with Bay Area.

fide means "by way of" and refers to information passed on by the person credited but that source did not personally obtain that information.

"pers. comm." refers to information passed on by "personal communication" by the person credited.

"pers. obs." means a "personal observation" of the author.

County notebooks: The county notebooks refers to a set of binders compiled by the author which includes noteworthy citations culled from *The Condor, North American Birds* and its predecessors, and the three local Audubon Society newsletters. This term is used in the text in just a handful of instances.

NAB Notebooks: The binders and, for more recent years, computer databases, for the northern California region of *North American Birds* magazine.

Audubon Society newsletters: *The Gull* (Golden Gate Audubon Society), *The Kite Call* (Ohlone Audubon Society), and *The Quail* (Mt. Diablo Audubon Society).

Species Accounts

American Goldfinch

GARDNER

CANADA GOOSE • *Branta canadensis*

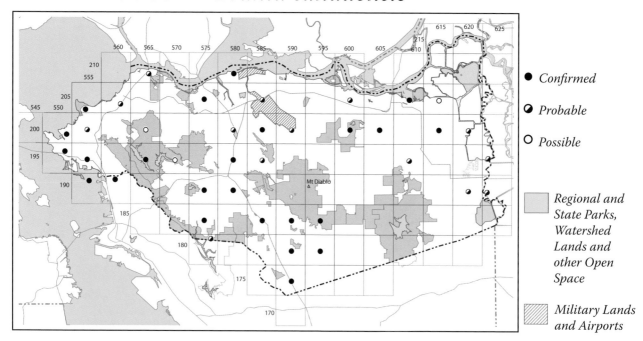

Many mistake the sound of honking Canada Geese over their neighborhood as a signal that the timelessness of migration is playing out over their very rooftops. Most often, however, this "migration" is from a city duck pond on one side of town to a golf course on the other.

Current status and distribution

The Canada Goose breeds widely throughout the western half of the county in most of the blocks containing significant ponds, reservoirs, city parks and golf courses. Gaps in the map generally reflect "hilly" blocks lacking significant amounts of freshwater. The species is most common in the central part of the county along the Interstate 680 corridor, where there are many city duck ponds and golf courses, as well as McNabney Marsh where the county's largest population resides. From 2002–2004 an average of 50 pairs were estimated to breed there (pers. obs.). A lack of habitat in the Diablo Range has prevented even a toehold there. In East County, it is most common at sewage treatment plants in Oakley, Brentwood and Byron but is generally absent from the southeast corner of the county where the few freshwater ponds tend to dry early in the breeding season. The species overall scarcity in East County, reflected in the atlas map, may be rectified in the coming decades as a plethora of golf courses and accompanying ponds have sprung up there in recent years.

Historical occurrence

The Canada Goose was unknown as a breeding bird anywhere in the Bay Area early in the 20th century (Grinnell and Wythe 1927). Grinnell and Miller (1944) cite the first nesting in the Bay Area sometime in 1932 at Crystal Springs Res., San Mateo County. It seems likely that the resident population of the Bay Area is descended from transplanted birds, rather than naturally occurring birds (see Shuford 1993 for a more thorough discussion). The first known nest record for Contra Costa County is at Brooks Island near Richmond in 1959 (Lidicker and McCollum 1979).

Breeding and natural history

The atlas project amassed forty-four records of breeding confirmations. Nests with eggs or adults occupying nests presumed to contain eggs were noted as early as 9 March; none was noted later than 14 May. The earliest detected precocial young was 21 April; nearly full-grown young were noted well into June.

Conservation

Based upon its wholesale adaptation to altered habitats, the future of the breeding Canada Goose population in Contra Costa County appears assured.

WOOD DUCK • *Aix sponsa*

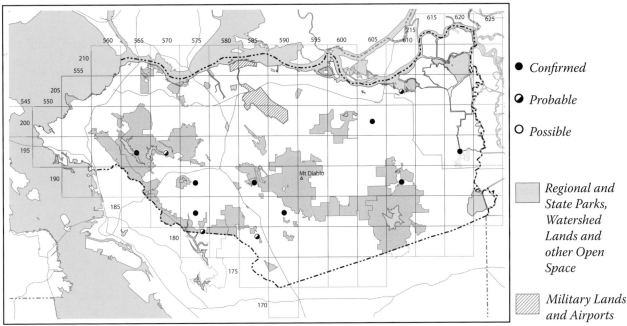

The true status of this, the county's most gaudily colored breeding bird, is confused due to the planting of adult birds and eggs at various (sometimes dubious) sites in the county. Origins, however, are quickly forgotten when one is confronted with the beauty of this sublime duck.

Current status and distribution

Nesting Wood Ducks were present almost exclusively in central portions of the county; none were found around Richmond and or in the north-central portion. The only known breeding station in East County is at Discovery Bay, a planned community built around water where the species has been known to utilize nest boxes since at least the early 1990s (county notebooks). Nesting "woodies" were present at Upper San Leandro Res., Lafayette Res., San Pablo Res., near downtown Walnut Creek, Marsh Creek Res., and at a small stock pond on Empire Mine Rd. just south of Antioch. At the latter location, there were no trees in the immediate vicinity, suggesting that they may have been planted at the site.

Wood Ducks prefer shady, wooded waterways and ponds in the few places such habitats occur in the county. Situations featuring rapidly moving water are inevitably shunned. Smaller ponds are also apparently preferred over larger ones, although shady coves around the margins of the large watershed reservoirs frequently host small flocks.

Wood Ducks most often nest in natural tree cavities as well as holes excavated by Pileated Woodpeckers and even Northern Flickers. Suitable cavities are generally scarce in the county and this is likely a prime reason for

their traditional rarity as breeders. In fact, the use of natural cavities has never been documented in Contra Costa County. In recent years, however, wooden nest boxes have been placed around ponds and reservoirs throughout the county, particularly in the Berkeley Hills.

Historical occurrence

The former status of the Wood Duck in Contra Costa County is unclear although it is unlikely that the species was ever common. Grinnell and Wythe (1927) state that they were historically present in the San Francisco Bay Area "in some numbers" but hadn't been detected in recent years. Contra Costa County was not mentioned in the summary, which isn't surprising considering a dearth of perennial streams and reservoirs. Of the four local watershed reservoirs, only two had recently been completed (San Pablo and Upper San Leandro), one was almost completed (Lafayette) and Briones wouldn't be completed until 1964.

19th century writers commented on the abundance of Wood Ducks in California and apparently as many as 100 could be shot in a single day in the Sacramento Valley. But by 1913 the species was felt to be on the verge of extinction in California, due mainly to excessive hunting and wholesale habitat destruction (Banks and Springer 1994). There was an increase in subsequent years but it either wasn't felt locally or it went undocumented until the early 1950s. A sighting of 400–500 birds at San Pablo Res. on 29 Nov 1952 (AFN 41: no.1) is far and away the largest number ever recorded in the county.

The fact that the Wood Duck was abundant in the

Sacramento Valley in the 19th century is suggestive of the possibility that the species may have once been common in eastern Contra Costa County as well. Although Wood Ducks are locally detected most often from the watershed reservoirs of the Coast Ranges, it seems more than likely that in the days before levee-building and drainage, their former stronghold would have been the marshes and sloughs of the Delta.

Breeding and natural history

All twelve atlas confirmations involved precocial young, with dates ranging between 30 April and 4 August; the bulk of them from June. It is unclear, however, how many of these records—if any—pertain to wild birds. In Monterey County, seven of eight records of precocial young were detected between 16 May and 6 June (Roberson and Tenney 1993). The date span for precocial young in San Mateo County was more protracted: 11 April through 25 August (Sequoia Audubon Society 2001). Mid-late summer records of precocial young presumably refer to second broods, something the species is particularly well known for.

Conservation

A dearth of both suitable habitat and nest cavities in Contra Costa County would seem to assure the continued scarcity of nesting Wood Ducks. The lack of natural nest cavities has been partially overcome by the widespread placement of nest boxes but the fact remains that there are few suitable places to put them.

GADWALL

GADWALL • *Anas strepera*

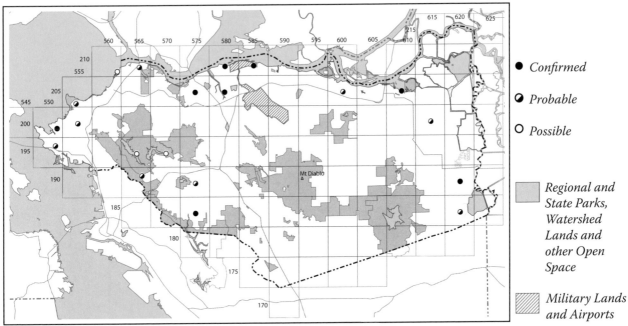

● *Confirmed*

◐ *Probable*

○ *Possible*

▨ *Regional and State Parks, Watershed Lands and other Open Space*

▨ *Military Lands and Airports*

Far and away the most understated of our local waterfowl, Gadwalls, particularly females, almost avoid detection by those who don't appreciate the subtleties of a study in browns. In fact, they are one of our more common breeding ducks despite the fact that breeding sites are relatively few.

Current status and distribution

Gadwalls were confirmed nesting in eight blocks along the western, northern and eastern boundaries of the county and in one block in the watershed lands at Upper San Leandro Res. The species was most common in the marshes around Concord and Martinez, as at McNabney Marsh where an estimated 12–15 pairs nested in 2002 (pers. obs.). The two confirmations from the eastern portion of the county were at sewage ponds at Oakley and Byron. Numerous pairs present on watershed reservoirs well into May hint that nesting may be more widespread in the Berkeley Hills than our confirmations indicate.

Historical occurrence

Because the Gadwall is now found so readily, it seems surprising that the species was once considered quite rare locally. In fact, Grinnell and Wythe (1927) knew of no records of Gadwall for either Alameda or Contra Costa Counties. Breeding in the Bay Area began as early as 1965 (Bousman 2007), but the first breeding record for Contra Costa County wasn't recorded until 30 June 1995 when two females were noted on nests at McNabney Marsh (FN 49: no. 5).

Breeding and natural history

The eleven atlas records of precocial young—dates ranging from 3 May to 21 June—suggest that Gadwalls in Contra Costa County begin to breed later than our other common breeding ducks such as Mallard and Cinnamon Teal. Data from the *San Mateo County Breeding Bird Atlas* strongly indicates that the local breeding season is a lengthier affair. Precocial young there were detected as early as 10 April and as late as 1 August (Sequoia Audubon Society 2001).

Conservation

Like many of our breeding waterbirds, the long-term future of nesting Gadwalls in Contra Costa County is wholly dependent upon the protection of dwindling wetlands.

MALLARD • *Anas platyrhynchos*

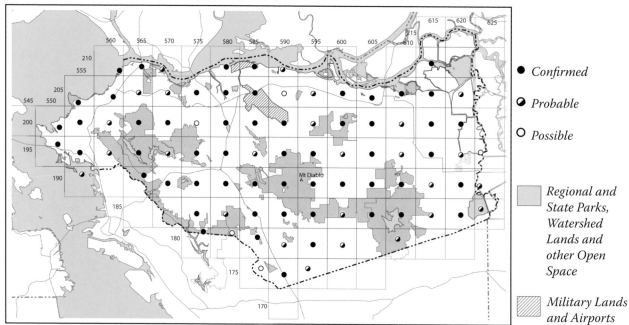

Legend:
- ● Confirmed
- ◑ Probable
- ○ Possible
- ▨ Regional and State Parks, Watershed Lands and other Open Space
- ▨ Military Lands and Airports

The incredibly adaptable Mallard is not only one of our most common breeding waterfowl but is one of the most widespread of all of Contra Costa County's breeding birds. Confirming Mallards was not a problem for the atlas team but discerning truly "wild" birds from domestic ones proved problematic, particularly when found at urban sites in association with rabble of questionable heritage.

Current status and distribution

Easily our most common breeding waterbird, the Mallard was detected in every complete block in the county, with confirmations in an impressive 56 blocks; the species was found to be probable in nearly every remaining block. The species was seemingly present everywhere in the county that was wet, including fresh and saline emergent wetlands, reservoirs, sewage ponds, duck ponds, golf courses, urban creeks and irrigation ditches.

Historical occurrence

Grinnell and Wythe (1927) considered the Mallard to be common residents of the Bay Area but it seems entirely possible that they have become more common still, particularly during the breeding season, due in great part to pervasive habitat alteration that has met their needs.

Breeding and natural history

Mallards were confirmed nesting an even one hundred times during the atlas project, with nearly all records based upon occupied nests or, especially, precocial young. Nine occupied nests were found 16 March through 4 July. Ninety records of precocial young were detected 26 March to as late as 7 August. Late records

of young hint at either a second brood (apparently rare in Mallards but see below) or re-nesting. The idea of re-nesting is supported by a dozen June records of pairs, as the pair bond is apparently broken in Mallards once the female begins to incubate. Mallards have also been found to be more likely to produce a second brood in some urban and "unnaturally crowded" situations (Drilling and others 2002).

Although the actual number of breeding pairs in most urban blocks is probably modest, more "natural" habitats may host large numbers of breeding pairs. McNabney Marsh, which was thoroughly surveyed during the breeding seasons of 2002–2004, had an estimated average of sixty-seven pairs (pers. obs.).

Conservation

The adaptability of the Mallard to a world molded for human use has likely assured its long-term success in Contra Costa County.

BLUE-WINGED TEAL • *Anas discors*

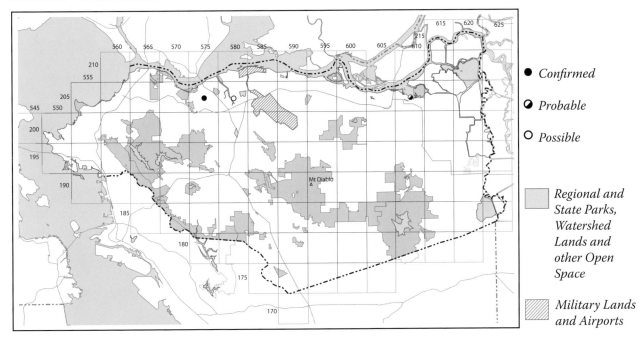

● *Confirmed*

◑ *Probable*

○ *Possible*

▨ *Regional and State Parks, Watershed Lands and other Open Space*

▨ *Military Lands and Airports*

Because Contra Costa County lies snugly within the range of the Cinnamon Teal and only at the very periphery of that of the dapper Blue-winged Teal, the sighting of a Blue-winged Teal in Contra Costa County has traditionally been a coveted moment for local birders and never more so than during the breeding season.

Current status and distribution

The Blue-winged Teal might best be considered very rare and sporadic nester in Contra Costa County (but note words of caution from Shuford below). On 25 May 2000, a male Blue-winged Teal was present at McNabney Marsh, possibly providing the first "summer" record for the county. On 8 June 2000 there were two males present but overshadowed by a well-studied female with ten tiny precocial young in tow, providing the first and only breeding record for Contra Costa County. Tantalizing was the discovery of four males and at least one female in a flooded, grassy field at the Iron House Sanitary District property in Oakley on the intriguing date of 10 June 2000. These birds were involved in vigorous courtship displays but, sadly, the field was drained shortly thereafter and the birds disappeared. On 7 June 2001 a male was along Waterfront Rd. near the Concord Naval Weapons Station, indicating the possibility of breeding there as well.

Historical occurrence

Grinnell and Wythe (1927) knew of only two instances of occurrence for the Bay Area, neither of which was in the East Bay. The first record for Contra Costa County may not have been until 1964 when one was found at Heather Pond, in what is today Walnut Creek's Heather Farm Park (county notebooks). In the ensuing decades a handful of birds were found annually in winter, most often at McNabney Marsh near Martinez. The first recorded nest record for the Bay Area involved precocial young in Santa Clara County 21 May 1974 (Bousman 2007).

Breeding and natural history

Neither the scant information compiled during the atlas project nor data culled from other published Northern California atlases is of much use in determining a nesting chronology—they are simply too rare as breeders. Blue-winged Teal are notably late migrants, often appearing well into June, with various atlases reporting numerous records of pairs or small groups that weren't thought to have remained to nest. It is possible that each of our three records, other than the possible breeding record, pertain to late migrants.

Conservation

Although we treat the above record as being a valid confirmation, Shuford (1993) sternly points out that even a cautiously identified female Blue-winged Teal with young is not a certain indication of "pure" breeding as the father may still have been a Cinnamon Teal. He further reasons that a number of sightings of accurately identified females with broods would reduce the likelihood of mixed-species pairs but this was not possible here.

CINNAMON TEAL • *Anas cyanoptera*

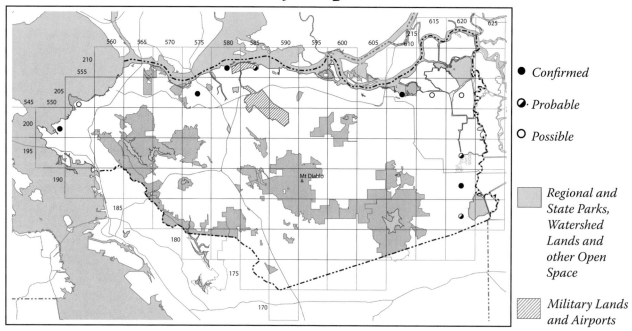

If the bird-lover confesses a somewhat languid interest in the old standbys of duckdom, Mallard, Widgeon, Shoveler, and the rest, the species which have quacked and spattered their way through literature for generations, it is a far different matter with our champion of the West. For him we are not ashamed to confess a fresh interest and a kindling of desire. Whether our attitude be that of sportsman, bird-lover or student, surely no more alluring spectacle could be afforded than that of a flock of these brilliant chestnut-colored ducks when they rise suddenly from a wayside pond at break of day.

> ❧ *William Leon Dawson (1923)*

The superb male Cinnamon Teal is one of the most beautiful of our breeding birds; the female, however, is somber and difficult to differentiate from the scarce but coveted Blue-winged Teal. Contra Costa County is blessed, in a sense, as the Cinnamon Teal is the second most common breeding duck in the county and is available for study year round.

Current status and distribution

The Cinnamon Teal was confirmed breeding at five widely scattered sites, each around the periphery of the county. The species was most common around McNabney Marsh (where an estimated 45 pairs were thought to breed in 2002) and Waterfront Rd. north of Concord. Additional breeding sites include Iron House Sanitary District near Oakley, the sewage ponds at the east end of Camino Diablo in Byron, and the marsh at the mouth of Wildcat Creek in Richmond. Pairs were detected elsewhere in the eastern part of the county but most were in temporarily flooded fields that tended to dry up too rapidly for completion of

breeding. It is likely that the species bred in inaccessible northern and eastern blocks.

In general, nesting Cinnamon Teal are found in non-tidal fresh emergent wetlands, but are occasionally found in more brackish saline emergent wetlands. Sewage ponds are also readily used if emergent vegetation is allowed to thrive.

Historical occurrence

Grinnell and Wythe (1927) were either unaware of any breeding records for Contra Costa County or didn't consider them important enough to merit citation. However, their mention of nesting records from adjacent Alameda and Solano counties, each of which enjoyed more thorough coverage in the early 20th century, suggests that breeding likely occurred but was never documented.

Breeding and natural history

The breeding season of the Cinnamon Teal in California (beginning with the first nest initiation to the last successful hatch) is believed to extend from late March to late July (Gammonley 1996). During the atlas, precocial Cinnamon Teal were noted as early as 16 April, suggesting that the nest was initiated by mid-March. The latest date for precocial young was 14 July.

Conservation

The future success of Contra Costa County's Cinnamon Teal population depends upon the protection of remaining wetlands. The retention of suitable habitat throughout the breeding season at the region's various sewage treatment facilities would further increase viability.

NORTHERN SHOVELER • *Anas clypeata*

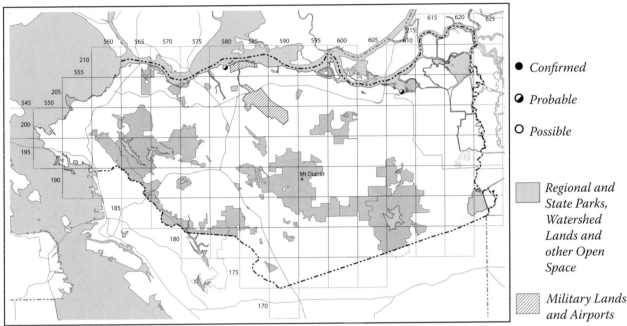

Confirmed

Probable

Possible

Regional and
State Parks,
Watershed
Lands and
other Open
Space

Military Lands
and Airports

This spoon-billed dabbling duck is a common and sometimes abundant winter resident on bodies of freshwater and yet the species is one of our scarcest breeding birds. In fact, the Northern Shoveler was never confirmed nesting during the atlas project.

Current status and distribution

Pairs of Northern Shovelers were present during the breeding season along Waterfront Rd. north of Concord on 3 June 1998, at McNabney Marsh on 13 May 2000, and at Iron House Sanitary District near Oakley on 20 May 2000. In 2002 a male was present at McNabney Marsh through at least 1 June. Each of these areas features the freshwater and/or brackish ponds needed for breeding, although conditions are subject to variations of quality from year to year. That the only breeding record comes from McNabney Marsh may be due in part to the fact that it is the most accessible and heavily watched freshwater marsh in the county.

Historical occurrence

The sole breeding record for Contra Costa County was furnished by a pair of adults with nine precocial young at McNabney Marsh on 30 June 1995 (FN 49: no. 2). Although the species was never recorded breeding prior to 1995, that may be an artifact of coverage, as the species is known to have bred at Hayward and Alvarado, Alameda County, in the 19th century (Grinnell and Miller 1944).

Breeding and natural history

The Northern Shoveler is a scarce breeding species in the Bay Area. Nevertheless, nearly forty records of precocial young were culled from local breeding bird atlases and the NAB notebooks. The earliest record of precocial young was 2 May in San Mateo County (Sequoia Audubon Society 2001), although the vast majority of such records are concentrated in the period from late May through early July.

Conservation

If the Northern Shoveler is to maintain even a limited summer presence in the county, the protection and creation of freshwater ponds is crucial.

NORTHERN PINTAIL • *Anas acuta*

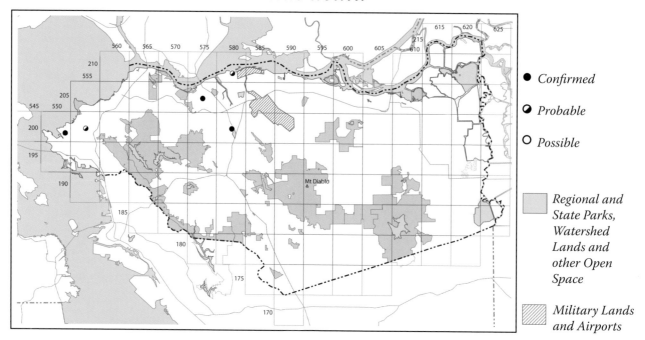

Confirmed

Probable

Possible

Regional and State Parks, Watershed Lands and other Open Space

Military Lands and Airports

The Northern Pintail, with conservative colors and an elegant profile, brings a simple grace to a select number of wetland sites in Contra Costa County.

Current status and distribution

Breeding Northern Pintail were detected at only three locations: near the mouth of Wildcat Creek in Richmond; near the Concord Airport; and, where the species is most common, McNabney Marsh near Martinez. Thorough surveys of McNabney Marsh in 2002 suggest that about 15 pairs bred that year. By 2004 that number had dropped to 6 to 7 pairs (pers. obs.). Pairs were also detected in June at the Concord Naval Weapons Station but breeding was never confirmed.

Breeding Northern Pintails may be found in saline and fresh emergent wetlands and ponds near the shores of both the San Francisco Bay estuary and the Delta.

Historical occurrence

Grinnell and Wythe (1927) cited two instances of breeding from Alameda County but were unaware of any such records from Contra Costa County. The first known breeding record for Contra Costa County was provided by a female with young at the Mt. View Sanitary District/McNabney Marsh complex on 22 June 1989 (NAB notebooks). Although the pintail was not found breeding in East County during the atlas project, a female with five young was at Iron House Sanitary District near Oakley 20 Aug 1995 (Quail 42: no. 2).

Breeding and natural history

The atlas project yielded eight records of precocial pintail spanning 25 April–8 June. In Northern California, the Northern Pintail is thought to typically arrive in breeding areas in March, with nest initiation extending from mid-March through mid-June. Hatching occurs between early May and early July (Austin and Miller 1995). The San Mateo atlas documents a longer nesting season, with records of precocial young extending from 28 March–10 August (Sequoia Audubon Society 2001). A record from Monterey County on 25 August suggests that the season may extend later still (Roberson and Tenney 1993).

Conservation

The Northern Pintail, because it is known to breed at just a handful of sites, is vulnerable to any type of disturbance during the nesting season. It is crucial that the few known sites be protected from development, predators and human disturbance.

NORTHERN PINTAIL

GREEN-WINGED TEAL • *Anas crecca*

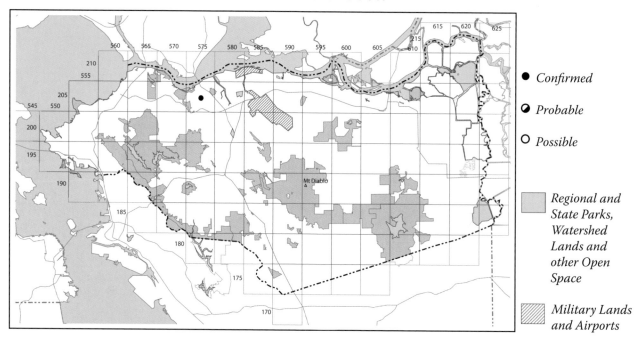

- • Confirmed
- ◓ Probable
- ○ Possible

Regional and State Parks, Watershed Lands and other Open Space

Military Lands and Airports

The handsome Green-winged Teal is a common sight on bodies of freshwater during the winter months but is extremely rare during the summer months. In fact, the only nest record for the county was obtained during the atlas project.

Current status and distribution

The Green-winged Teal was noted only twice during the atlas project, each time at McNabney Marsh near Martinez. A single male, possibly a late migrant, was present 5 May 1998. A female with three half grown precocial young 2 Aug 2000 provided the only nest record for Contra Costa County. Although it is possible that birds went undetected at locations to which we had no access, it is clear that the Green-winged Teal is an extremely rare breeder in the county.

Historical occurrence

Grinnell and Wythe (1927) mentioned nesting at Alvarado, Alameda County, a county where nesting has been noted periodically in recent decades. It is unclear if the species was historically absent from Contra Costa County as a breeding bird or if coverage was simply insufficient.

Breeding and natural history

The only Contra Costa County breeding confirmation involved three half-grown young at McNabney Marsh on 2 Aug 2000. A compilation of Northern California nest records (data *fide* W. Bousman) shows nests with eggs spanning 4 April–7 July, with most records from late May and throughout June. The date span for eight records of precocial young spans 22 May–9 July, suggesting that the confirmation obtained during the atlas may have been later than most.

Conservation

Unlike other dabbling ducks, the Green-winged Teal breeds most abundantly in the forested wetlands of Canada, rather than in the imperiled prairie pothole region. Johnson (1995) suggested that this may have allowed the population to increase while many other dabbling duck numbers declined. There seems to be little concern for the Green-winged Teal in North America but the few remaining freshwater marshes of Contra Costa County are in dire need of protection.

RUDDY DUCK • *Oxyura jamaicensis*

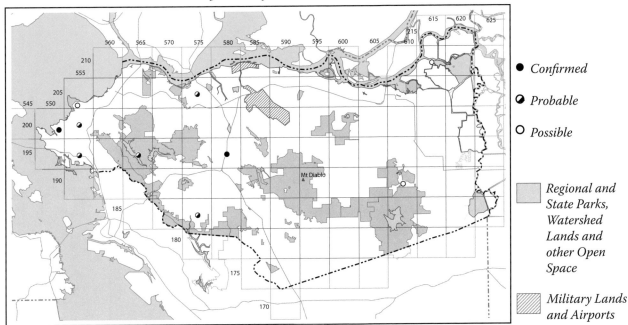

This dapper diving duck with cinnamon plumage and sky-blue bill is a common winter resident in the county on both open saltwater and freshwater ponds. During summer, however, the species is a very scarce and local nester, known in only two sites.

Current status and distribution

It was a surprise to find that the Ruddy Duck is such a scarce breeder in Contra Costa County. The only breeding confirmations came from near the mouth of Wildcat Creek at Richmond and the ponds at Heather Farm Park in Walnut Creek. There were additional records of pairs at San Pablo and Upper San Leandro reservoirs, McNabney Marsh near Martinez, Marsh Creek Res. west of Brentwood, and Iron House Sanitary District near Oakley. McNabney Marsh was checked particularly thoroughly during the atlas project and in succeeding years but despite the presence of a handful of birds each summer the species has never been confirmed breeding there.

Local Ruddy Ducks apparently prefer to nest in dense cattails or reeds on the margins of permanent ponds.

Historical occurrence

The Ruddy Duck was known to Grinnell and Wythe (1927) to nest at Alvarado and Niles, Alameda County. It is unclear when the first Contra Costa County nesting was recorded.

Breeding and natural history

The Ruddy Duck was confirmed on only two occasions during the atlas project, making it difficult to establish a sturdy breeding chronology. Precocial young were at Richmond 12 May 2001 and Heather Farm Park, Walnut Creek 9 June 2001. Pairs were noted in 6 additional blocks between April and June. Precocial young in Monterey County were noted as early as 27 April and as late as 26 September (Roberson and Tenney 1993). The San Mateo Atlas reported a similarly late record of precocial young from 25 September and an even later one from 15 October (Sequoia Audubon Society 2001).

Conservation

Breeding Ruddy Ducks prefer freshwater ponds, a habitat that has been systematically destroyed in recent decades. The protection of existing habitat is crucial. Of further benefit would be encouragement of emergent vegetation throughout the breeding season at sewage treatment plants.

RING-NECKED PHEASANT • *Phasianus colchicus*

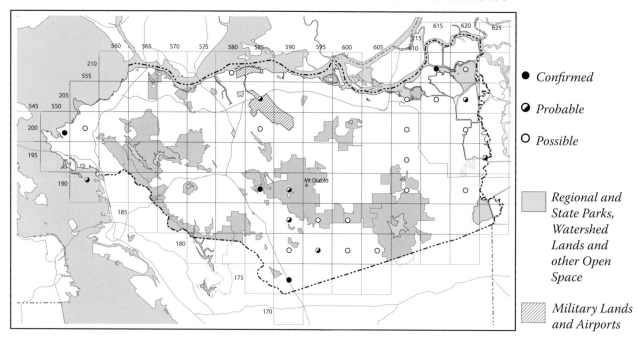

- ● Confirmed
- ◐ Probable
- ○ Possible

▨ Regional and State Parks, Watershed Lands and other Open Space

▨ Military Lands and Airports

This stunningly resplendent pheasant, introduced from Asia during the 19th century, is a conspicuous resident of agricultural East County. The long-term viability of the species, however, may be dependent upon stocking by hunting clubs.

Current status and distribution

During the atlas project, the Ring-necked Pheasant was present in four general regions: Richmond; San Ramon Valley and vicinity; Concord; and, most abundantly, in East County. Although only four confirmations were obtained, the species was recorded in 28 blocks and the atlas map seems to be an accurate representation of its current range.

The Ring-necked Pheasant in East County is partial to agricultural settings featuring grains, and alfalfa fields. Such habitats are exclusive to East County—local and apparently dwindling populations in Western and Central County are almost exclusively found on hillsides of open grasslands.

Historical occurrence

The California Fish and Game Department first introduced this handsome Asian pheasant as early as 1885 (Grinnell and Miller 1944). Grinnell and Miller included the delta region as one of the species centers of abundance in the state. The earliest known nest record for Contra Costa County is a set of eggs taken at Crockett 30 May 1933 (MVZ #2544).

Breeding and natural history

The majority of the records in the atlas database involve "singing" males recorded at various times during the breeding season. Seemingly mated pairs were noted as early as 12 March. A total of four confirmations were achieved: a nest with eggs was found at Richmond 25 April and precocial young were detected three times 3 June through 20 July.

Conservation

Probably because the Ring-necked Pheasant is an introduced species, there is a dearth of available information to be found in local Audubon Society sightings columns. The sentiment in the local birding community that populations have been shrinking in recent years is boldly confirmed by Christmas Bird Count data for the three long-term East Bay counts. The Oakland CBC no longer records any pheasants while the Contra Costa CBC is now averaging only one or none (National Audubon Society 2002).

Although the number of pheasants in Central and Western Contra Costa County appears to be shrinking, stocking by hunting clubs complicates their true status in East County. Whether or not East County populations can maintain themselves without continuing introductions is anyone's guess.

WILD TURKEY • *Meleagris gallopavo*

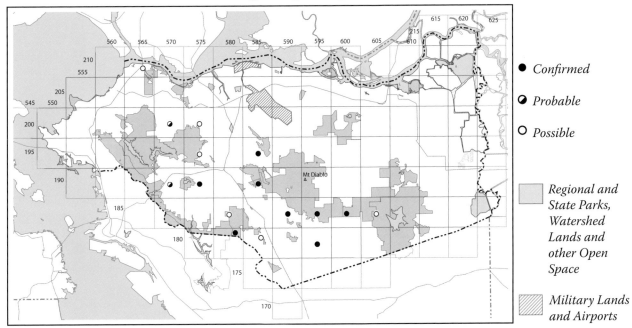

Once an introduced species with a limited range in the East Bay (primarily in southeastern Alameda County), the feverish rate of Wild Turkey colonization of the woodlands of Contra Costa County has been stunning. And, based on anecdotal evidence from local "chat-lines", this spread has continued well into the post-atlas era.

Current status and distribution

The Wild Turkey breeds locally west of the Interstate 680 corridor, mainly around Las Trampas Regional Park, Lafayette and Martinez. There was also a single July record from the Crockett area. The species was more widely distributed on the western and southern flank of Mt. Diablo where it was often noted invading suburban neighborhoods immediately adjacent to the state park. Sightings from previously unoccupied locations seemed to have accelerated even faster after the atlas was completed, with sightings of adults and young from throughout the Berkeley Hills, including at Tilden and Wildcat Canyon Regional Parks. It seems only a matter of time until each of the county's woodlands echoes with gobbles.

The preferred habitat of the Wild Turkey has traditionally been open oak woodlands with a grassy understory but in recent years the species has rapidly expanded into residential settings.

Historical occurrence

The "liberation" of Wild Turkeys in California began as early as 1877 and yet by 1944 the species wasn't thought to be firmly established anywhere in California (Grinnell and Miller 1944). The turkeys of southeast Alameda County were released by 1965 (Bousman 2007)

and by 1976 were "well established" along Mines Road (county notebooks). The first conclusive evidence of breeding followed in 1986 (AB 40: no. 3). The earliest report from Contra Costa County may have been a report from Morgan Territory Rd. 23 May 1981 (Quail 28: no. 1), though this area appeared unoccupied during the years of the atlas.

Breeding and natural history

The Wild Turkey was confirmed breeding in 8 blocks, a number that would be significantly higher if fieldwork had taken place just a few years later. Meager data collected during the atlas suggests that courtship takes place mainly March through mid-May with young out and about as early as 22 May and as late as 7 July.

Conservation

The recent boom in the Wild Turkey population has shifted talk from the protection of Wild Turkeys to the protection of the vegetation of suburban backyards. Although it is unclear how common the practice has become, the "removal" of turkeys from suburban settings is apparently taking place.

CALIFORNIA QUAIL

CALIFORNIA QUAIL • *Callipepla californica*

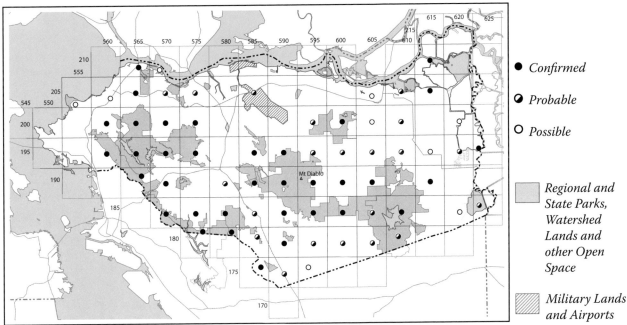

California Quail, with its distinctive *"chi-ca-go"* call and subdued but highly intricate plumage, is an enjoyable presence in Contra Costa County's woodlands.

Current status and distribution

The California Quail breeds throughout wooded portions of the Coast Range and locally in the eastern portion of the county. The only gaps in the atlas map are the Bay plain around Richmond, suburban neighborhoods around Concord and Pittsburg and a handful of agriculture-dominated blocks in the Central Valley. Small populations may have inhabited some of these gaps, particularly those away from Richmond.

In Contra Costa County, the California Quail occurs in coastal scrub, chamise and mixed chaparral, brushy woodlands, and riparian settings with substantial undergrowth. In the eastern portion of the county the species persists in isolated areas of willows and brambles. Numbers are hanging on, though declining, in suburban gardens with sufficient cover along the Interstate 680 corridor. Some forests of the Berkeley Hills are too densely forested for the species, but because these forests never occupy particularly large acreages this isn't reflected in the atlas map. Extensive grasslands and marshlands are also shunned but this too is reflected only in the northern and southeastern portions of the map.

Historical occurrence

Although the California Quail was historically more abundant and ubiquitous, there are so few early accounts of this species that the extent of its historical distribution and numbers is uncertain.

Breeding and natural history

Pairs of California Quail were observed as early as 3 March but were not detected in numbers until April. All fifty-five breeding confirmations during the atlas project were based on observations of young. Young were noted as early as 16 May but most appeared from late June through mid-July. The last fledglings, presumably capable of flight, were detected 7 September.

Conservation

Although the future of the California Quail seems secure in protected parklands and watersheds, the species has slowly begun to disappear from suburban settings, likely due to habitat destruction (*i.e.* the clearing of undergrowth) and predation by domestic cats. Such losses are expected to increase in the future.

41

Pied-billed Grebe • *Podilymbus podiceps*

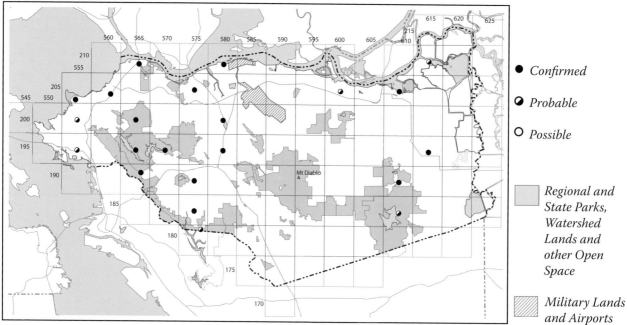

● *Confirmed*

◖ *Probable*

○ *Possible*

▢ *Regional and State Parks, Watershed Lands and other Open Space*

▨ *Military Lands and Airports*

The Pied-billed Grebe, particularly during the nesting season, is a bird of pond edges with emergent vegetation for nest-anchorage and shelter. While in open water the species habitually acts like a feathered periscope, ready to dive at a moment's notice. There is a noticeable population bulge during migration periods and in winter, and at such times the Pied-billed Grebe is routinely found in significant numbers on large bodies of open water and even in salt water harbors.

Current status and distribution

Nesting Pied-billed Grebes are most often encountered in the western half of the county, in part due to the presence of numerous large watershed reservoirs. In the southeast portion the species is relegated to reservoirs; however, recently built ponds, particularly on golf courses, may eventually host breeding birds if shoreline vegetation is allowed to sprout. The species was conspicuously absent from almost the entire center of the county with nesting along the Interstate 680 corridor known only at McNabney Marsh and Heather Farm Park in Walnut Creek. It is most surprising that much of the northern marshes were apparently unoccupied, though perhaps some birds did breed in areas to which there was no access. A paucity of nest sites in the arid Diablo Range is less surprising. The only known nest sites are on the eastern flank at Marsh Creek Res. and possibly at Los Vaqueros Res.

Historical occurrence

Grinnell and Wythe (1927) suggest that Pied-billed Grebes were unknown as breeders in Contra Costa County, although it seems highly likely that the species was simply missed due to scant attention from ornithologists early in the century.

Breeding and natural history

During the atlas, nests with eggs were noted as late as 15 July while precocial young were noted as early as 28 April and as late as 5 August. These dates, however, are clearly a better indication of when most fieldwork took place than when the species actually nests, as the Pied-billed Grebe is known to nest very early and very late. In 2005 an adult with two striped fledglings was at Briones Dam on the early date of 19 February (D. Wight, pers. comm.). There are at least two records from Alameda County of precocial young well into November (county notebooks).

Conservation

The long-term future of nesting Pied-billed Grebes is dependent upon the protection of freshwater sites with emergent vegetation. Nesting opportunities would increase if sewage treatment plant operators, as well as owners of private ponds, were to allow shoreline vegetation to thrive during the breeding season.

PIED-BILLED GREBE

WESTERN GREBE • *Aechmophorus occidentalis*
CLARK'S GREBE • *Aechmophorus clarkii*

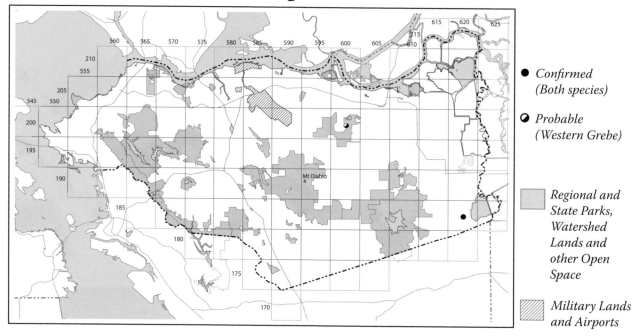

● Confirmed
(Both species)

◑ Probable
(Western Grebe)

▨ Regional and
State Parks,
Watershed
Lands and
other Open
Space

▨ Military Lands
and Airports

The Western Grebe and the Clark's Grebe, considered for a full century to be different color phases of a single species, have long been noted for their stunning, graceful courtship displays, most notably the "rushing ceremony" in which the pair runs on the surface of the water.

Current status and distribution

Both the Western Grebe and the Clark's Grebe are common and conspicuous winter residents on bodies of salt and freshwater. Members of this species pair have long been noted in the summer on San Francisco Bay, far from breeding habitat, but only recently have birds begun to exhibit breeding behavior.

On 18 Sept 2000, pairs of both Western and Clark's grebes were discovered building nests at Clifton Court Forebay near Byron in the southeast corner of the county. It is unknown if there was any successful breeding. A pair of Westerns was noted in suitable breeding habitat at Antioch Municipal Res. on 6 June 2002. The first proven successful nesting for an *Aechmophorus* grebe was confirmed 6–13 June 2004 when a pair of Clark's with two small young was found at San Pablo Res. Also present were an additional thirteen Clark's and four Westerns (Quail 50: no. 50). Another late nest attempt at Clifton Court Forebay was noted 27 Aug 2004. On that day, 50+ Clark's were on nests or nest building, though once again the eventual outcome is unknown (Quail 49: no. 10).

Nesting *Aechmophorus* grebes typically occupy large, open bodies of water (with a surface area of at least several square kilometers) with a border of emergent vegeta-

tion (Storer and Nuechterlein 1992). Such conditions are rarely met in Contra Costa, however.

Historical occurrence

Grinnell and Wythe (1927) were aware of Bay Area nesting since 1885 only at Lake Merced, San Francisco. It is doubtful that there was ever any suitable habitat in Contra Costa County until reservoirs began to be constructed early in the 20th century.

Breeding and natural history

In San Diego County, the Western Grebe has been noted breeding throughout the year, possibly more so than any breeding species in that county, so perhaps local records of late nest building aren't unusual. There the peak of nesting is May through early July, including chicks 19 Apr and 21 June, but chicks have been noted throughout the winter months (Unitt 2004). Clark's Grebes in San Diego County have a similar nesting schedule, with egg laying from mid-April through early August. Winter nesting is apparently less common there, although two nearly full-sized young were found 10 January (Unitt 2004).

Nests in Monterey County were thought to involve "pure" species pairs (Roberson and Tenney 1993) but the San Diego Atlas (Unitt 2004) found widespread hybridization. At one lake it appeared that birds were choosing mates almost randomly.

Conservation

Future breeding attempts by Western and Clark's Grebes are wholly dependent upon the presence of suitable habitat at the county's freshwater reservoirs.

DOUBLE-CRESTED CORMORANT • *Phalacrocorax auritus*

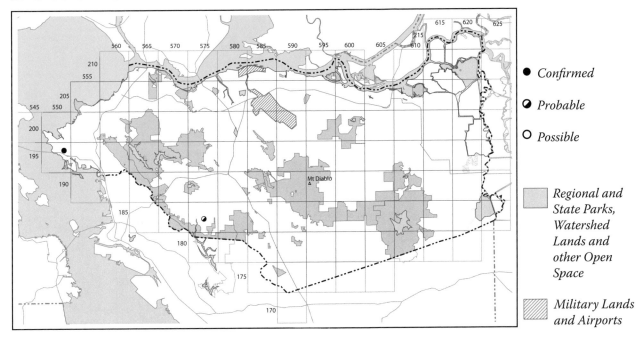

● *Confirmed*

◐ *Probable*

○ *Possible*

▨ *Regional and State Parks, Watershed Lands and other Open Space*

▧ *Military Lands and Airports*

Although the Double-crested Cormorant is one of the least glamorous of Contra Costa County's breeding birds, the species is a common and conspicuous sight at open water sites throughout the county that can provide sufficient fish. As a breeding bird, however, the species is relegated to a single known site.

Current status and distribution

The only known Double-crested Cormorant nest site in Contra Costa County is the Richmond-San Rafael Bridge. This is a surprise, as the species is known to nest in trees around ponds, reservoirs and watercourses elsewhere in the Bay region. As indicated by the atlas map, the Double-crested Cormorant was noted foraging in, or flying over, much of the western third of the county, particularly the watershed reservoirs of the Berkeley Hills. The species was less common in the eastern portion of the county; birds there in the summer may be foraging away from a Central Valley nest colony. In fact, a modest colony on Venice Island, just east of Bethel Island in adjacent San Joaquin County, was first established in 1998 and by 2005 had increased to perhaps forty nests (W. Holt, pers. comm.).

Historical occurrence

Grinnell and Wythe (1927) cite nesting only on the Farallon Islands and at Seal Rocks near the Golden Gate. The species was unknown as a breeding bird (and it is unlikely that the species was overlooked) in the East Bay until 1984 when five nests were found at the east end of the Richmond-San Rafael Bridge on 3 July (AB 38: no. 6).

Breeding and natural history

The lone confirmation during the atlas project was of occupied nests on the Richmond-San Rafael Bridge 4 Apr 1998. Birds on the Farallon Islands, as well as birds nesting on the bridges of San Francisco Bay, are said to return to nest sites beginning in mid-March (Shuford 1993). In San Mateo County, occupied nests were noted as early as 7 April. Nests with young were detected 8 June–16 July (Sequoia Audubon Society 2001).

Conservation

The most significant threat to the county's lone nest colony would appear to be the potential for an oil spill, particularly since a constant stream of oil tankers passes beneath their bridge abode.

PELAGIC CORMORANT • *Phalacrocorax pelagicus*

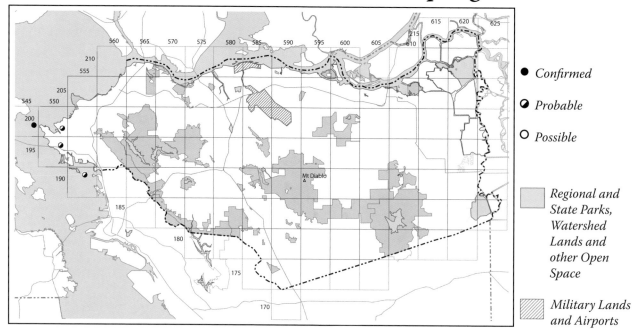

Confirmed

Probable

Possible

Regional and State Parks, Watershed Lands and other Open Space

Military Lands and Airports

The "Violet-green Cormorant" is a common sight along the cliffs of coastal California but this pencil-necked piscavore is far less common inside the bay where suitable breeding habitat is a scarce commodity.

Current status and distribution

The only known nest site in Contra Costa County is a sporadically utilized cliff face on West Brother Island near Pt. San Pablo. Pairs were noted at several nearby sites, including Bird Rock near Brooks Island and Red Rock adjacent to the Richmond-San Rafael Bridge. It is still unknown if the species breeds at these sites though Red Rock seems to offer particularly suitable habitat.

Nesting colonies are typically found on headlands and island cliffs (Hobson 1997) but the species is known to utilize human-made structures, as it does along Cannery Row in Monterey (Roberson and Tenney 1993).

West Brother Island is one of a pair of small rock islands just off the Richmond shoreline. East Brother Island was long ago leveled for the construction of a lighthouse but West Brother has been spared and currently hosts a large breeding population of Western Gulls. The island itself is low and overall flat on top but it does rise abruptly, providing a short but steep cliff on the flanks, the preferred nesting substrate for Pelagic Cormorants.

Historical occurrence

The Pelagic Cormorant was noted in small numbers inside San Francisco Bay and San Pablo Bay throughout the 20th century (Grinnell and Miller 1944) but the vast majority of records are from outside of the breeding season. Nesting was unsuspected in Contra Costa County

until the 1990s. Three nests on West Brother Island on 19 April 1995 provided Contra Costa County's first nest record. Thirteen nests were recorded on 21 May 1995 but the site was not checked again that season (FN 49: no. 3). On 6 April 1996 six occupied nests were noted. Nesting was not noted again until 25 May 2002, the final year of the atlas, when a single adult was noted on a nest.

Breeding and natural history

The lone nesting confirmation during the atlas period was an adult on a nest 25 May 2002. Apparently territorial pairs were discovered in blocks 550-195 and 550-200 on 17 May 1998 and another pair was thought to be visiting a possible nest site 20 June. The San Mateo County atlas team noted the carrying of nest material and occupied nests as early as 23 March and nests with young on 8 and 11 July (Sequoia Audubon Society 2001). In Monterey County, a nest with eggs was noted as early as 10 April and as late as 3 June; nests with young were tallied between 27 May and 20 August (Roberson and Tenney 1993). In Sonoma County, occupied nests were noted as late as 23 July (Burridge 1995).

Conservation

The lapse in nesting records between 1996 and 2002 does not reflect a lapse in coverage as the island was checked in each of the intervening years. Perhaps the El Niño events in the late 1990s, which decimated seabird populations along the coast, were responsible although this is conjecture. This meager population will continue to be inordinately prone to El Niño events and oil spills.

AMERICAN BITTERN

AMERICAN BITTERN • *Botaurus lentiginosus*

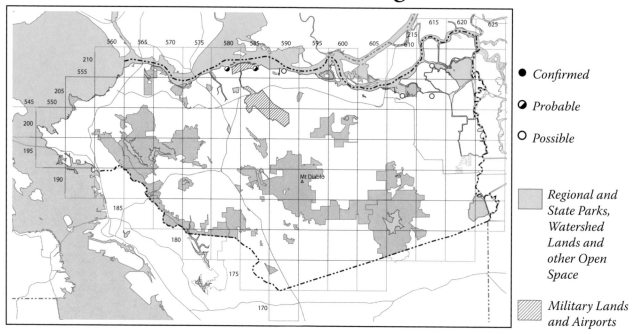

The American Bittern is an odd, mysterious bird. It is rarely seen, except for the occasional individual with its neck craned to the sky, blending with surrounding marsh plants. It is only somewhat more often heard and typically just at dawn and dusk during the breeding season. At that time the American Bittern emits eerie, booming calls, for which it has been dubbed "stake-driver" and "thunder-pumper".

Current status and distribution

During the atlas project, the American Bittern was found in only two portions of the county: in the marshes in north-central county around the Concord Naval Weapons Station and in the northeastern corner around Big Break, Jersey Island and Bethel Island. Although Grinnell and Wythe (1927) considered the species to be resident at Richmond, we found no evidence that it still occurs there. While some suitable habitat in the county, particularly in the east, may not have been surveyed due to access problems, the atlas map is probably an accurate depiction of the species' current range.

The American Bittern primarily inhabits fresh emergent and brackish saline emergent wetlands (Gibbs and others 1992). The growth of tall, emergent vegetation, particularly bulrushes and cattails, is most important for nesting, although the species forages in sparser wetlands and even the edges of tidal marshes.

Historical occurrence

Grinnell and Wythe (1927) listed the American Bittern as a resident at Martinez and Richmond, but the species appears to be long extirpated from the latter lo-cality. There are also a few sightings in the 1980s and early 1990s from the Byron area. Although a few bitterns may persist there, this area was adequately covered during the atlas project and no bitterns were detected.

Breeding and natural history

Although coverage of marsh habitat was light, bitterns were detected nine times during the atlas project. On seven occasions single birds were noted. The best evidence of probable breeding was provided by one adult bittern chasing another away from an apparent territory on the Concord Naval Weapons Station 4 June 1998.

Conservation

While the American Bittern may not have been common in the county historically, it is presumably much less numerous today due to loss of suitable breeding habitat. Many sites with documented or suspected breeding, such as Jersey and Bethel Islands, are unprotected.

GREAT BLUE HERON • *Ardea herodias*

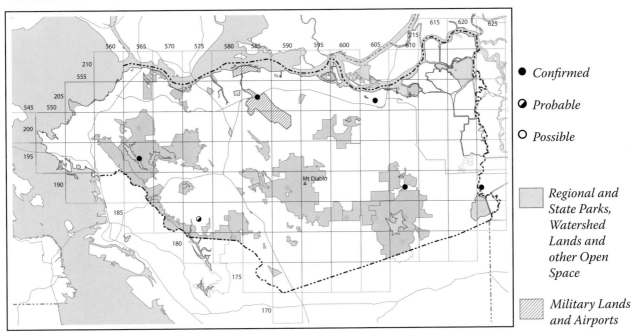

The stately Great Blue Heron is the most commonly encountered heron in Contra Costa County, found wherever there is water. Water isn't even a prerequisite as the species is often seen stalking dry pastures and agricultural fields in search of small mammals.

Current status and distribution

Despite being such a constant presence throughout much of the county, the Great Blue Heron was found breeding at just five locations: San Pablo Res.; in Clyde north of Concord; on West Island (Sacramento County); in Marsh Creek Res. near Brentwood; and on tiny Eucalyptus Island near the northeast corner of Clifton Court Forebay. An additional nest colony in eucalyptus trees in suburban Alamo, said to have been established in the late 1990s, contained six nests in 2003, four in 2004, and five in 2005 (Kelly and others 2006).

The heronry at San Pablo Res. is the only current site that has been monitored to any significant extent. Twelve nests were first noted in 1991 and numbers increased to as high as thirty-seven by 2004 (John P. Kelly, pers. comm.).

The Great Blue Heron typically nests high in tall trees with water either immediately adjacent or very close by. At West Island and Marsh Creek Res. nests were placed in Fremont cottonwoods. The remaining sites were built in eucalyptus, a common occurrence in lowland California.

Historical occurrence

Grinnell and Wythe (1927) were apparently unaware of breeding by Great Blue Herons in Contra Costa County through at least 1927 and it seems that at that time the spe-cies occurred rarely if at all in the county. The MVZ and the WFVZ, however, are in possession of eight egg sets, six of them taken before the *Directory to the Bird-Life of the San Francisco Bay Area* was published. Six of the sets were taken at Brentwood between 1915 and 1929, so the species clearly maintained at least a limited presence in the eastern portion of the county. On a side note, the two remaining sets were said to be taken in 1893 at the north shore of the mouth of Redwood Creek but this doesn't make sense as all but the headwaters of Redwood Creek are in Alameda County and Redwood Creek is merely a tributary to San Leandro Creek. Nesting has also been documented at several additional sites: along Bear Creek Rd. near Orinda by Curl in 1956 and 1957; at Montair Elementary School, Danville with two nests in 1992 and one in 1993 before the nest trees were removed (Kelly and others 2006); along Pinole Valley Rd. where a single nest was found in 1996 (John P. Kelly, pers. comm.); and at Brooks Island near Richmond in 1994, 1995 and 1997, with a high nest count of just four in 1995 (John P. Kelly, pers. comm.).

Breeding and natural history

Nesting can start rather early. Of eight egg sets at the MVZ and the WFVZ, the earliest was taken 12 March and the latest was 12 May. During the atlas, birds appeared to already be sitting on eggs at Eucalyptus Island on 24 Feb 1998 and nests with young were noted there that same year as early as 16 April. The latest occupied nest found during the atlas (contents unknown) was at West Island 14 June. 2000.

Conservation

The heronries at San Pablo Reservoir, and to a lesser extent at Marsh Creek Reservoir, are afforded some protection but those at Clyde, West Island and Eucalyptus Island are vulnerable to nest-site destruction. The latter two sites are also immediately adjacent to popular boating locations where the summertime din can be nearly unbearable.

GREEN HERON

GREAT EGRET • *Ardea alba*

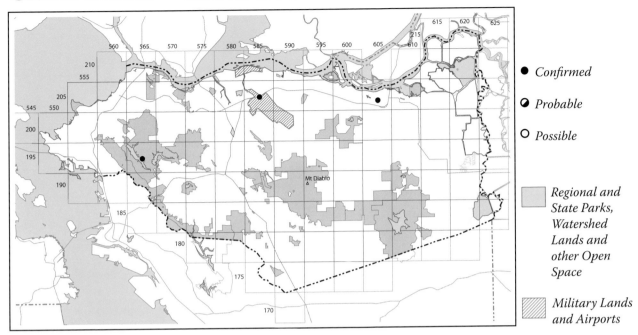

● *Confirmed*

◑ *Probable*

○ *Possible*

▨ *Regional and State Parks, Watershed Lands and other Open Space*

▨ *Military Lands and Airports*

This hunted wild thing, whose image few of us have seen, and whose name had almost become a memory, is at liberty now to put on her bridal array of dazzling linen and snowy plumes. She may grace our horizon upon her migratory passages, or she may light up our swamps when she deigns to pause for rest and amphibian refreshment. There is none left to molest or to make her afraid.

🖋 *William Leon Dawson (1923)*

Current status and distribution

Great Egrets grace wet areas throughout the county but were found nesting at only two sites during the atlas project; a third site was discovered just over the Contra Costa County line in Sacramento County. A traditional nesting colony at San Pablo Reservoir was active throughout the atlas project, and a small colony discovered during the atlas project in 1999 was on a hillside at Clyde, near the Concord Naval Weapons Station. The Sacramento colony was found on West Island, north of Antioch. Great Egrets were observed nesting there in 2000 and 2002, the only years this site was checked.

The Great Egret was noted at many locations during the breeding season. Most of these birds presumably were on long foraging trips away from nest sites. However, it is possible, or even likely, that some of these birds were near nest sites that were not discovered during the atlas project.

Egrets at San Pablo Reservoir and at Clyde built their nests in eucalyptus trees; those at West Island nested in cottonwoods.

Historical occurrence

It is remarkable that the Great Egret nests here at all as the species was completely extirpated from the San Francisco Bay region by 1880, mainly due to the dogged determination of the plume hunters of the late nineteenth and early twentieth centuries. Not a single Great Egret was recorded in the region again until 1925, when twelve birds were found in the Suisun Marshes of Solano County (Grinnell and Wythe 1927). The first returnees to Contra Costa County were two birds at Avon, north of Concord, on 25 Dec 1933 (Stoner 1934). It is unclear if they bred here prior to 1880, but it is said that there were "one or two to every marsh" around San Francisco and San Pablo Bays (Grinnell and Wythe 1927). It is also unclear when breeding recommenced.

Breeding and natural history

All four nesting confirmations during the atlas project involved occupied nests. Dates ranged from 2 April to 14 June; the early date likely represents nests with eggs, the latter date nests with young. During the Monterey County atlas project, nest occupation began in mid-March, with young in the nest in early May and fledging occurring by mid-June (Roberson and Tenney 2003). In San Mateo County, nest building was detected 14 April and a nest with young was found as late as 1 August (Sequoia Audubon Society 2001).

Conservation

Great Egrets are common and conspicuous residents in Contra Costa County. However, the total number of breeding birds is small enough that the overall population is vulnerable to nest site disturbance and destruction.

51

SNOWY EGRET • *Egretta thula*

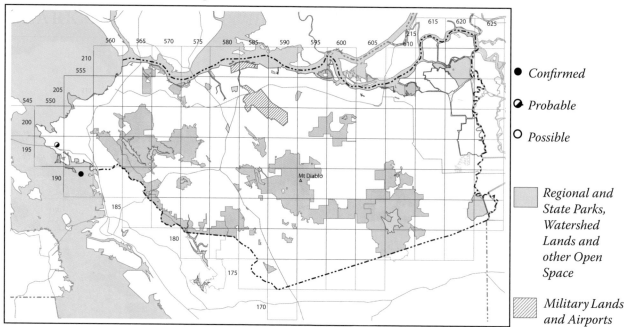

- ● *Confirmed*
- ◕ *Probable*
- ○ *Possible*

■ *Regional and State Parks, Watershed Lands and other Open Space*

▨ *Military Lands and Airports*

The dainty Snowy Egret is widespread in the ponds, marshes and wet fields that dot the western, northern and eastern periphery of the county, particularly in winter. However, the species breeds only sporadically in Contra Costa County and, although it did breed one year during the atlas project, the Snowy Egret has seemingly once again receded from the scene.

Current status and distribution

The only known Snowy Egret nest site in Contra Costa County in recent memory is Brooks Island near Richmond. Nesting first occurred there in 1991 when ten nests were found (John P. Kelly, pers. comm.). This site reached maximum numbers of nests in 1994 when 95 nests were counted. In 1995 there were still eighty-nine nesting pairs but the species disappeared thereafter (John P. Kelly, pers. comm.). The species made a brief reappearance during the atlas project in 2000 when eight pairs were present but the site was again abandoned and has yet to be reoccupied (John P. Kelly, pers. comm.).

Historical occurrence

Grinnell and Miller (1944) state that the Snowy Egret was presumed extinct in California by the early 1900s, a casualty of the thriving plume trade. Grinnell and Wythe (1927) knew of no historical records for the East Bay so if the species ever did occur it was likely prior to the last quarter of the 19th century. The first breeding evidence documented for California wasn't provided until W. L. Dawson found a nest in Merced County in 1914 (*fide* W. Bousman). Grinnell and Miller further state that by 1943 the Snowy Egret was again fairly common in "favored

places." The first known nesting for Contra Costa County was at Browns Island north of Pittsburg where an estimated 100 pairs were nesting in kangaroo thorns in 1962 (AFN 16: no. 5).

Breeding and natural history

The *San Mateo County Breeding Bird Atlas* (Sequoia Audubon Society 2001) uncovered the following breeding chronology: adults were noted carrying nest material on 25 April and nest building on 14 April; a nest with eggs was found 12 April; nests with young were discovered on ten occasions spanning 12 May–29 June; and fledglings were recorded 3 June–27 July.

Conservation

The Brooks Island nest site is well protected from human disturbance, although a Red Fox was noted on the island in 1996, possibly contributing to the failure of the colony that year (Kelly and others 2006). In 1982, eggs in San Francisco Bay were found to be contaminated by organochlorines and mercury (Parsons and others 2000).

GREEN HERON • *Butorides virescens*

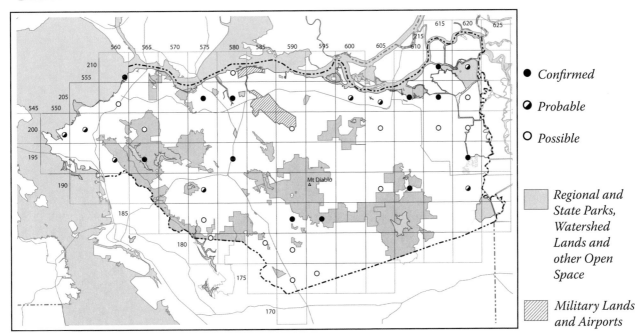

- ● *Confirmed*
- ◖ *Probable*
- ○ *Possible*

▨ *Regional and State Parks, Watershed Lands and other Open Space*

▨ *Military Lands and Airports*

The Green Heron is an inconspicuous, habitual loner of Contra Costa County's wooded watercourses, sloughs and ponds. Were it not for the species' loud, curious "cluck" note, usually given in flight, they would be seen even less often. Paradoxically, this little heron regularly chooses areas of constant human presence for nest sites, to the disdain of those residing below the nest tree.

Current status and distribution

The Green Heron is an uncommon breeding bird in freshwater habitats throughout much of the county. The only notable exceptions were in the drier portions of the Diablo Range, particularly around Mt. Diablo State Park, and in the extensive grasslands south of Mt. Diablo. Although the atlas map might appear to show the Green Heron to be particularly common in East County, it is unlikely that more than a handful of East County blocks support more than one or two breeding pairs.

Green Heron nests in Contra Costa County have long been noted in close proximity to human settlements, a fact not often mentioned in the literature. Although the species seems to utilize saline emergent wetlands elsewhere in its range, Northern California nesters are devoted exclusively to freshwater (Shuford 1993) and (Roberson and Tenney 1993); this is certainly the case in Contra Costa County.

Historical occurrence

Although neither Grinnell and Wythe (1927) nor Grinnell and Miller (1944) cite breeding for Contra Costa County, this is surely an artifact of light coverage in comparison with other local counties.

Breeding and natural history

The atlas project uncovered sixteen breeding confirmations in 11 different blocks. These scant data indicate that local Green Herons build their nests from mid-March (earliest was 18 March) through late April and occupy them from early April to even late June (latest was 24 June). Fledglings were recorded on six occasions between 17 May and 11 July. An additional report of an occupied nest 11 August was, if interpreted correctly, an extremely late confirmation.

Although some of the "possible" and "probable" evidence may pertain to either late migrants or early post-breeding wanderers, most were in May and thus assumed to be nesting in the area.

The Green Heron is most common in Contra Costa County in April and again in August and September, when migrants bolster the local population. Thus, birds found during these months away from known breeding sites are best considered transients.

Conservation

Green Heron populations have likely suffered greatly due to the disturbance and destruction of freshwater and riparian habitats but current population levels could be maintained by vigilant protection of these habitats.

BLACK-CROWNED NIGHT-HERON • *Nycticorax nycticorax*

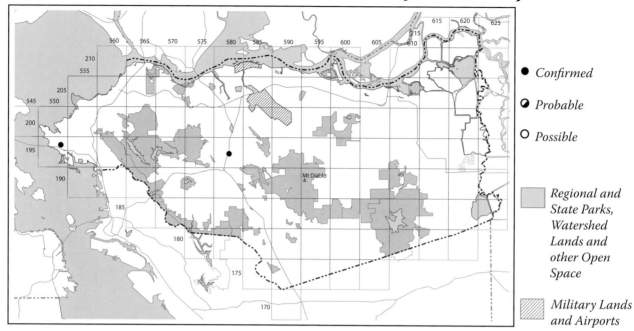

Every investigator of cat-tails and "tules," those giant bulrushes of California, has been startled in his course, at some time or other, by the eruption of an unsuspected company of gray ghosts. They had marked his approach as they stood about in grave dignity, silent, motionless, and disapproving; but their color had blended so well with that of the cover that the intruder blundered on, unmindful that he was invading precincts sacred to Nycticoracine slumbers.

꙳ William Leon Dawson (1923)

The hunch-backed Black-crowned Night-Heron is found only locally in Contra Costa County and is most often seen either hunkered deep into willows or in flight—particularly in early morning or evening, while commuting from foraging areas to nest sites or roosts.

Current status and distribution

Just a small handful of Black-crowned Night-Herons is known to breed in Contra Costa County. The only currently known site is at Heather Farm Park in Walnut Creek. A colony at Brooks Island was active from 1991 when thirty-one nests were counted, through 1995 when there were a whopping 251 nests. The entire heronry collapsed in 1996 (John P. Kelly, pers. comm.). A smaller colony was briefly reestablished in 2000 and contained thirteen nests, but has been inactive in the ensuing years.

In California, Black-crowned Night-Herons are known to nest in a wide variety of situations, including within woodlands (particularly on islands), in stands of emergent wetland vegetation, and even in tall grass. Thus it is surprising that the species is such a rare and local breeder in Contra Costa County.

Historical occurrence

Although breeding in Contra Costa County was unknown at least through 1944, this is almost certainly due to a lack of observers in appropriate portions of the county. On 17 Apr 1962, eighty birds were flushed from a heronry at Browns Island north of Pittsburg (a site no longer occupied by any breeding herons), providing the first known evidence of breeding for the county (AFN 16: no. 5).

Breeding and natural history

Small numbers of night-herons began to breed at Heather Farm Park in 2000. On 8 May an adult was on a nest and by 27 June the nest contained four tiny fledglings. In 2001 an adult was on a nest on 29 April. On 13 May there were chicks in the nest. On 18 May a second nest was found, this one with two chicks. Young were off the nest by 4 June. In 2003 there were chicks as early as 10 May and fledglings by 29 May. A different pair had young in the nest 16 June–10 July, one of which fledged 12 July. These two young, incidentally, were almost wholly white (H. Harvey, pers. comm.).

The variance in timing noted above is apparently typical of this species. The onset of breeding in Monterey County has varied from early April to as late as the end of May. In 1992, young were still in the nest in early August (Roberson and Tenney 1993). At colonies in south San Francisco Bay, Gill (1977) noted nesting as early as 4 March, peaking in mid-May.

Conservation

With only two known nest sites and just a handful of breeding pairs, the presence of breeding night-herons is clearly tenuous, though it is unclear exactly what could be done to bolster their numbers.

TURKEY VULTURE • *Cathartes aura*

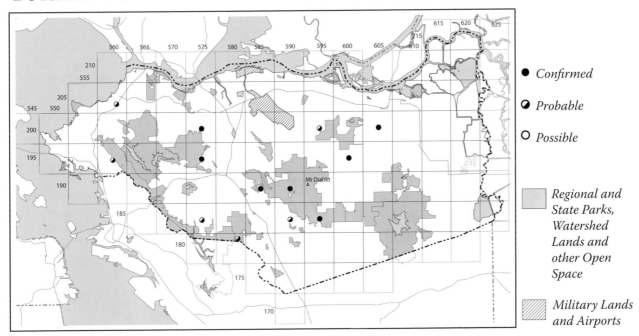

- ● Confirmed
- ◑ Probable
- ○ Possible

▨ Regional and State Parks, Watershed Lands and other Open Space

▨ Military Lands and Airports

A close-up view of a Turkey Vulture reveals a face only a mother, or a birdwatcher could love, but in the air the species becomes incredibly graceful, soaring for hours on end in search of carrion. Although a conspicuous presence in the airspace of the entire county, an actual nest is a prized find; it seems certain based on the number of birds present during the breeding season that some nests went undetected and that a large percentage of the birds present likely didn't breed, possibly because the species requires several years to reach maturity.

Current status and distribution

The Turkey Vulture is a common sight in Contra Costa County but nests are restricted to a handful of locations in the Coast Range. The species was confirmed nesting at six locations during the atlas, including two locations at Briones Regional Park and four locations in or near Mt. Diablo State Park. Although airborne birds were noted commonly over the Richmond area and East County, the species is unknown to have ever nested there.

Turkey Vultures will feed in nearly any location which offers an easy landing but most prefer open grasslands and agricultural areas which offer easy viewing while on the wing. Their choice of nest sites is far more stringent, however. In the American west, nearly 90% of nests are found in caves or on cliff ledges (Shuford 1993) and this is true for the few nests found during the atlas project.

Atlasers were unfortunately inconsistent in their use of the observed, possible and probable categories. In the interest of conservatism, all records of single birds have been omitted from the map. Further, it is likely that some records of "probables" refer to two birds simply foraging together or pairs not necessarily in the block where they were nesting.

Historical occurrence

Grinnell and Wythe (1927) considered the Turkey Vulture to be a summer visitant, mostly in the interior.

Breeding and natural history

Data collected during the atlas suggests that birds may be on eggs as early as 24 March with hatched-young around mid-May. Fledglings were noted 1 and 18 July with an additional report of 10 May. A carefully identified set of eggshells was found in a small cave on Mt. Diablo on 22 July 1999. There are ten egg sets in the collections of the MVZ and the WFVZ that were taken from Contra Costa County, all during the narrow window of 30 March-26 April. Of the five that include a location, four are from on or near Mt. Diablo and the fifth is from Rocky Ridge in Las Trampas Regional Park.

Because the Turkey Vulture regurgitates food for the young, nests in remote rocky locations, doesn't carry nest material, and spends a great deal of time away from the nest, the species is very difficult to confirm nesting.

Conservation

Turkey Vultures have been persecuted for being potential carriers of livestock diseases and for preying upon newborn or weak livestock, generally due to mistaken assumptions based upon the presence of birds at carcasses (Kirk and Mossman 1998). Locally, one might suspect that nest site disturbance and encroaching urban development might be more significant long-term threats.

OSPREY • *Pandion haliaetus*

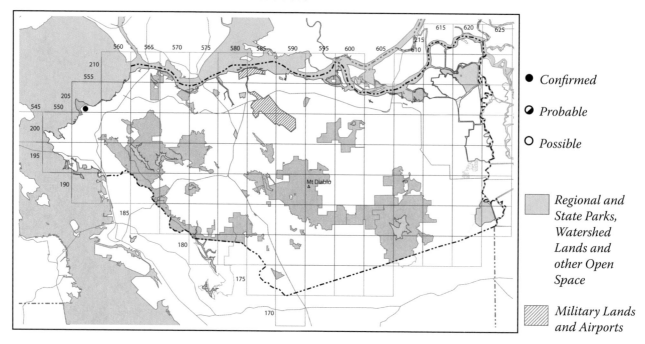

The Osprey is an uncommon migrant and wintering bird in Contra Costa County with the vast majority of sightings coming from August through April. Although migrants and commuters may be seen virtually anywhere in the county, most sightings are of wintering birds frequenting the Richmond shoreline and the watershed reservoirs of the Berkeley Hills. Breeding birds, however, are amongst the rarest of the rare with but a single confirmation during the atlas project.

Current status and distribution

The sole nest detected during the atlas project was near Point Pinole Regional Shoreline. The species is also frequently recorded southwest along the bayshore, particularly at Pt. Isabel Regional Shoreline. Inland the Osprey is most often found hunting at the watershed reservoirs of the Berkeley Hills and, since its recent completion, at Los Vaqueros Res. at the eastern edge of the Diablo Range.

Numerous records from April–June in bayside Richmond blocks and from the watershed reservoirs suggest that an additional pair or two may have bred somewhere in the county and simply avoided detection. On the other hand, Ospreys are known to forage as far as 20 km from the nest site and thus birds noted over inland reservoirs may be commuting to the Pinole nest site or another unknown site elsewhere. This idea is bolstered by the fact that neighbors north of San Pablo Res. have reported fish falling from the sky (R. Hartwell, pers. comm.)!

Necessary conditions for breeding Osprey include a steady, easily accessible supply of fish within 10–20 km of the nest site, shallow water where fishing is easier, and open elevated nest sites free from predators (Poole and others 2002). In coastal California the species uses tall trees almost exclusively (Shuford 1993). The Pinole nest, however, was in an artificial tower. Elsewhere, the Osprey has responded well to artificial nest towers but the one such tower in the county, one constructed at San Pablo Res., has been used only for perching (R. Hartwell, pers. comm.).

Historical occurrence

Historically it is unclear if the Osprey nested in the county but by the time of Grinnell and Wythe the species was known in the Bay Area only from the Russian River region (Grinnell and Wythe 1927). Grinnell and Miller (1944) state that the Osprey was formerly much more common but "now (1944) much reduced in numbers, and known nesting stations few." There are no published records of Ospreys for Contra Costa until the 1950s when at least five sightings were recorded in *The Gull*. Sightings remained noteworthy until the early 1980s when they began to be recorded regularly. A nest, likely the first for Contra Costa County, was reported at Briones Res. in 1990 (county notebooks).

Breeding and natural history

Just a single pair of Osprey was confirmed nesting during the atlas project, that being a pair on a nest at Pinole 2–19 May 1998. In Napa County (Napa-Solano Audubon Society 2003), nest building was noted 30 April and 30 May, a nest with young was found on 15 May and a fledgling was recorded 1 July. The Sonoma atlas found an occupied nest on 30 March and a nest with young on 1 July, suggesting that the breeding cycle is a lengthier affair than our meager data would suggest (Burridge 1995).

Conservation

Osprey populations during the 20th century suffered significant declines due to pesticides, particularly DDT and DDE (Poole and others 2002). In Contra Costa County, however, Ospreys are undoubtedly more common than at any time during recorded history, despite the presence of just one known breeding pair. It is possible that the more widespread erection of artificial nest platforms may lure a handful of additional birds to nest.

WHITE-TAILED KITE

WHITE-TAILED KITE • *Elanus leucurus*

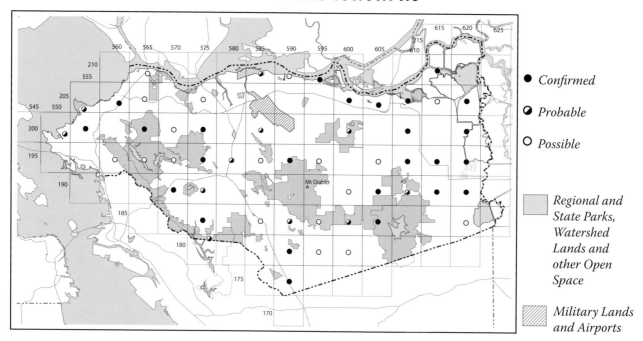

- ● *Confirmed*
- ◐ *Probable*
- ○ *Possible*

▨ *Regional and State Parks, Watershed Lands and other Open Space*

▨ *Military Lands and Airports*

Perhaps the most elegant of our breeding birds, the White-tailed Kite is a familiar sight in Contra Costa County. Although most abundant in winter when populations are bolstered by birds from the north, significant numbers nest throughout the county wherever suitable foraging habitats have been spared from development.

Current status and distribution

Breeding kites are most readily found in the eastern portion of the county where significant amounts of grassland, agricultural fields, pastures, and, to a lesser extent, marshlands, persist amongst increasing development. Elsewhere in the county, suitable habitat is more localized, although the species can still be fairly common in grasslands and oak savannah in the central portion of the county, as around Crockett, Martinez, Concord and south of Mt. Diablo. The species also commonly forages in the marshlands of North County but such situations rarely afford favorable nest sites so nests tended to be found further inland. A few pairs have also managed to hang on in the Richmond area.

Nests sites are typically immediately adjacent to favored foraging areas and are quite often in a single, isolated tree. In the Berkeley Hills and Diablo Range, nests are occasionally found on densely forested hillsides of native habitat but this is the exception rather than the rule. A large percentage of nests detected during the atlas, particularly those found in the Central Valley and around suburban areas in Central County, were placed near the crowns of planted conifers, especially in redwoods and Monterey pines.

Historical occurrence

The earliest known nest record for the county is based upon an egg set which was collected 28 Mar 1915 by Gurnie Wells (WFVZ #23191). Grinnell and Wythe (1927) state that they were "rather rare" in the Bay Area despite being common until the late 1890s. Grinnell and Miller (1944) further this notion but hint at signs of a recovery.

Breeding and natural history

The White-tailed Kite was confirmed breeding thirty times in 24 blocks. Eight records of birds either nest-building or carrying nest material ranged from 13 February–8 April. A report from 6 June has been discounted because of the extremely late date; it seems more likely that the bird was carrying food. A single nest with young was found 28 April and adults were seen carrying food three times from 7–22 May. Adults were noted on occupied nests (contents unknown) on ten occasions from 19 March to 21 May, with an additional record on the very late date of 14 June. Fledglings were noted on six occasions between 18 May and 12 July with an additional report from 4 August.

Conservation

The White-tailed Kite has regained and maintained a significant presence in Contra Costa County but the future of the species should not be taken for granted. Due to suburban plantings, nest sites now exist in embarrassing amounts but foraging habitats are being usurped at alarming rates—especially in East County and in areas east of San Ramon.

NORTHERN HARRIER • *Circus cyaneus*

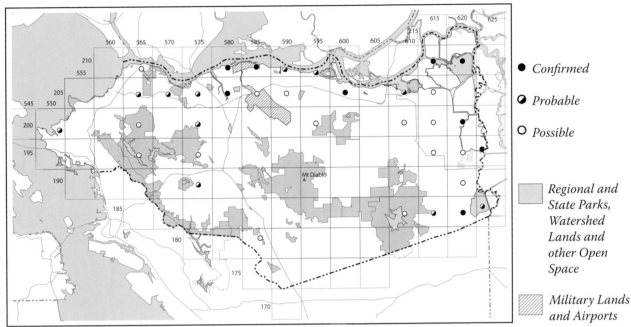

Rocking and wheeling over grasslands, marshlands and weedy fields in search of small mammals or songbirds, the Northern Harrier is one of the county's more recognizable breeding birds. The species becomes particularly entertaining during the breeding season when it begins boisterous courtship displays that include spectacular midair food transfers of hapless mammals and reptiles.

Current status and distribution

Nearly all nesting harriers in Contra Costa County are found in the extensive marshes of North County and the open fields of East County, with smaller numbers in the hilly grasslands around Crockett and Port Costa. Other than an agitated pair in the marshes near Pt. Richmond on 25 Apr 1998 we found no substantial evidence of breeding in the western portion of the county where contiguous amounts of habitat appear too small to support a breeding population. The species was also completely absent during the breeding season from the central and southern portion of the county, even from the extensive grasslands south of Mt. Diablo.

A quintessential bird of open country, the Northern Harrier forages and nests in fresh and saline emergent marshes, open grasslands and in weedy, bramble-choked fields. Although nests are generally well concealed, they are often quite close to roads and other disturbances. Even though the actual nest may be well hidden from view, its presence is constantly betrayed by the bird's habit of calling noisily and by the male carrying prey to the nest while the female incubates and protects the newborns.

Historical occurrence

Neither Grinnell and Wythe (1927) nor Grinnell and Miller (1944) knew of nesting anywhere in the East Bay, either in lightly visited Contra Costa County or in comparatively heavily birded Alameda County. Because the species is currently a fairly common nester in Contra Costa County it is tempting to speculate that it may have always done so and was simply overlooked. But Grinnell and Miller specifically state that breeding acreage had been greatly reduced, with numbers of breeding birds following suit. Furthermore, they cited no breeding instances any closer than Buena Vista Lake, Kern County.

Breeding and natural history

The atlas uncovered thirteen instances of confirmed breeding in 9 blocks, eleven of which involved males carrying food to occupied nests. Except for an early record of 1 April, dates ranged from 6 May to 26 June. Atlasers submitted many reports of single birds in March and early April, many of which have been omitted from the map as such reports were conservatively treated as pertaining to wintering birds or migrants.

Conservation

The long-term future of the Northern Harrier in Contra Costa County is clouded by the species' fondness for wetlands and open grassy fields. Such habitats are diminishing rapidly, particularly in the eastern portion of the county. Primarily due to habitat destruction, the Northern Harrier has been given Third Priority status as a California Bird Species of Special Concern (Shuford and Gardali 2008).

SHARP-SHINNED HAWK • *Accipiter striatus*

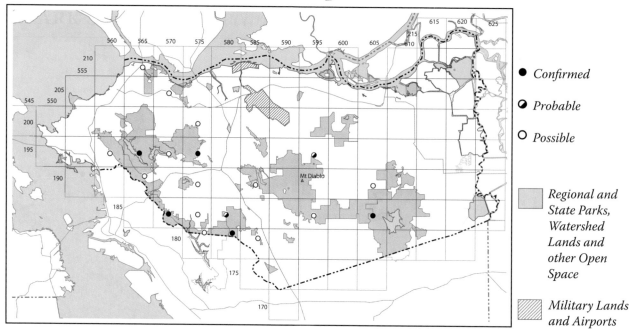

● *Confirmed*

◑ *Probable*

○ *Possible*

▨ *Regional and State Parks, Watershed Lands and other Open Space*

▨ *Military Lands and Airports*

A wave of vocal despair sweeps the woodland, and each individual is seen to be fluttering abjectly while it utters those chittering distress notes. Not the devil himself, appearing suddenly in a congregation of worshippers, could occasion such consternation as comes to the little feathered folk cringing before the expected blow. The blow must fall and some one must die.

    🐦 *William Leon Dawson (1923)*

Current status and distribution

The Sharp-shinned Hawk is among the most secretive of the county's nesting birds and it appears far more than likely that it is also one of the rarest. Although "sharpies" were noted widely in the county through early May, such birds have been treated here as migrants, leaving just a handful of breeding season sightings. It is clear that habitat needs of this species dictate an absence from anywhere in the county except wooded portions of the Coast Range. Further, based upon a small amount of data, it would appear that the species is more numerous in the more densely forested Berkeley Hills than in the more arid Diablo Range.

Because so few nests have ever been found in the county, an accurate depiction of suitable breeding habitat is difficult. Nests in the Diablo Range portion of Santa Clara County were found in "dense, broadleaved evergreen forests of Coast Live Oak and California Bay on north-facing slopes with nearly complete canopy closure" (Bousman 2007). Additional nests in Santa Clara County were found in open oak woodland with gray pines and a partly open canopy and in a dense stand of California bay in coastal oak woodland (Bousman 2007).

Historical occurrence

Grinnell and Wythe (1927) cite nesting from San Leandro and Berkeley, Alameda County so it is probably safe to assume that breeding was taking place in adjacent Contra Costa County. A citation of adults feeding young at the Diablo Country Club on the western flank of Mt. Diablo on 27 May 1950 would likely represent the first nesting confirmation for the county but the early date is suggestive that these were misidentified Cooper's Hawks (Gull 32: 27).

Breeding and natural history

The Sharp-shinned Hawk was confirmed nesting just three times during the atlas project. Adults were noted feeding young 4 July 2002 at Briones Regional Park, a nest with young was found 6 July 1998 at Las Trampas Regional Park west of Danville, and an adult was seen feeding young at Upper San Leandro Res. 9 July 2002. An occupied nest at Morgan Territory Regional Park on 8 May 2002 was thought to have been a Sharp-shinned Hawk but the adult was seen only briefly. Because the nest was in an oak (unusual for this species) and because the early date might be more indicative of a Cooper's Hawk, this sighting is best considered hypothetical.

Conservation

The Sharp-shinned Hawk, because it is so secretive during the nesting season, has received relatively little attention from researchers. Habitat requirements for nesting seem poorly understood and have tended to be summarized in only general terms. However, it would appear that forest degradation from logging is their most significant range-wide threat. Remsen (1978) placed the Sharp-shinned Hawk on the California Bird Species of Special Concern list, although they have been removed from the latest list (Shuford and Gardali 2008).

COOPER'S HAWK

COOPER'S HAWK • *Accipiter cooperii*

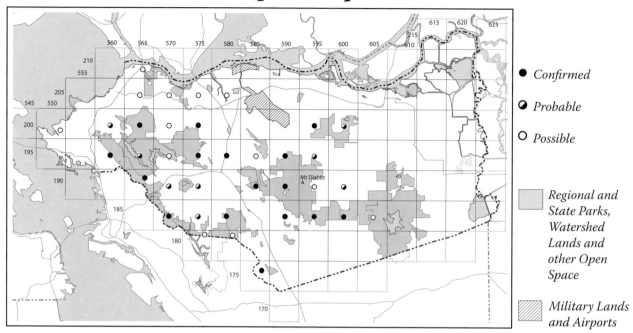

Long thought to be rare breeding birds in Contra Costa County, it now appears that the Cooper's Hawk is far more common here than most would have imagined. And, because the species is reclusive during the breeding season and prefers remote nest sites, it seems likely that the Cooper's Hawk is more common still than the map would indicate.

Current status and distribution

The Cooper's Hawk is an uncommon and usually furtive nester throughout all of the wooded portions of the Coast Range. Although breeding bird atlas projects for Alameda (R. Richmond, pers. comm.) and Santa Clara counties (W. Bousman, pers. comm.) found numerous nests in urban and suburban parks and neighborhoods, we obtained no such confirmations in Contra Costa County. The species is thus completely absent as a breeding bird from the Bay plain around Richmond, from the urbanized Interstate 680 Corridor, from the Pittsburg/ Antioch area, and from the Central Valley portion of the county.

The Cooper's Hawk nests in a far wider variety of vegetation types than the closely related Sharp-shinned Hawk, ranging from relatively dense coastal oak woodlands and even particularly dense stands of Blue oak woodland to riparian corridors in canyon bottoms.

Historical occurrence

Grinnell and Wythe (1927) knew of breeding Cooper's Hawks only in Marin and Sonoma counties. The first nesting confirmation for Contra Costa County appears to have been a nest at Reliez Valley near Lafayette 15 May 1932 (Gull 14:6). The impression given by Grinnell and Wythe that Sharp-shinned Hawks were more commmon locally than Cooper's is contrary to our current understanding and the possibility remains that some early nests were attributed to the wrong species.

Breeding and natural history

The only record of a bird carrying nest material was at Briones Regional Park 26 Mar 2000. Occupied nests (contents unknown but earlier dates presumably pertaining to eggs, later dates to young) were found from 21 April–29 June. Nests with young were detected 17 June–20 July and fledglings were noted 3–29 July. A set of eggs taken at Reliez Valley near Lafayette 11 Apr 1933 is slightly earlier than any in our small sample (MVZ #2565).

Conservation

Statewide concerns for Cooper's Hawk populations led them to be designated as a Third Priority Species of Special Concern (Remsen 1978), but they have not been included on more recent lists. While pesticides and unscrupulous falconers are considered threats, habitat destruction remains the most pressing concern.

RED-SHOULDERED HAWK • *Buteo lineatus*

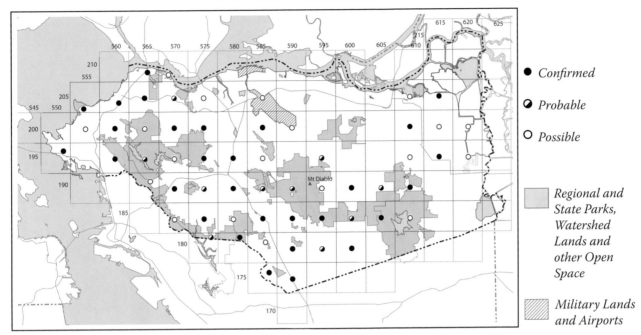

● *Confirmed*

◐ *Probable*

○ *Possible*

▨ *Regional and State Parks, Watershed Lands and other Open Space*

▨ *Military Lands and Airports*

Far and away one of our most beautiful nesting birds, the Red-shouldered Hawk is also one of our greatest success stories. In the past quarter of a century these masters of the roadside have staged a well-documented invasion of forested areas throughout the county, going from an extreme rarity to a common sight in a short time.

Current status and distribution

Red-shouldered Hawks occur throughout the county. Most neighborhoods in Central County have a pair of nesting birds, particularly those that are more forested or feature even a slender riparian corridor. In fact, it is in these residential settings where they are most common. They are also found with regularity in protected park settings, particularly those with streamside habitats. Proper habitat is most commonly found in the Berkeley Hills; in the Diablo Range they are generally much less common. In recent years they appear to have begun to colonize the eastern portion of the county, but there they remain quite scarce and localized. They were notably absent from some of the residential areas around Pittsburg and Antioch, from the northeastern portion of the Diablo Range around Black Diamond Mines, and from the southeastern portion of the county that is almost purely grassland and agriculture.

Birds in wild settings often nest in California Sycamores, but the majority of nests discovered during the atlas project were built in introduced eucalyptus.

Historical occurrence

Grinnell and Wythe (1927) considered them rare and local residents of the interior valleys of the Bay Region. Although they make no mention of any sightings from Contra Costa County, sets of eggs were collected at Oakley in East County 18 Apr 1915 (MVZ #7646) and 2 Apr 1921 (WFVZ #44128). The next known sightings for the county are of one north of Orinda 23–30 September and one at Pinole 29 November, both in 1953 (AB 2: 54). The first known nesting since 1915 wasn't documented until 1979, when a pair with a fledgling was noted near the north end of Morgan Territory Rd. south of Clayton in June of that year (county notebooks). It remains unclear whether or not the Red-shouldered Hawk was a regular member of the breeding avifauna early in the century, but it is clear that the increase in the later part of the twentieth century was a true range expansion, rather than the result of increased coverage.

Breeding and natural history

The atlas team managed to amass thirty-seven breeding confirmations in an incredible 32 blocks. Adults were noted either carrying nest material or building nests on the widely scattered dates of 3 and 23 March, 17 April, and 30 May. In the latter case the adult may have actually been carrying food rather than nest material. Occupied nests with contents unknown were found 15 March–16 May, nests with young were recorded 17 May–7 July, adults were seen carrying food 7 May–8 June, and fledglings were present 27 May–17 July.

63

Conservation

The lure of the abundant eucalyptus for nesting Red-shouldered Hawks likely bodes well for this species' continued success in Contra Costa County, even with further degradation of the county's riparian corridors.

RED-SHOULDERED HAWK

SWAINSON'S HAWK • *Buteo swainsoni*

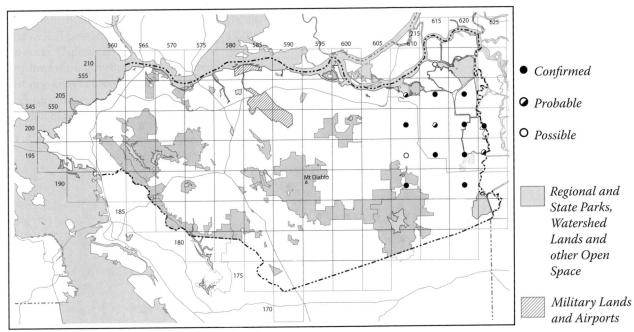

Surely one of the highlights of the atlas project was the surprising find that the Swainson's Hawk is a widespread (though numerically uncommon) nester in eastern Contra Costa County. A signature bird of Central Valley riparian habitats, local birds have thankfully adapted to less than pristine situations and established themselves as true players of the East County avifauna.

Current status and distribution

A glance at the atlas map reveals one of the least complicated ranges of any of our nesting birds. Each of our nests was found east of the Diablo Range (though one near Marsh Creek Res. was just barely so) and from Jersey Island in the north to Byron in the south.

The locations of Swainson's Hawk nests were a major surprise. Often associated in California with extensive riparian habitats, no such habitats exist in East County. Our nests were almost evenly split between isolated cottonwood trees and small clumps of introduced eucalyptus, a few of them immediately adjacent to well-traveled highways. A handful of nests were found in large oaks though oaks are quite scarce in East County. These choices of nesting trees are surprising since urban pairs at Davis and Stockton overwhelmingly prefer planted conifers (England and others 1997).

Even though some nests, notably one in an oak just east of Marsh Creek Res., are on the verge of the Diablo Range, it would appear that the open, rolling hills (such as those around Deer Valley and Briones Valley) are rarely, if ever, utilized by foraging birds.

Historical occurrence

The only historical nesting confirmations of this handsome buteo involved three eggs collected at "Mt. Diablo" 22 Apr 1898 (SBNHM #12186; *fide* W. Bousman) and a nest with three eggs collected from a cottonwood between Brentwood and Oakley on 9 May 1915 (Grinnell and Wythe 1927). In the years immediately preceding the start of the atlas it was becoming clear that Swainson's Hawks had increased locally but it was unclear when this increase had taken place. Concentrated birding in East County in the early 1980s turned up this species on only rare occasions. No such efforts were undertaken again until the early 1990s and at that time the species was readily found, indicating that the increase occurred sometime between the mid-1980s and the early 1990s.

Breeding and natural history

Ten breeding records from 9 blocks were obtained during the atlas project. Birds were noted building nests on two different occasions, each on 26 March. Occupied nests (contents unknown) were recorded five times between 11 April and 3 May. Adults carrying food were noted three times between 6 May and 22 June.

Conservation

The recent invasion is a welcome event but it is unfortunate that it may be quite short-lived. Although the Swainson's Hawk has apparently adapted well to crops (such as alfalfa) that don't grow too tall for foraging and which contain sufficient prey, current wholesale development is consuming the agricultural areas of East County at a fantastic rate. On the bright side, birds occupying low-lying areas in the far eastern portion of the county may be spared as little construction has occurred in these flood-prone areas. The Swainson's Hawk has been listed as state threatened by the California Department of Fish and Game (2006) and placed on Audubon's Watchlist 2002 at the level of yellow. Because Swainson's Hawk populations in California are thought to be expanding, the species was not included on the most recent List of California Birds Species of Special Concern (Shuford and Gardali 2008).

SWAINSON'S HAWK

RED-TAILED HAWK • *Buteo jamaicensis*

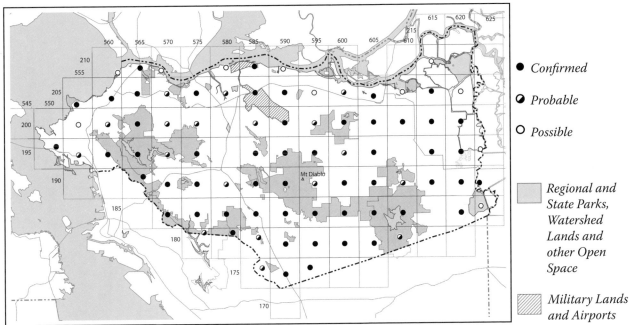

With a fondness for conspicuous perches in settled areas, the Red-tailed Hawk seems to be one of the few birds that is equally familiar to birders and non-birders alike.

Current status and distribution

During the atlas project, the Red-tailed Hawk was confirmed in a hefty 54 blocks and found to be probable in 18 others. This includes nearly every single complete block.

The Red-tailed Hawk forages in open grasslands and agricultural areas throughout the county. Nest sites are usually near the top of tall trees that offer commanding views of foraging areas, although transmission towers are also frequently used, particularly in East County. Many nests are built on hillsides, which further increases their view. In native habitats the nest sites tend to be in small clumps of trees in areas of fragmented forests or savannah which have patches of open grassland interspersed throughout. In the eastern half of the county, where forests thin out dramatically, the trees most commonly chosen for nesting are introduced eucalyptus. This is true in both the open grasslands north and south of Mt. Diablo and in East County, where nearly every clump is occupied. One set of transmission towers, which runs roughly northwest to southeast from Jersey Island to Clifton Court Forebay, features a basket-like construction near the top of the tower that has proven a perfect fit for Red-tail Hawk and Common Raven nests. In fact, nearly every single tower is occupied by one or the other during the spring and summer months.

Historical occurrence

No significant changes in status or distribution can be discerned from the scant amounts of published local data. Early authorities considered them common, a situation that appears to have changed little.

Breeding and natural history

Nesting of the Red-tailed Hawk was confirmed on eighty-six occasions during the atlas project. Birds were noted carrying nest material on ten occasions with dates ranging from 22 January–14 May. There are records from Contra Costa County of birds building nests by mid-December. Reports of nest building in April through mid-May may well refer to the adding of "decoration" described by Palmer (1998). Birds on nests were recorded thirty-four times as early as 9 March to as late as 2 June. Most of these reports likely refer to nests with eggs but some of the later records may have been nests with young that couldn't be seen. This seems to agree with data from the MVZ and the WFVZ. Of twenty-one egg sets in those collections taken from Contra Costa County, all were collected between 8 March and 5 May. Nests with young were tallied fourteen times 13 April–24 June. Thirteen reports of fledglings ranged from as early as 30 May to as late as 20 July.

Conservation

Urbanization in the Richmond and Central County areas must have usurped a significant amount of suitable habitat, but forest fragmentation, planting of eucalyptus windbreaks, and the construction of transmission towers has probably been more than adequate compensation.

GOLDEN EAGLE • *Aquila chrysaetos*

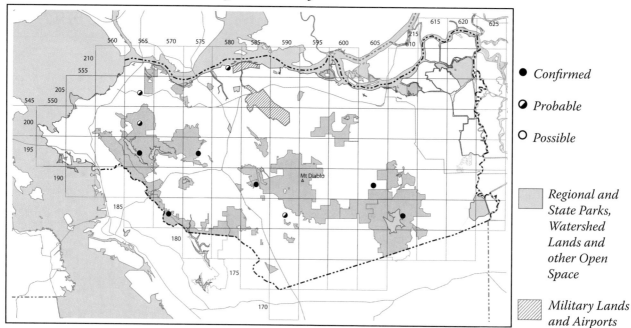

Confirmed

Probable

Possible

Regional and State Parks, Watershed Lands and other Open Space

Military Lands and Airports

Massive, majestic and mortal enemy to ground-squirrels everywhere, the Golden Eagle is in a struggle against urban sprawl to maintain its local role as a symbol of wildness in a place becoming less wild with each passing day.

Current status and distribution

The Golden Eagle is an uncommon and local nester in Contra Costa County. At least three pairs nested in the Berkeley Hills, the most prominent being the well-watched pair that nested on the radio towers at Sibley Regional Park. Although it isn't clear from the map, the Golden Eagle is much more common in the Diablo Range, with several pairs nesting in the vicinity of Los Vaqueros Res. alone.

A pair of Golden Eagles requires a massive home range. In the western U.S. the species forages over home ranges that average 20–33 km² (Kochert and others 2002). These huge territories are significant for one obvious reason—the amount of contiguous suitable habitat in Contra Costa County is not large and is steadily shrinking.

Historical occurrence

Although Grinnell and Wythe (1927) make no specific mention of nesting Golden Eagles in Contra Costa County, they do mention nesting, at least formerly, in the hills "near Berkeley." The MVZ and the WFVZ have a combined six egg sets taken in Contra Costa. The earliest was 28 Feb 1926 (location unknown) and the latest was 16 Apr 1887 at Sycamore Valley (present day Danville). Two of the sets are recorded as being from Brentwood but it is assumed they were taken from the Diablo Range west of town.

Breeding and natural history

The atlas team confirmed nesting eagles on ten occasions in 6 blocks. Nest building was recorded as early as 16 December. Occupied nests (contents unknown) were noted four times 9 March–24 April; nests with young were seen 17 March and 12 April. The lone record of a fledgling was detected 21 May. There are six sets of eggs in the possession of either the MVZ or the WFVZ, the dates of discovery spanning 28 February–16 April.

Conservation

For such an awe-inspiring bird, few species face the number of threats to their survival than does the Golden Eagle. Throughout its range, the Golden Eagle is subjected to a litany of dangers: collisions with vehicles and power lines; shooting (occasionally in an organized manner by sheep ranchers); poisoning; harvesting; pesticides; lead; nest-site disturbance; and, of course, habitat degradation and destruction. In Contra Costa and adjacent Alameda counties, eagles face an additional threat from the wind turbines in the Altamont Pass Wind Resource Area. Sixty-one mortalities were detected in the Diablo Range between 1994–1997, 37% of which were due to turbine strikes. A further 16% were caused by electrocutions (Hunt and others 1999). It is unclear if the local breeding population can continue to survive with such high rates of mortality.

AMERICAN KESTREL • *Falco sparverius*

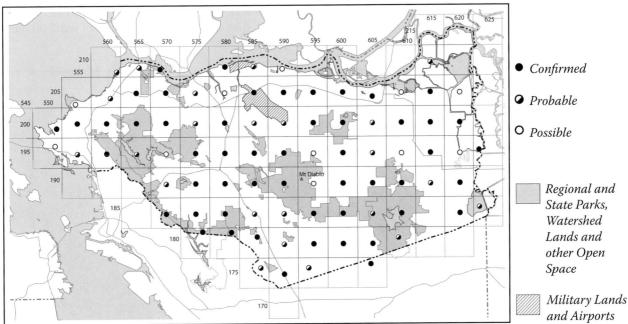

This compact, handsome falcon may be our most common and widespread breeding raptor, even more common than the Red-tailed Hawk, and has adapted well to roadsides and surprisingly small parcels of habitat.

Current status and distribution

The American Kestrel is found in nearly every nook and cranny of Contra Costa County and it is likely that the species was present even where there are blank spots on the map. The species is readily found in valley and blue oak woodlands, grasslands, and even around vacant lots and freeways if sufficient prey is available.

Unique amongst our breeding raptors, the American Kestrel requires suitable nest cavities, usually woodpecker excavations, however, the species has been noted entering holes in large transmission towers.

Historical occurrence

Early commentators considered the American Kestrel to be a common resident and, although historical comparisons are difficult, little seems to have changed in the ensuing decades.

Breeding and natural history

Atlasers amassed sixty-five breeding confirmations of the American Kestrel. Happily, none of the reports were of birds carrying nest material, as Kestrels aren't known to do so. Occupied nests (contents unknown) were noted from 9 March through 16 August; the nest on the latter date likely pertains to a second nesting attempt, something the species is now known to do and was felt to happen in Monterey County (Roberson and Tenney 1993).

Four records of nests with young were noted 23 May–10 June. Adults were seen carrying food on nineteen occasions 7 April–2 June but some of the April records may well have been of males carrying food to females on nests. Thirty reports of fledglings ranged from 7 May–20 July with the majority detected in very late May and in June.

Each of the four egg sets from the county now at the WFVZ was taken between 14 and 30 April; the lone set housed at the MVZ was collected 9 May.

Conservation

Because the American Kestrel is an obligate cavity nester, the conservation of large, often dead trees with woodpecker holes is crucial to its continued well-being in wilder areas of the Coast Range.

PEREGRINE FALCON • *Falco peregrinus*

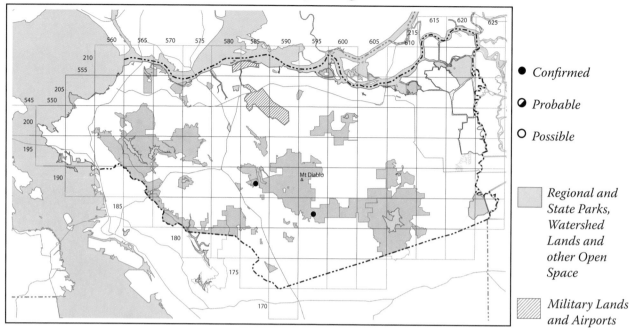

The legend for the map reads:

- ● Confirmed
- ◐ Probable
- ○ Possible

Regional and State Parks, Watershed Lands and other Open Space

Military Lands and Airports

The dashing figure of a Peregrine Falcon hurtling over a mudflat in hot pursuit of a flock of shorebirds or throttling a hapless pigeon over an urban area is a sight many thought would never be seen again in Contra Costa County, or anywhere else for that matter. Once one of North America's rarest breeding birds, the reemergence of the embattled Peregrine Falcon as a viable member of the continent's avifauna was witnessed throughout the atlas project.

Current status and distribution

During the winter months, the Peregrine Falcon is a scarce but widespread presence, most often on transmission towers that allow viewing of concentrations of shorebirds and ducks. During the breeding season, however, the species is restricted to cliffs on Mt. Diablo and to several of the major bridges. Breeding at each of these sites is due to their reintroduction by man. These sites provide commanding views and plenty of prey nearby, as well as a minimum of disturbance.

Historical occurrence

Grinnell and Wythe (1927) considered the Peregrine Falcon to be a rare and local resident, citing Mt. Diablo as one of the Bay Area's few nest sites. There are at least six eggs sets at various museum collections, all apparently from Mt. Diablo, the earliest being four eggs collected on Mt. Diablo 8 Apr 1883 (WFVZ #52694). As recently as 1944 Grinnell and Miller still considered the species to be "fairly common for a hawk."

Breeding and natural history

Atlasers confirmed Peregrine Falcons breeding on four occasions, all on Mt. Diablo. An occupied nest was found 31 May, a nest with young was noted 14 May, and fledglings were detected 11 and 19 June. The date span for local egg sets spans 30 March–22 May.

In Monterey County, the local breeding season is believed to extend from mid-February to August (Roberson and Tenney 1993). The San Mateo atlas project confirmed Peregrine nesting on sixteen occasions. Nest building was recorded on 7 March and actual occupation of a nest was noted 10 March. Nests with young spanned 16 April–24 May. Fledglings were tallied 2–30 June (Sequoia Audubon Society 1991).

Conservation

From the 1940s to the 1970s, the nearly global use of organochlorine pesticides such as DDT caused the accumulation of toxins in the prey of the Peregrine Falcon, which in turn built up in Peregrines. Although few direct fatalities were documented in North America, the most unfortunate implication was reproductive failure due to eggshell thinning. In 1969, just a single pair was able to raise young in California (Herman and others 1970). The recovery of the Peregrine Falcon has coincided with the discontinuation of the use of DDT in the U.S. in the 1980s (White and others 2002).

Once listed as a federally endangered species, this species has, with massive and expensive human assistance, increased in numbers and been de-listed.

PRAIRIE FALCON • *Falco mexicanus*

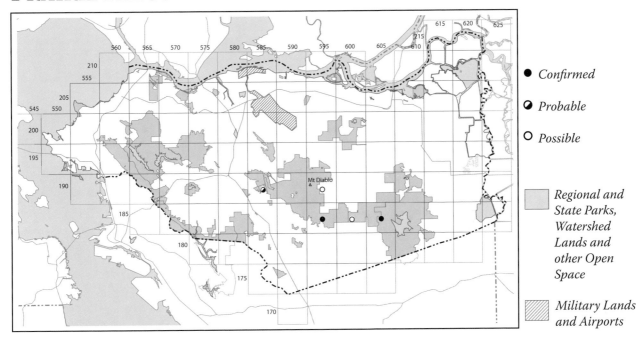

Confirmed

Probable

Possible

Regional and State Parks, Watershed Lands and other Open Space

Military Lands and Airports

Ruthless he is, and cruel as death; but ah, isn't he superb! To recall his image is to obtain release from imprisoning walls, glad exit from formal gardens and the chipping of sparrows. To recall his scream is to set foot on the instant upon the bastion of some fortress of the wilderness... A plague on your dickey birds!

> *William Leon Dawson (1923)*

The Prairie Falcon is an archetypal bird of the arid American west, foraging over grasslands and nesting on rocky cliff ledges. Such wildness is rare in Contra Costa County, however, and so too are breeding Prairie Falcons.

Current status and distribution

Breeding Prairie Falcons in Contra Costa County are completely restricted to the portion of the Diablo Range that includes Mt. Diablo State Park and areas immediately eastward. There the species occupies sites high upon rocky cliff faces, as in Pine Canyon at Mt. Diablo and at Morgan Territory Regional Preserve. The Berkeley Hills are almost entirely lacking in suitable cliff nest sites. A site at Las Trampas Regional Park west of Danville where eggs were collected in 1920 was unoccupied during the atlas project. Single East County records from Jersey Island on 24 April and Orwood Rd. near Byron on 24 June likely pertain to wide-ranging foragers or early post-breeding dispersants, as the species does not breed in that area.

Historical occurrence

Grinnell and Wythe (1927) cite nesting from not only Mt. Diablo but also Redwood Canyon between Oakland and Moraga, an area from which nesting has never even been suspected in the modern era. There is an additional egg set at MVZ taken 4 Apr 1920 at Rocky Ridge (now in Las Trampas Regional Park). There are an astounding 25 sets of eggs from Contra Costa County at the WFVZ. The first known nest record is an egg set collected at Pine Canyon, Mt. Diablo on 25 Mar 1882 by none other than C. E. Bendire (United States Natural History Museum #B20644).

Breeding and natural history

Because atlasers had little time to spend with an individual species, only scant amounts of Prairie Falcon data was collected during the atlas project. An occupied nest was found 8 May and fledglings were spotted 20 and 25 June. Egg sets from Contra Costa County at the WFVZ were collected in a narrow window between 29 March and 12 May (seventeen of them in April). In Monterey County, occupied nests were found 12–28 April and a nest with young was detected 23 April; other nests with young were tallied 14 May–9 June. In Napa County, an occupied nest was found as early as 1 April and a nest with young was reported 17 May.

Conservation

Because the Prairie Falcon has such stringent habitat requirements and because such habitats are so scarce in Contra Costa County, it is unlikely that there are more than five or so breeding pairs. The species is particularly vulnerable to disturbance from rock climbers and poachers. The Prairie Falcon appeared on early California Bird Species of Special Concern lists but is not included in the most recent version (Shuford and Gardali 2008

BLACK RAIL • *Laterallus jamaicensis*

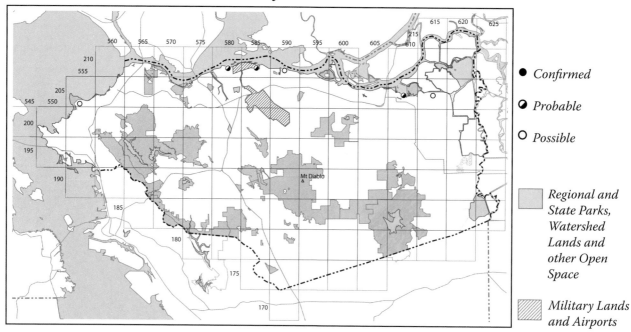

Confirmed

Probable

Possible

Regional and State Parks, Watershed Lands and other Open Space

Military Lands and Airports

Now dye the bird the color of swamp muck, and set it to playing hide-and-seek in a situation where it has every advantage of obscurity, and you have issued an ornithological challenge whose piquancy is felt by every amateur and fought for by every professional.

⟶William Leon Dawson (1923)

Although seeing a Black Rail in Contra Costa County defies most would-be observers, this species is comparatively easy to hear in certain places at certain times. Despite its reputation as a rarity, the Black Rail actually is a reasonably common resident, especially in North County marshes.

Current status and distribution

The Black Rail is most common in the marshlands of North-Central County from Martinez east to about Pittsburg, including (at least formerly) some of the low-lying marshy islands north of the shoreline of Suisun Bay. Much of this habitat is protected by the State of California or owned by the military. Evens and others (1991) detected Black Rails "in low to moderate abundance" in the remaining wetlands between Pt. San Pablo and Pt. Pinole in the Richmond area. The lone record in that area during the atlas was a singing bird 15 May 1999.

The species status along the Antioch shoreline is less certain. There is likely suitable habitat in this area, but it was inaccessible during the atlas project. Farther east, beyond the Antioch Bridge, numerous pairs were detected on the south side of "Big Break" around the Iron House Sanitary District. This site, named because of a levee breach resulting in the complete loss of a former

island, hosted at least 10 pairs of birds during the atlas project. Although Evens and others (1991) sampled the Delta, they did so less thoroughly than other areas and found no rails in Contra Costa County.

The vegetation in the three main regions of occupation in Contra Costa County (Richmond, North County, and Delta) differs markedly. Suitable habitat in the San Pablo Bay Area (Richmond) is dominated by pickleweed and California cord grass, saltgrass, seaside arrow-grass, marsh jaumea, alkali heath and gumplant. In the delta, marshes are dominated by tule, bulrush, cattail and common reed (Evens and others 1991).

Besides vegetation requirements, Black Rails in the San Francisco Bay estuary apparently also require an unrestricted tidal flow and a continuous upland transition zone (Evens and others 1991).

Historical occurrence

Grinnell and Wythe (1927) knew the Black Rail only as a "fairly common fall and winter visitant." Grinnell and Miller (1944) refer to it as a permanent resident but knew of no nest records for the San Francisco Bay system. However, Evens and others (1991) cite a set of eggs collected from Newark, Alameda County, in 1911 and an abandoned nest, "reportedly of a Black Rail", found at Pinole in 1976. Manolis (1978) surveyed Black Rails in central California and succeeded in detecting them at Pinole (3 singing); Pt. Pinole (a single bird); Mallard Island north of Pittsburg (two to three heard, one seen); and at Big Break near Oakley (three calling). On 11 Nov 1994, a single Black Rail was heard calling at Piper Slough on Bethel Island (Quail 41: no. 5) and up to three birds were heard sporadically through at least 11 June 1997, presumably breeding there (Quail 43: no. 11). The habitat was altered shortly thereafter, and the rails ostensibly abandoned the site.

It seems very likely that the Black Rail was breeding in the marshes of Suisun and San Pablo bays throughout the 20th century but was overlooked due to its secretive habits and marshy haunts.

Breeding and natural history

Because the Black Rail in western North America is thought to be mostly sedentary (Eddleman and others 1994), it is assumed that they bred in each of the blocks in which they were recorded. The atlas database contains little more than records of singing males, which are of little use in defining a breeding chronology. Egg laying by Black Rails in California apparently ranges from 10 March to 6 July, centering on 1 May (Eddleman and others 1994).

Conservation

Black Rail populations have suffered greatly from the fragmentation and loss of suitable wetland habitats, particularly around San Francisco Bay where it has been estimated that 95% of historical wetlands have been drained. Such losses have undoubtedly caused a severe decline in local populations, leading to their designation as State Threatened in 1971 (CDFG 2005). Long-term survival of Black Rails in Contra Costa County, and throughout their range, will clearly depend on the zealous protection of surviving wetlands.

BLACK RAIL

CLAPPER RAIL • *Rallus longirostris*

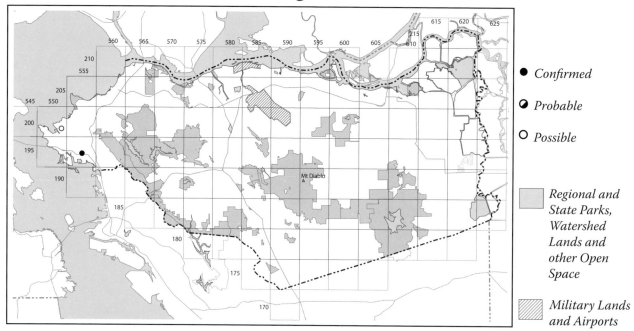

• *Confirmed*

◑ *Probable*

○ *Possible*

▨ *Regional and State Parks, Watershed Lands and other Open Space*

▨ *Military Lands and Airports*

The "Marsh Hen," once considered locally abundant in the Bay Area, is now a scarce and localized resident of the mostly inaccessible coastal marshes of Contra Costa County, a victim of widespread habitat destruction.

Current status and distribution

The Clapper Rail in Contra Costa County is known with certainty from just a handful of saline emergent marshes in West County, including the area around Meeker Slough north of Pt. Isabel, near the mouth of Wildcat Creek and near Pinole. There is a record from Martinez Regional Shoreline in North County from 29 May 1979 (county notebooks) but other reports from Central County have all come second hand.

The Clapper Rail is usually found in saline emergent wetlands featuring numerous tidal channels. The most common plants in this habitat include cord grass, pickleweed and salt grass. Shuford (1993) lists six important factors for breeding Clapper Rails: well-developed sloughs and tidal channels; extensive stands of cord grass; dense vegetation for cover and nest sites; intertidal mudflats; tidal channels with gradually sloping banks; stands of cord grass for foraging; abundant vertebrate food resources; and transitional habitat between the salt marsh and upland vegetation for protection during high tides.

Historical occurrence

Grinnell and Wythe (1927) assert that the Clapper Rail was once common in the marshes of south San Francisco Bay but, although once common elsewhere around the bay, were now only rarely reported, including a sighting from San Pablo 26 October 1919. Grinnell and Miller

(1944) considered the species to be "locally abundant" in the marshes of "Santa Clara, San Mateo and Alameda; formerly, and in part again recently, marshes on northern and eastern side of this bay, in Marin, Napa, Sonoma, Contra Costa and extreme western Solano counties."

Although the Clapper Rail has clearly been long present in Contra Costa County research, particularly by Bousman (2007), has turned up no breeding confirmations for Contra Costa County.

Breeding and natural history

The only confirmation during the atlas project, and possibly the first for Contra Costa County, involved precocial young at Meeker Slough north of Pt. Isabel 24 June 2001. The Santa Clara County atlas cites eggs from 3 April–16 July. Downy young were noted as early as 13 July and as late as 17 August (Bousman 2007).

Conservation

Clapper Rails in the San Francisco Bay estuary are represented by the race *obsoletus*, which once ranged at least as far south as Monterey County and as far north as Humboldt Bay, Humboldt County (Grinnell and Miller 1944). The widespread destruction of the salt marshes of the San Francisco Bay estuary, as well as heavy hunting pressure early in the late 19th and early 20th centuries, was primarily responsible for almost catastrophic population declines. The emergence of the non-native Red Fox in the 1980s was almost enough to drive the subspecies to extinction and in 1991 the total winter population was estimated to be just 500 birds (Bousman 2007). The "California" Clapper Rail is currently listed as Endangered by both California and the federal government.

VIRGINIA RAIL • *Rallus limicola*

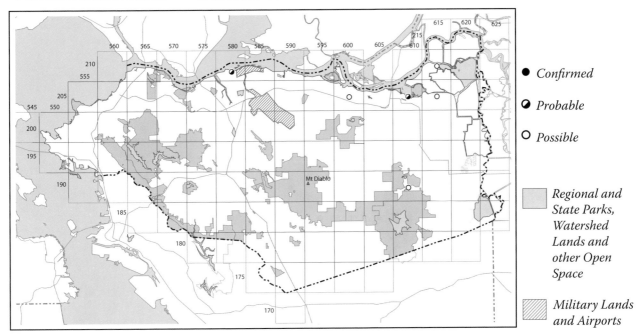

● *Confirmed*

◑ *Probable*

○ *Possible*

▨ *Regional and State Parks, Watershed Lands and other Open Space*

▨ *Military Lands and Airports*

The Virginia Rail is a secretive denizen of dense, marshy habitats where it is usually detected only when it emits one of its strange vocalizations, the most distinctive of which is a descending series of oink-like grunts. Based upon atlas data, the Virginia Rail is an uncommon and very local breeder in Contra Costa County who resides exclusively in imperiled freshwater marshes.

Current status and distribution

Although no breeding confirmations were achieved, the Virginia Rail is presumed to have bred in a handful of blocks in the northeastern portion of the county and at Marsh Creek Res. on the eastern flank of the Diablo Range. Elsewhere in the county there are few ponds or reservoirs where suitably dense marsh vegetation has been allowed to thrive for extended periods of time. The wetlands of West County are salt marshes, seemingly unsuitable for breeding Virginias. Although they are known to occasionally nest in such situations (Conway 1995), they are unknown to do so in nearby Marin County (Shuford 1993). Just two summer records were recorded from the extensive brackish marshes north of Concord—an area where they are truly abundant in winter. The remaining breeding season sightings during the atlas project were from areas of fresh emergent vegetation, including tidal areas near Oakley and around a few freshwater ponds, including Marsh Creek Reservoir.

Historical occurrence

Grinnell and Wythe (1927) cite no nest records for Contra Costa County but considered them to be fairly common residents of the bay counties. Thus, they prob-

ably bred in Contra Costa County where suitable habitat was rarely or never visited by researchers.

Breeding and natural history

The strongest indication of breeding was an individual engaged in territorial defense on the Concord Naval Weapons Station 4 June 1998. The other sightings involved "singing" birds during the breeding season. A few early April sightings are not included on the map as they may have been either wintering birds or migrants.

The handful of haphazard sightings collected during the atlas project is of little use in compiling a nesting chronology, nor is much data easily available for nearby areas. In Monterey County, precocial young were detected 21 and 27 May (Roberson and Tenney 1993). In Napa County, precocial young were tallied 6 and 8 June. Burridge (1995) reported distraction displays as early as 26 April and precocial young as late as 15 July in Sonoma County. In San Mateo County, precocial young were found as early as 15 May and as late as 11 August (Sequoia Audubon Society 2001). Finally, in Marin County, Shuford (1993) reported precocial young as early as 1 May.

Conservation

A preference for fresh emergent wetlands places the Virginia Rail in an extremely vulnerable position in Contra Costa County, where such situations have probably never been common and are only becoming less so. Their future here is wholly dependent upon the protection of the remaining freshwater marshes.

COMMON MOORHEN • *Gallinula chloropus*

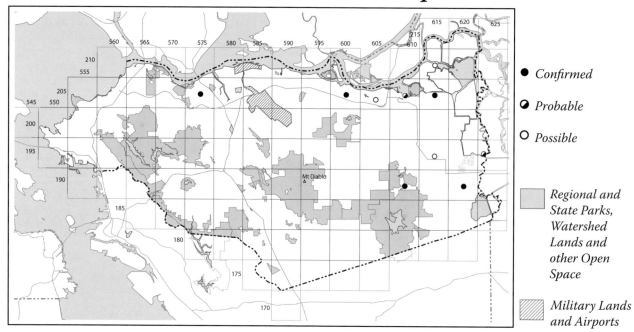

Confirmed

Probable

Possible

Regional and State Parks, Watershed Lands and other Open Space

Military Lands and Airports

This "Red-billed Mudhen", though nearly a dead-ringer for the ubiquitous American Coot, is far scarcer and more localized than its white-billed relatives. Although probably never common, its numbers have decreased steadily in recent decades due to the wanton destruction of freshwater habitats.

Current status and distribution

The Common Moorhen is present locally on select freshwater ponds and in the reedy sloughs and ditches of East County. The species is completely absent during the breeding season from the Richmond area and the Berkeley Hills. In Central County the species is known only from McNabney Marsh and the nearby Mt. View Sanitary District sewage treatment plant. Birds found in winter in the marshes of North County aren't known to nest locally though access to these areas is spotty and breeding birds could have been overlooked. Marsh Creek Res. in the hills just west of Brentwood is the only known breeding station in the Diablo Range. As the map shows, the Common Moorhen is most often encountered in East County, where it favors marshy freshwater ponds and sewage ponds.

Historical occurrence

Surprisingly, Grinnell and Wythe (1927) knew of only three records of Common Moorhen from the San Francisco Bay counties, although that included apparently recently hatched birds near Hayward, Alameda County, in 1904. Grinnell and Miller (1944) included the suitable marshlands of the Sacramento and San Joaquin Valleys in their range so it seems certain that a lack of Contra Costa records, particularly in East County, is due to a lack of coverage rather than a true absence.

Breeding and natural history

Just five breeding confirmations were obtained for this secretive and local species. Adults were noted carrying nest material on 13 and 22 April and precocial young were discovered on three occasions within the narrow window of 2–10 June.

Conservation

Although the Common Moorhen doesn't appear on any "watchlists," this is clearly a bird on which the scientific and birding communities need to keep a close eye. The species preference for freshwater marshes seems to leave it highly vulnerable to the kinds of habitat losses that have already occurred in Contra Costa County and throughout California.

COMMON MOORHEN

AMERICAN COOT • *Fulica americana*

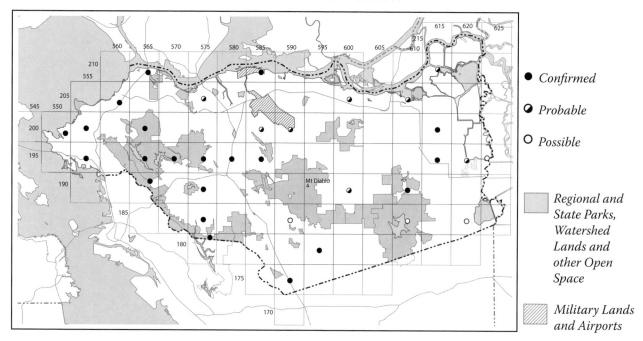

- ● Confirmed
- ◑ Probable
- ○ Possible

▢ Regional and State Parks, Watershed Lands and other Open Space

▨ Military Lands and Airports

Often uncharitably referred to as "mudhen", the American Coot is our only member of the rail family that is common, widespread or conspicuous, and for that it deserves at least a measure of our respect.

Current status and distribution

The American Coot was confirmed breeding in many blocks in the western third of the county but was found only locally even in those blocks. Nesting in the Berkeley Hills was confined to the watershed reservoirs but elsewhere in the county most nests were at sewage ponds, city duck ponds and golf courses.

Historical occurrence

Because so little has been published in local sightings columns about the American Coot, it is impossible to detect any changes in its status and distribution. It is entirely possible, however, that the widespread construction of ponds at sewer treatment plants, golf courses and city parks has boosted the local population at least somewhat.

Breeding and natural history

The American Coot was confirmed nesting thirty-five times during the atlas project, about half of the time based upon the presence of precocial young. Strangely, our three records of adults carrying nest material fall between 27 May and 26 June! Adults occupying nests presumed to contain eggs were found five times between 30 April–18 June. Of twenty-three records of precocial young, two were from April (earliest was 18 April), 10 were from May, six were from June, three were from July and the remaining two were from August, the latest being 17 August.

Of interest is the fact that the earliest breeding record for North America was a nest with ten eggs in central California on 23 Jan 1936; the latest, said to be from the San Francisco Bay Area, involved three adults with three young near a nest 21 Sept 1967 (Brisbin and others 2002). Records such as these suggest that a dearth of fieldwork early in the season caused us to miss much of the early breeding cycle and possibly some of the late breeding cycle.

Gullion (1954) did extensive work with breeding coots at Lake Temescal, Alameda County and at Jewel Lake in Tilden Park, Contra Costa County (where Coots no longer breed). Double brooding was found in five of six pairs that successfully raised an earlier brood.

Conservation

As with other species that nest on freshwater ponds, breeding American Coots would benefit greatly if emergent vegetation is allowed to flourish around the margins of the many artificial ponds that have been constructed in recent decades, particularly at sewer treatment plants and golf courses.

KILLDEER • *Charadrius vociferus*

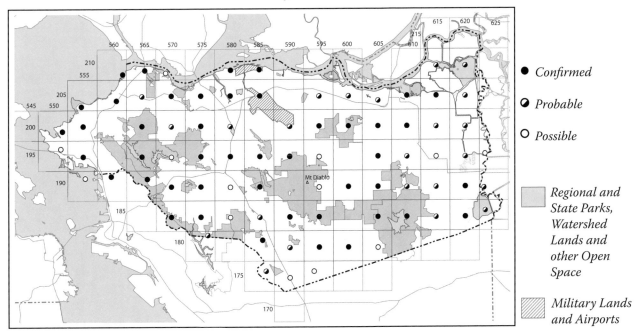

Confirmed

Probable

Possible

Regional and State Parks, Watershed Lands and other Open Space

Military Lands and Airports

Vociferus is the arch accuser of the human race, and as sure as a mere man sets foot upon a portion of the domain which she counts her own, every ingenuity of alarm is brought to bear upon him, every passion and prejudice of the wild things is appealed to, and the miserable son of Adam is denounced as a wrecker of homes, an ogre and an outcast. ⟶ *William Leon Dawson (1923)*

The Killdeer, with its urgent, high-pitched vocalizations given both day and night, is one of the more familiar birds of shore and neighborhood alike. The fact that it is amongst our most widespread breeding birds is a testament to its adaptability to human presence and altered habitats.

Current status and distribution

During the atlas project, Killdeer were present and breeding in every corner of the county with confirmations in 45 blocks and "probable" pairs in many of the remaining blocks; even the few blank spots on the map probably had birds present somewhere. The species is partial to gravel parking lots and road shoulders, abandoned railroad beds, muddy edges and levees of ponds, and rocky creek bottoms, often in close company with humans.

Historical occurrence

Strangely enough, Grinnell and Wythe (1927) knew of Bay Area nesting only at Golden Gate Park, San Francisco and from Alameda County. The first certain nesting in Contra Costa County was a set of eggs taken at Antioch in 1933 (MVZ #4235). Still, it seems highly improbable that the Killdeer was truly such a scarce nester in Contra Costa early in the 20th century.

Breeding and natural history

Fifty-two breeding confirmations were obtained during the atlas project. Adults were noted on nests (eggs presumed) 1 March through 2 June, suggesting at least a second brood. Distraction displays, which qualify as a confirmation for Killdeer, were noted on thirteen occasions from 11 April to 19 June. Twenty-eight records of fledglings or precocial young (atlasers often appear to have used these categories interchangeably) ranged from 26 March to 2 July (most from April and May), again an indication of at least a second brood.

Conservation

One can only wonder how many Killdeer, which nest in precarious situations, are stepped on or run over. Yet its adaptation to roadsides, gravel lots and playing fields would seem to suggest that its long-term future here is very bright indeed.

BLACK OYSTERCATCHER • *Haematopus bachmani*

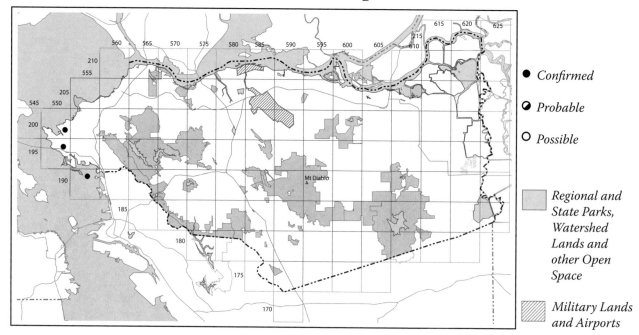

● *Confirmed*

◑ *Probable*

○ *Possible*

▨ *Regional and State Parks, Watershed Lands and other Open Space*

▨ *Military Lands and Airports*

Bringing a taste of the rocky Pacific shoreline to Contra Costa County, this comical shorebird is one of our scarcest and most localized breeding birds. This Johnny-come-lately was a welcome addition to the local avifauna upon first arrival a little over two decades ago and its modest numbers ensure that it will continue not to be taken for granted.

Current status and distribution

The Black Oystercatcher is known to breed at just a few sites in the Richmond area. Known sites include Bird Rock, a small rock adjacent to Brooks Island, and West Brothers Island near Pt. San Pablo. Nesting may also occur at a handful of additional sites, particularly Red Rock, a 179-foot rocky island near the Richmond-San Rafael Bridge. In addition to rocky breeding sites, the species is routinely found foraging and roosting on the multitude of breakwaters in the area. Outside of the breeding season the species is regularly present as far to the northeast as Pt. Pinole Regional Shoreline but there is no suitable nesting habitat at that site.

Historical occurrence

The Black Oystercatcher was known only from the Farallon Islands and Tomales Pt., Marin County by Grinnell and Wythe (1927). The first records from the East Bay apparently were not until June of 1982 when a single bird was found at the Bay Bridge Toll Plaza, Alameda County (AB 36: no. 6). The first Contra Costa sighting followed quickly when one was found at "Castle Rocks" (should have been Castro Rocks) 29 Dec 1982 (AB 37: no. 3). The first nesting confirmation is from Brooks Island in June and July of 1984 (AB 38: no. 6).

Breeding and natural history

The atlas project managed to confirm nesting on one occasion each in three different blocks. A nest with eggs was detected 17 May 1998, precocial young were noted 17 May 1998, and an occupied nest was found 20 June 1998. The 17 May record of precocial young is notably early as hatching is June–August on the Farallon Islands and precocial young were not noted in Monterey County until 23 June (Roberson and Tenney 1993). The early date for the San Mateo Atlas was 10 June (Sequoia Audubon Society 2001).

Conservation

Currently listed only as a Yellow List Species on the Audubon's Watchlist (2002), this is a species that bears watching, particularly locally. In Contra Costa County it is unlikely that there are more than 5–7 breeding pairs, leaving them vulnerable to nest site disturbance or destruction, predators and oil spills.

BLACK OYSTERCATCHER

BLACK-NECKED STILT • *Himantopus mexicanus*

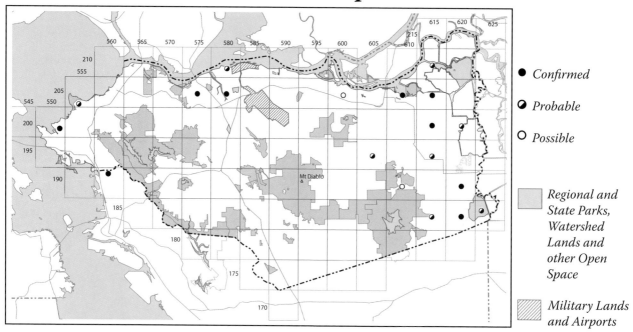

Confirmed

Probable

Possible

Regional and State Parks, Watershed Lands and other Open Space

Military Lands and Airports

Quite possibly the most absurdly constructed of any of our breeding birds, the Black-necked Stilt trundles about marshes and pond edges on preposterously long legs that appear better designed for a heron than a shorebird.

Current status and distribution

Like many waterbirds, pockets of breeding Black-necked Stilts are found locally in the Richmond area, in North County (most notably at McNabney Marsh where up to 25 pairs breed annually), and in east county, where most successful nesting takes place at artificial ponds. Numerous nesting attempts during the atlas project in East County, specifically around the Byron Airport and on Jersey Island, were ultimately abandoned when seasonal wetlands dried up or were drained before completion.

Historical occurrence

Although Grinnell and Wythe (1927) were aware of breeding in the Bay Area only in Hayward, it seems likely that the species bred somewhere in the county, probably in the eastern portion, but it was never recorded. It is doubtful, however, that the Black-necked Stilt was historically common since the vast majority of modern nests occur in manmade habitats which were unavailable earlier in the 20th century.

Breeding and natural history

Mated pairs of stilts were recorded nineteen times beginning as early as 3 March. Six occupied nests (contents unknown but eggs presumed) were tallied 12 April–8 June; nests with eggs were found 25 April–19 May. The earliest spindly precocial young were detected 27 April, the latest on 8 June. Although our early confirmations appear similar in timing with other Bay Area atlas projects, precocial young were detected in San Mateo County as late as 25 August, suggesting we missed later breeding efforts (Sequoia Audubon Society 2001).

Conservation

Although difficult to quantify, numerous predators, including the Common Raven and the introduced Red Fox, likely pose a serious threat to nesting stilts. In East County, where the stilt breeds locally and probably far less commonly than in earlier times, man's ravenous appetite for new housing is consuming potential habitat at breakneck speed.

BLACK-NECKED STILT

AMERICAN AVOCET • *Recurvirostra americana*

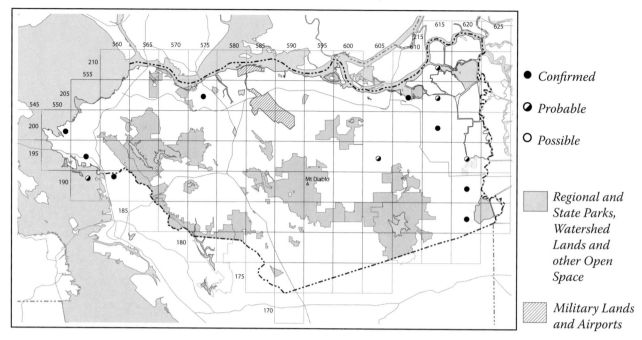

Confirmed

Probable

Possible

Regional and State Parks, Watershed Lands and other Open Space

Military Lands and Airports

This stately shorebird with a curious upturned bill is a common sight on the mudflats of San Francisco and San Pablo Bays during migration and in winter but during the breeding season the species is restricted to a handful of primarily artificial interior nest sites.

Current status and distribution

The distribution of the American Avocet during the breeding season in Contra Costa County nearly mirrors that of the Black-necked Stilt, with which it often breeds in close quarters. It is a scarce breeder in the Richmond area, an uncommon and somewhat local breeder in the marshes north of Concord, and fairly common but still local in East County. Although freshwater marshes with suitable water levels, such as McNabney Marsh near Martinez, are particularly prized, most nesting now occurs on levees at sewage ponds, as in Oakley and Byron.

Historical occurrence

The American Avocet was unknown as a breeder in the San Francisco Bay Area at least through 1927 (Grinnell and Wythe). By 1944, Grinnell and Miller listed occasional nesting in the Bay Area, at least near Palo Alto, Santa Clara County. Statewide, Grinnell and Miller (1944) considered the species to be common in the Central Valley and thus the species likely bred somewhere in eastern Contra Costa County but was never recorded. Numerous citations in American Birds throughout the 1950s–1960s suggest a population that was rapidly increasing, though no guesses as to why this occurred are offered.

Breeding and natural history

Apparently mated pairs of avocets were noted as early as 28 March and as late as 10 June. Ten occupied nests (eggs assumed) or nests with eggs were recorded 25 April–6 June. Precocial young were found on six occasions 13 May–6 June. The breeding season is likely far longer than our data would indicate, as evidenced by the documentation of precocial young in San Mateo County from 6 April–15 July (Sequoia Audubon Society 2001).

Conservation

The Common Raven and introduced Red Fox pose a serious threat to the American Avocet, particularly during the breeding season. The paving over of East County is also usurping suitable habitat, although that may be compensated for at least somewhat by the presence of sewage treatment plants, a presence which will surely increase as populations there burgeon.

SPOTTED SANDPIPER • *Actitis macularius*

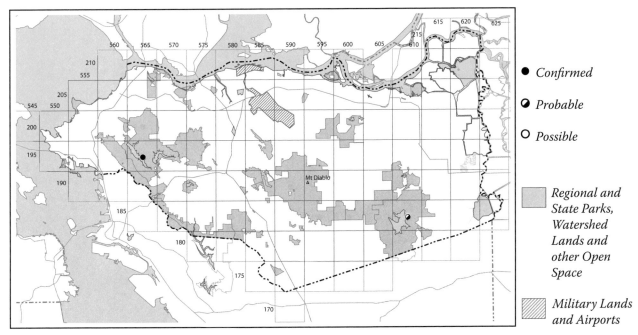

Once quite appropriately known as the Teeter-tail, the Spotted Sandpiper is found throughout its breeding range on sandy or cobbled streambed habitats or along lakeshores. Such habitats are very scarce in Contra Costa County and thus breeding Spotted Sandpipers are rarely spotted.

Current status and distribution

Because so little suitable habitat exists in Contra Costa County there are but two known breeding stations: a traditional site at the Pittsburg Power Plant along the shore north of Pittsburg and a new site at San Pablo Reservoir that was first discovered during the atlas project. The atlas team didn't visit the Pittsburg site during the project.

Nesting Spotted Sandpipers may nest in a wide variety of aquatic settings but birds in the Bay Area show a strong preference for sites featuring extensive rocks and gravel. Such sites are typically along the banks of sluggish streams but may also be along the shores of lakes and large ponds. Although such conditions are not common in Contra Costa County it remains surprising that the species has been confirmed nesting at just two sites.

Historical occurrence

Both Grinnell and Wythe (1927) and Grinnell and Miller (1944) knew of breeding in the Bay Area only in Sonoma County. Because the nesting population in the East Bay County is so tiny and local, it wouldn't be surprising for the species to be overlooked. This is especially true since one breeding station, San Pablo Res., was only eight years old at the time of Grinnell and Wythe and the power plant at Pittsburg was not yet in existence.

Breeding and natural history

The lone confirmation during the atlas project involved fledglings at San Pablo Res. on 3 July 1998. A pair at Los Vaqueros Res. on 19 May 2000 was intriguing and may well involve true breeding birds rather than late migrants. A few additional sightings were reported but were from relatively early in the season and at spots where breeding seems unlikely.

A likely nesting chronology of local breeding is suggested by data from nearby counties. In Monterey County, agitated adults and pairs were detected 11 May–13 July (Roberson and Tenney 1993). In Napa County, precocial young were noted on four occasions 30 June–11 July (Napa-Solano Audubon Society 2003).

Conservation

Because so little truly suitable breeding habitat exists in Contra Costa County (none of it "natural") and probably never has, the Spotted Sandpiper appears destined to remain a very rare and local nester. There truly is no suitable habitat to either protect or restore.

WESTERN GULL • *Larus occidentalis*

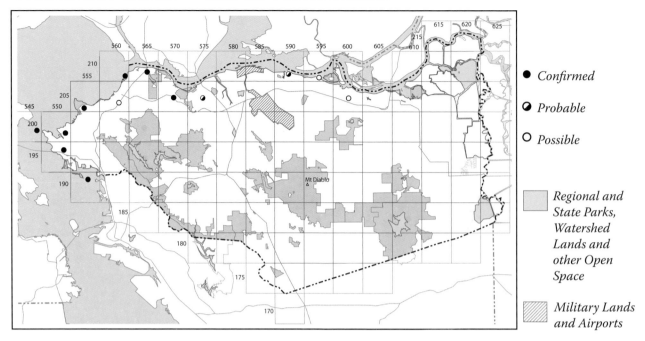

Confirmed

Probable

Possible

Regional and
State Parks,
Watershed
Lands and
other Open
Space

Military Lands
and Airports

As human populations have increased in Contra Costa County, so too has the population of certain species of birds. Amongst the most prominently conspicuous is the Western Gull, that raucous, dark-backed scavenger so familiar to those who frequent the waterfront. The Western Gull is quite scarce away from areas close to the San Francisco Bay Estuary.

Current status and distribution

During the atlas project, the Western Gull was present and breeding in eight waterfront blocks from Richmond eastward through the Carquinez Straits to Martinez. Further east, the species was noted on several locations around Bay Point and Pittsburg, including a begging fledgling on a sandbar near McAvoy Yacht Harbor, Bay Point, on 10 June 2001. The species was noted still further east at Antioch in March but no sign of breeding was ever detected.

In the Richmond area, the Western Gull heavily utilizes the few rocks whose tops manage to poke above the surface, most notably West Brother Island and Red Rock. The species also make uses of the many pilings and channel markers that dot the open bay. It forages on the open bay and mudflats but is also commonly found lurking in parking lots and city parks where food scraps are to be had. Of particular interest is the dump in North Richmond where thousands of these birds may be seen foraging at any one time. Although numbers present there are obviously highest in winter there are nevertheless too many birds there in summer to represent only local breeders. Birds seem to be commuting here from distant nest sites to partake in the bonanza and it is likely

that this becomes even more prevalent in years of low food productivity on the nearby Pacific Ocean.

Historical occurrence

Grinnell and Wythe (1927) considered the Western Gull to be an abundant resident, found throughout the year inside San Francisco Bay but nesting only at Pt. Reyes and the Farallon Islands. By 1944 the species was nesting on piers of the San Francisco Bay Bridge in San Francisco and Alameda counties (Grinnell and Miller 1944). The first nest record for Contra Costa County appears to have been from 1952 when a vacant nest was found on Red Rock near the Richmond/San Rafael Bridge (Johnston 1952). Forty pairs with young were noted in 1962 on West Brother Island (AFN 21: no. 5).

Breeding and natural history

The Western Gull was confirmed just thirteen times during the atlas, a surprisingly low total, ten of them based on adults occupying nests found between 4 April–19 June. A nest with eggs was found 17 May. The first adult seen feeding a begging youngster was 10 June.

Conservation

The seemingly eager adaptation by the Western Gull to food sources and nest sites made available by humans would appear to place it in a secure position in Contra Costa County.

CALIFORNIA GULL • *Larus californicus*

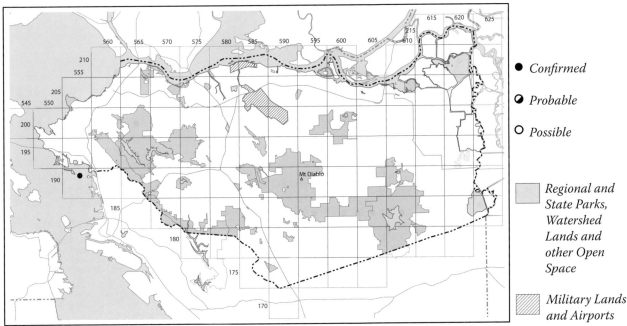

Confirmed
Probable
Possible

Regional and State Parks, Watershed Lands and other Open Space

Military Lands and Airports

The California Gull is the most prominent inland gull, often found feeding on scraps in city parks and parking lots and loitering on shopping center rooftops. This commonness, however, is not indicative of its status during the breeding season, as nesting has been confirmed on just one occasion in Contra Costa County.

Current status and distribution

One of the most surprising discoveries of the atlas project came when researchers found the first and only nest for Contra Costa County amongst the Caspian Tern colony on Brooks Island on 14 June 2000 (*fide* S. Bobzien; details to be published elsewhere). The nest was apparently abandoned. The species nested there in subsequent years and in larger numbers—we await the publication of further details.

Historical occurrence

As of 1944 (when Grinnell and Miller was published), the California Gull was not yet known to breed in the East Bay. It is unlikely that the species was overlooked. The first Bay Area nesting was near Alviso in 1980 (Bousman 2007). It appears that the first known East Bay nesting was at Leslie Salt near Newark, Alameda County, where nine nests were found 21 June 1983 (AB 37: no. 6). By 1985 there were 270 nests at the same location (AB 39: no. 3). Nesting colonies throughout the South Bay have shown an explosive growth rate in recent years (Bousman 2007).

Breeding and natural history

Egg laying in south San Francisco Bay is said to begin in mid to late April, with a mean time for incubation of 26.6 days. Fledglings depart the parental territory at the age of 40–60 days (Winkler 1995). In Santa Clara County, however, adults have been noted constructing nests as early as 26 March. Egg-laying has been noted from 18 April to 2 May. An adult was noted on a nest as late as 15 August (Bousman 2007).

Conservation

Brooks Island, already under the protection of the East Bay Regional Parks District, may represent the only suitable nesting habitat anywhere in Contra Costa County, and there the species will have to compete with several hundred pairs of Caspian Terns.

LEAST TERN • *Sterna antillarum*

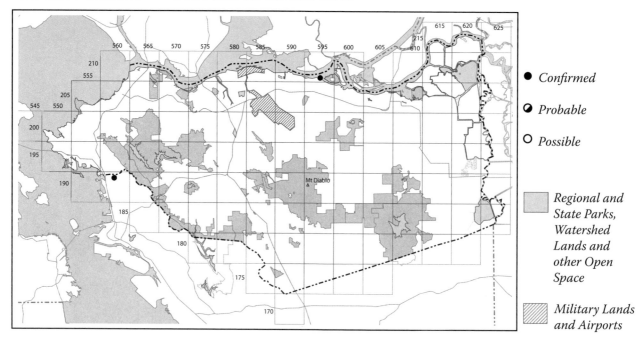

Confirmed

Probable

Possible

Regional and State Parks, Watershed Lands and other Open Space

Military Lands and Airports

Truth to tell, the shores of California no longer offer safe asylum to these tender children of the tropics. They still nest with us, or try to, but the odds are against them. The playgrounds of humanity, as we boast our southern shores to be, is no fit place for birds like these.

> ⁂*William Leon Dawson (1923)*

Although a tern in all respects, its tiny size and curved wings give the rare Least Tern a distinctly swift-like appearance when seen in flight. The subspecies which breeds in California, *S. a. Browni*, is federally endangered, its continued existence the result of extensive management and protection from predators.

Current status and distribution

A small colony at the Pittsburg Power Plant along the riverfront north of Pittsburg had been the lone nesting site in the county since the species was first detected there in 1982; in fact it was the most northerly nest site in western North America until the establishment of a new colony at Grizzly Island, Solano County, just across Suisun Bay, in 2006. The colony has always been modest in size, with a low of just one pair in 1986 and a high of 15 pairs in 2000 (L. Collins, pers. comm.).

In 2000, a new colony was established on a man-made shell mound at the northeast corner of the Albany Crescent, just within the boundaries of the county. That year there were at least 6 nests (L. Turnstall, pers. comm.). On 16 July 2001 there were five adults on nests and three chicks and on 27 May 2002 they were once again noted nesting (L. Turnstall, pers. comm.). Although they may have been present during the following breeding seasons,

they weren't reported again until six birds were noted there in late May 2006. On that day, copulation was also noted (C. L. Greenberg, pers. comm.).

Historical occurrence

Grinnell and Wythe (1927) were aware of just one definite record of this diminutive tern for the San Francisco Bay Area, that being two birds in Alameda, Alameda County, on 19 Aug 1923. Grinnell and Miller (1944) added a record from Alvarado, Alameda County, also in August of 1923, but cite Moss Landing, Monterey County as the northernmost breeding station in the state. By the 1930s small numbers, probably representing post-breeding wanderers from Monterey Bay nesting colonies, were beginning to be found annually, mostly around Alameda, including an adult feeding three immature birds on 2 Aug 1959 (AFN 14: no. 1). Another citation (AFN 19: no. 5) is of fifteen adults carrying fish to fledged young at the mouth of Alameda Creek 31 July 1965. The species was finally proven nesting when three nests were found in Alameda, Alameda County, in June of 1967 (AFN 21: no. 5). The first record for the Pittsburg breeding site, and apparently for Contra Costa County as a whole, was on 5 July 1982 when three birds were found (Quail 29: no. 2).

Breeding and natural history

The sparse data accumulated during the atlas project documented occupied nests 27 May–16 July and chicks 25 June–16 July. Least Terns in San Francisco Bay are said to generally arrive in late April, lay most eggs in May and early June, hatching in June and early July, and fledging in late June through August. The vast majority of birds have departed for points south by late August (Roberson and Tenney 1993).

Least Tern colonies are known to shift during the breeding season in response to heavy predation and this seems to have occurred at the Alameda Naval Air Station Colony in 2006, possibly explaining the late copulation report from the Albany Crescent, and even the nesting in Solano County (J. Luther, pers. comm.).

Conservation

Although numerous human activities, including hunting, plume collecting and habitat destruction, have served to severely diminish Least Tern populations, colonies within the San Francisco Bay Estuary are now most vulnerable to feral dogs and cats, Red Foxes and other mammals, and birds such as American Kestrels and Burrowing Owls.

AMERICAN AVOCET

CASPIAN TERN • *Hydroprogne caspia*

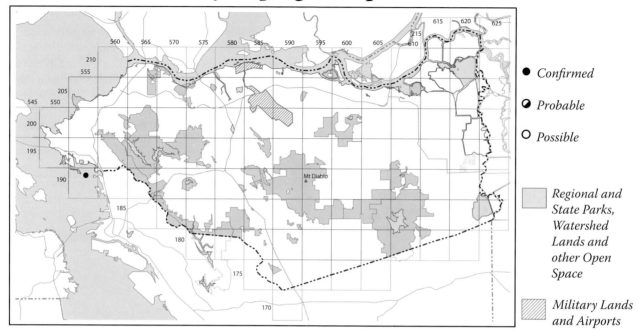

- ● *Confirmed*
- ◑ *Probable*
- ○ *Possible*

Regional and State Parks, Watershed Lands and other Open Space

Military Lands and Airports

Few wildlife spectacles in Contra Costa County can match the Caspian Tern colony on Brooks Island at the height of the breeding season. The sheer number of birds arriving from, or heading off to, distant foraging grounds, in combination with a rasping din that can easily be heard from the distant Richmond Shoreline, is unforgettable.

Current status and distribution

As of 2008, Brooks Island hosts the only tern colony in Contra Costa County and, in truth, there seem to be no other suitable candidates. Although the Caspian Tern will nest on levees around salt ponds, geologic factors have conspired to prevent the creation of such ponds locally. This summer resident is widely found in small numbers foraging on the watershed reservoirs of the interior and is commonly found deep into the delta. For example, the species is common in summer around Big Break and Bethel Island. Since the nearest known nest site is Brooks Island (about 50 miles to the west!) it is assumed that at least most of these birds are commuting from Brooks Island to distant, productive fishing grounds. This theory is bolstered by the fact that birds in places such as Antioch are often noted heading overland to the west with fish in their bills.

Historical occurrence

The first nesting within San Francisco Bay was confirmed in 1922 in southern Alameda County. However, Grinnell and Miller (1944) believe that the species was nesting there by at least 1916. Another large colony was established at the Alameda Naval Air Station in 1985 (AB 39: no. 3) but the beaches of Brooks Island apparently went unoccupied until 1995 when several hundred pairs nested (pers. obs.).

Breeding and natural history

The earliest returning bird was detected 28 March, probably later than the average first arrival for Contra Costa County, as one was seen at Brooks Island on 1 Mar 1995 (Quail 41: no. 8). Caspian Tern courtship and copulation may begin upon arrival on the breeding grounds. Territories are established and nest scrapes constructed within about four days of arrival. The first eggs are laid 2–3 weeks after arrival, with the egg-laying period generally lasting 4–5 weeks. In South San Francisco Bay, week-old chicks have been documented as early as 21 May. The young fledge at an age of about 37 days (Cuthbert and Wires 1999).

Conservation

Brooks Island is currently protected as an East Bay Regional Park and thus the main concern is continued vigilance against nest-site disturbance. This lone nest site would seem to be highly vulnerable to the possibility of an oil spill due to its position immediately adjacent to busy shipping lanes.

ROCK PIGEON • *Columba livia*

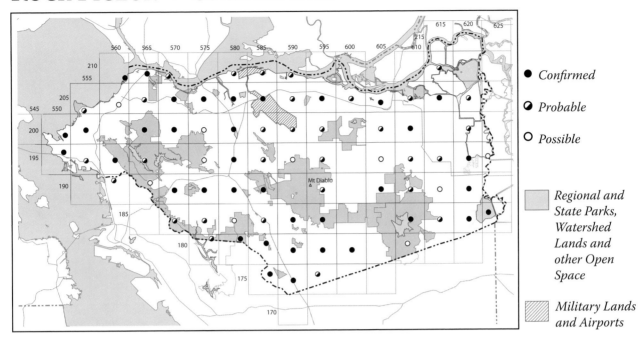

Few birds garner less respect than the beleaguered Rock Pigeon. Its practice of nesting around human settlements and leaving behind mountains of droppings has done little to bolster its image of a "rat with wings."

Current status and distribution

The lowly Rock Pigeon is a permanent resident around human settlements throughout the county. The species is very nearly absent away from such situations but, sadly, there are very few even moderately extensive areas of the county that don't contain buildings and thus the atlas map shows the species to be present at least somewhere in most blocks. The only sizable gaps are in watershed lands near Briones Reservoir and on the southern and eastern flank of Mt. Diablo.

A true opportunist, the species is readily found picking on scraps around shopping centers as well as feeding in agricultural fields and barren hillsides. The Rock Pigeon typically constructs its nests under the protective cover of opened buildings, although efforts in the form of netting and spikes appear to be on the increase in recent years.

Historical occurrence

It is unclear when the Rock Pigeon, first introduced in the eastern U.S. by European settlers in the early 17th century, became established in settled areas of Contra Costa as early writers such as Grinnell and Wythe ignored the species.

Breeding and natural history

Adult Rock Pigeons carrying nest material or nest building were detected on ten occasions 10 March–23 May, with an isolated record from 27 June. Occupied nests make up the bulk of our confirmations, with twenty-one tallied from 2 April–16 August. Adults feeding young were noted three times between 20 May–16 June. Fledglings were found four times from 22 April–17 July. Such a modest number of confirmations for a conspicuous bird living amongst us is probably indicative of a low level of interest in this introduced species amongst local birders.

Conservation

Not surprisingly for such an unpopular bird, the words "Rock Pigeon" and "conservation" are rarely uttered in the same sentence. None of the published Northern California atlases mention population declines and it is likely that the Contra Costa County population has at least held its own, if not increased, in recent decades.

BAND-TAILED PIGEON • *Columba fasciata*

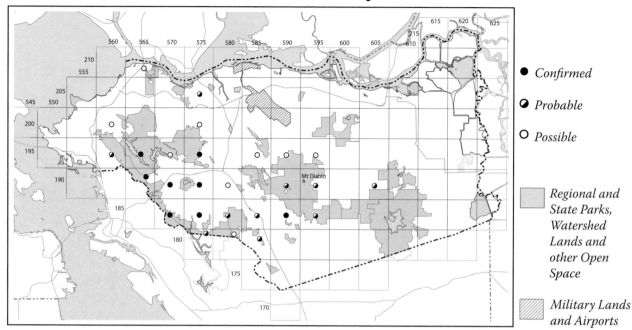

The Band-tailed Pigeon is a fairly common breeding bird in the heart of its local range in the Berkeley Hills, where the species forages in oaks and madrones. Elsewhere, however, the species is very rare and apparently nests only sporadically.

Current status and distribution

The fog-shrouded Berkeley Hills are the local stronghold of the Band-tailed Pigeon; the species is common nowhere else in the county. It is most often found in the vicinity of Tilden and Redwood Regional Parks in the western Berkeley Hills where it prefers coastal oak woodlands and localized stands of Monterey pines. The Band-tailed Pigeon decreases in numbers but remains present east to about Lafayette and Danville, areas featuring mature, well-wooded neighborhoods. In the Diablo Range the species is a sporadic wintering bird and scarce, extremely erratic breeder. As shown on the map, the species was confirmed in only one block in the Diablo Range. Although it is difficult to separate true breeding birds from wintering birds, presence from well into May and through the summer months strongly suggests that the Band-tailed Pigeon likely nested at some point during the atlas in each of the indicated blocks. The species has never been recorded in East County.

Historical occurrence

The Band-tailed Pigeon was unknown to Grinnell and Wythe (1927) as occurring in the East Bay in summer. The species was thought to possibly be breeding in Thornhill Canyon at East Oakland, Alameda County in 1955 (AFN 9: no. 4). The first confirmed East Bay breeding was at Strawberry Canyon near Berkeley, in Alameda

County, around 1960 (Condor 64:445). The first Contra Costa County breeding came in 1966 in Orinda (AFN 21: no. 4). A nest was found at Sunset Picnic Area, Mt. Diablo State Park, on 29 April 1979 (Kite 6:79), which likely represented the first breeding record for the Contra Costa County portion of the Diablo Range.

Breeding and natural history

The Band-tailed Pigeon was confirmed breeding nine times in a total of 8 blocks. An adult building a nest was detected 18 April. Occupied nests were recorded four times: 23 and 28 April, 29 July and 17 October. The latter date likely refers to a second or even a third brood as this species can nest at almost any time of the year. A new fledgling was found in coastal Monterey County 7 Dec 1989 (Roberson and Tenney 1993)! Adults feeding young were detected 12 June and 12 September, again indicating multiple broods. It is unknown how common such late nesting is here as very little atlasing was done after mid-August.

Conservation

The numbers of birds detected on breeding bird survey routes has decreased consistently in recent decades, with an average of –2.7%/year in California between 1966–1998 (Keppie and Braun 2000). Specific reasons for this decline are obscure, although habitat degradation and outright loss has likely been a significant factor. The species is currently a Yellow List Species on the Audubon Watchlist 2002.

MOURNING DOVE • *Zenaida macroura*

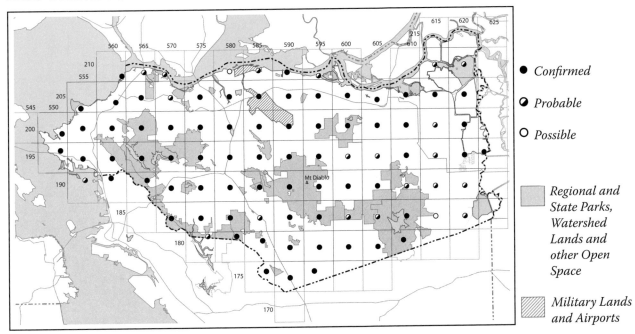

The tender, impassioned notes of the Mourning Dove are not only the most familiar, the most characteristic and commonplace, but the most lyric and soulful as well, the most romantically moving of any in the American chorus. Though the love-lorn swain blows but a single note, the sound sets a myriad chords to vibrating, -hope, memory, and desire, no less than sadness. Gentle melancholy, the sickness of springtime, is really the budding of desire, the yearning of the Live One for his complement, the Also Living. **❧ William Leon Dawson (1923)**

Scarcely noticed because of its constant presence around our homes and offices, the Mourning Dove is one of Contra Costa County's most successful breeding birds. Unlike the messy Rock Pigeon, this dainty dove and its nest is generally a welcome addition to front porches and planter boxes in the county's suburbs.

Current status and distribution

Clearly one of the most common and widespread of Contra Costa County's breeding birds, it was probably only limited coverage that prevented the species from being confirmed in each atlas block. This arch-type edge species can be found foraging in nearly any open habitat and is commonly found nesting in open oak woodlands, riparian corridors, planted eucalyptus windbreaks, city parks and suburban settings. Neighborhood nesters were commonly noted occupying nests on eaves and in planter boxes.

Historical occurrence

The breeding status of the Mourning Dove is likely little changed over the past century, as Grinnell and Wythe (1927) considered the species to be common, particularly in the interior. One apparent change, however, is its winter status, as Grinnell and Wythe considered it to be absent from the Bay Area during late winter.

Breeding and natural history

An abundance of Mourning Dove data was accumulated during the atlas project. Over 375 individual records include ninety-seven confirmations. The earliest recorded pair was 2 February. Adults found carrying nest material were detected on twenty-six occasions between 7 March and 2 August while birds noted actually nest-building were found another fifteen times 15 March–11 August. Eleven records of nests with eggs were tallied 2 March–8 June. An additional twenty-nine records of occupied nests were found 7 April–4 July. Nests with young were recorded four times from 17 April to 17 June. This number surely would have been higher were it not for the fact that most atlasers were able to confirm this species early in the season, thus reducing the attention paid to them later in the season. A nest with eggs on 5 September was reported by the San Mateo County atlas (Sequoia Audubon Society 2001), suggesting that the breeding season may extend significantly later than the atlasing season.

Conservation

Since it almost appears as if Contra Costa County was designed specifically with the Mourning Dove in mind, its future in Contra Costa County appears extremely bright.

BARN OWL • *Tyto alba*

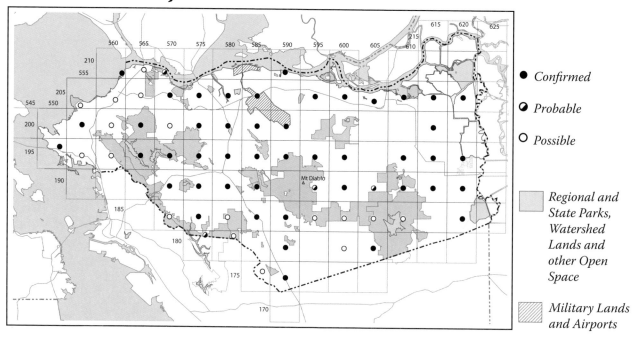

● *Confirmed*

◐ *Probable*

○ *Possible*

◻ *Regional and State Parks, Watershed Lands and other Open Space*

▨ *Military Lands and Airports*

Easily the most cosmopolitan of our local owls, the curious rasping calls of the Barn Owl are commonly heard over suburban neighborhoods throughout the county. Looking up at just the right spot might enable a brief view of these ghostly-white nocturnal predators.

Current status and distribution

The Barn Owl is fairly common and widespread in Contra Costa County, occupying a wide variety of natural and altered habitats. It is quite possible that the Barn Owl bred in every atlas block, something that can be said for just a handful of species. The species is apparently common around the Bay plain in Richmond and the open grasslands around Crockett and Port Costa. The species is less common throughout much of the Berkeley Hills because open habitats are less extensive. The Barn Owl is a constant presence throughout the residential Interstate 680 corridor as well as in the Diablo Range, particularly so in the extensive grasslands north and south of Mt. Diablo. It seems clear that the species is most common in East County where significant parcels of grasslands, weedy fields and agricultural fields continue to persist and the planting of fan palms appears to be almost habitual.

Historical occurrence

DeSante and George (1994) felt that Barn Owl populations in the west had increased during the 20th century due to agricultural practices and an increase in nest sites. Both Belding (1890) and Grinnell and Wythe (1927), however, felt that the Barn Owl was already common in both the East Bay and the Bay Area as a whole. The first

known nest record for Contra Costa County is assumed to be a set of three eggs collected 14 miles from Oakland 24 March 1887 (WFVZ #48211).

Breeding and natural history

The lone record obtained of a nest with eggs was recorded 13 April. Three egg sets from Contra Costa County in the possession of the MVZ range from 30 March–30 April. Nests with young were detected on five occasions 22 May–5 July. Fledglings were tallied twelve times 9 June–25 July. An additional thirty-eight records of abandoned or injured fledglings were obtained from the Lindsay Wildlife Museum Wildlife Hospital, greatly fleshing out the atlas map, but dates were not obtained. A record of a fledgling from Sonoma County on 12 April suggests that some early breeding was missed during the atlas project (Burridge 1995); a late record of a fledgling from San Mateo County (Sequoia Audubon Society 2001) on 28 October further suggests that the breeding season may extend far longer than our data might suggest. The vast majority of these records originated from residential settings.

Conservation

The future of the Barn Owl in Contra Costa County depends upon the protection of the open grasslands where it feeds, this probably being a more important limiting factor than the availability of suitable nest sites. The construction of artificial nest sites, in the form of either empty buildings or nest boxes, has probably compensated for the loss of local grasslands but clearly that trend cannot continue forever.

WESTERN SCREECH-OWL • *Megascops kennicottii*

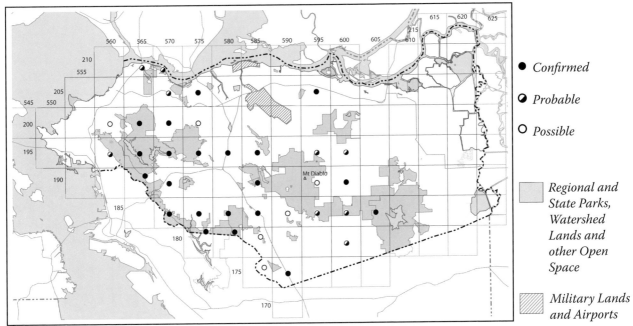

● *Confirmed*

◗ *Probable*

○ *Possible*

▨ *Regional and State Parks, Watershed Lands and other Open Space*

▨ *Military Lands and Airports*

This woodland gnome is found in forested areas throughout Contra Costa County and even blesses the yards of many "woody" neighborhoods, where lucky residents may be serenaded by the species' curious nocturnal bouncing ball calls.

Current status and distribution

Although not as conspicuous as the larger Barn or Great Horned Owls, it is possible that the Western Screech-Owl is the most abundant owl in the county, certainly within the confines of the Coast Range. The Western Screech-Owl is thought to breed throughout the wooded areas of the Coast Range, including areas along the western edge of the Berkeley Hills and the eastern edge near Mt. Diablo that are blank on the atlas map. Gaps in the central portion of the county are likely occupied as well. Such deficiencies are explained by a dearth of nocturnal atlasing as well as easy access via public roads. The species is unknown from the Central Valley portion of the county, (it is conceivable that it occurs very locally), in the marshes of North County, and the extensive grasslands south of Mt. Diablo, except along a few wooded drainages.

The species is most common in blue oak and valley oak woodlands with a sparse understory, but is also found around the edges of coastal oak woodlands. Screech-Owls are also present around riparian strips in the canyon bottoms of the Diablo Range but it would seem as if adjacent oak woodlands are the lure. They are absent from forests that are too dense or which feature an extensive understory.

Historical occurrence

Grinnell and Wythe (1927) described the Western Screech-Owl as a common resident with a preference for oak woodlands, exactly the same situation as exists currently.

Breeding and natural history

Adults thought to be entering occupied nests were detected on 17 April and 14 May and adults feeding young were noted 1 and 13 June. The bulk of the fifteen atlas confirmations involved fledglings, each of whom was detected within the narrow date span of 23 June–6 July. The presence of fledglings is clearly more prolonged as the Monterey atlas reported them as early as 9 May (Roberson and Tenney 1993) and San Mateo as late as 25 July (Sequoia Audubon Society 2001). A report of a fledgling in Sonoma County on 20 March is at severe odds with other published data for this species (Cannings and Angell 2001).

Conservation

Although not reflected in the atlas map, a loss of oak woodland habitats to development, especially in the central portion of the county, has likely caused local declines, although not enough to threaten their long term prospects.

GREAT HORNED-OWL • *Bubo virginianus*

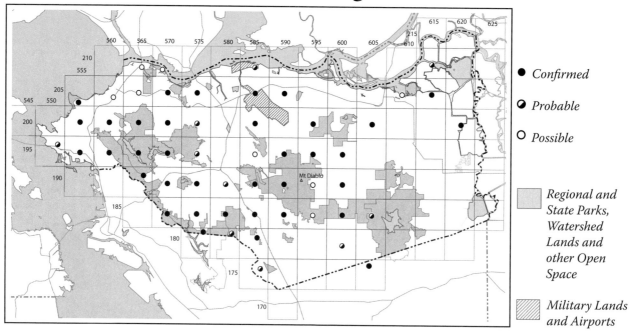

Confirmed
Probable
Possible

Regional and State Parks, Watershed Lands and other Open Space

Military Lands and Airports

He loves the darkness because his deeds are evil; and after the protecting sun has set, woe betide the mole or rabbit, Partridge, Jay, or chanticleer, who dares to stir where this monster is a-wing.

William Leon Dawson (1923)

This, the most feared member of the local nocturnal avian community, is widespread and common throughout the county, even in sparsely wooded suburban areas. The species' haunting duets, which likely strike fear in the heart of every other bird within earshot, is one of the characteristic nighttime noises of Contra Costa County.

Current status and distribution

Although numerically less common than many of the county's breeding birds, the Great Horned Owl would likely have been detected in every block in the county if more nocturnal fieldwork had been conducted. The glaring gap in the map for the southeastern portion of the county is, with a fair amount of certainty, due purely to a lack of effort. The species is found in a wide variety of situations: the edges of dense forests, open woodlands, grasslands, agricultural settings and suburban neighborhoods.

Historical occurrence

The status of the Great Horned Owl has remained unchanged during the past century.

Breeding and natural history

Local Great Horned Owls are known to breed early and likely even earlier than our data suggests. Occupied nests were detected on eight occasions between 26 March

and 6 May; nests with young were detected six or more times from 29 April–23 June. Nests often proved easy to detect in trees yet to leaf out. Fledglings were detected twenty-two times with dates spanning 1 May–3 July with single late reports from 6 August and 5 September. Some of the earliest dates of fledglings may actually refer to young birds near the nest yet not able to fly rather than true fledglings. A nest with young was found at Fort Ord, Monterey County, as early as 25 February (Roberson and Tenney 1993), indicating that the breeding season begins earlier than our data suggests.

Conservation

No significant threats to the health of local Great Horned Owl populations are evident, although habitat destruction will continue, particularly in East County.

NORTHERN PYGMY-OWL • *Glaucidium gnoma*

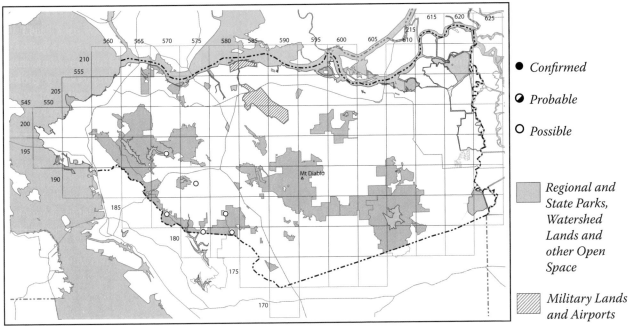

Legend:
- ● *Confirmed*
- ◑ *Probable*
- ○ *Possible*
- ▨ *Regional and State Parks, Watershed Lands and other Open Space*
- ▨ *Military Lands and Airports*

The true status of the Northern Pygmy-Owl in Contra Costa County has long vexed local birders and, unfortunately, the atlas project was unable to shed much light on the issue. Although significant parcels of seemingly suitable habitat dot the countryside, the "toot" of the pygmy-owl seems to be heard only sporadically in terms of both season and location.

Current status and distribution

The Northern Pygmy-Owl was detected in two blocks at Las Trampas Regional Park west of Danville and near Lafayette. It seems baffling that the species went unreported elsewhere in the Berkeley Hills but the Marin atlas team, working in what might seem to be more preferable habitats, detected the species on just three occasions in two blocks. Shuford (1993) was at a loss to explain its near absence there, particularly in comparison with nearby Sonoma County, with which it shares broad habitat similarities. The Sonoma atlas (Burridge 1995) turned up sightings in 36 blocks. The species' perceptible absence in the Contra Costa County portion of the Diablo Range is similarly vexing since the pygmy-owl is fairly common in similar habitats in southeastern Alameda County.

The Northern Pygmy-Owls recorded during the atlas were present in coastal oak woodlands featuring coast live oaks and California bay. The Northern Pygmy-Owl went undetected in the Diablo Range during the atlas project but it seems likely that the species occurs quite sparingly and simply avoided detection. In the Diablo Range portion of Santa Clara County, the Northern Pygmy-Owl was found nesting in shady canyons of California bay and occasionally California sycamore. At higher eleva-

tions the species inhabits oak and gray pine woodlands with a dense layer of manzanita and other shrubs, usually along a stream course (Bousman 2007). In southeastern Alameda County, the species appears to prefer oak woodlands with a strong component of gray pines (Robert J. Richmond, pers. comm.).

It seems logical that increased nocturnal coverage—the bane of most, if not all, atlas projects—would have revealed at least a few additional sightings. And yet, a dearth of historical sightings from the county, in addition to results from the atlas project, would seem to suggest that the species is truly a very scarce breeder in Contra Costa County.

Historical occurrence

Unknown to Grinnell and Wythe (1927) from anywhere in the East Bay but noted at Arroyo Mocho, Alameda County by Grinnell and Miller (1944), it still seems likely that the Northern Pygmy-Owl was present locally in Contra Costa County but was overlooked, just as it is now, because of its scarcity and unpredictability.

Breeding and natural history

Published data from Bay Area breeding bird atlases includes twelve records of fledglings or adults feeding young, with dates ranging from 7 June–27 July; local nesting would presumably follow a similar schedule.

Conservation

The vast majority of seemingly suitable pygmy-owl habitat in Contra Costa County is protected within the confines of regional parks, watersheds and Mt. Diablo State Park.

BURROWING OWL • *Athene cunicularia*

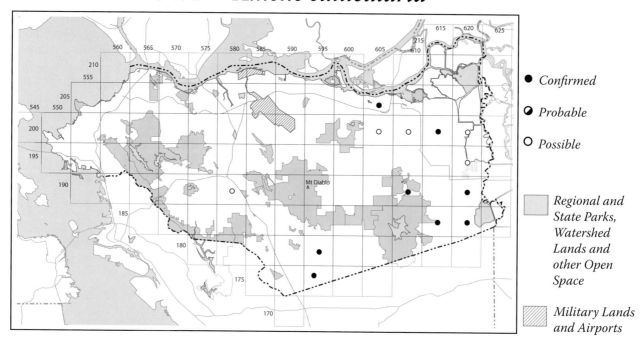

Confirmed

Probable

Possible

Regional and State Parks, Watershed Lands and other Open Space

Military Lands and Airports

"Billy Owl" is the humorous and half affectionate name bestowed by all good Californians upon this familiar sprite of the roadside, this authentic genius of open spaces. Like an elfin sentry the bird challenges from this earthen mound, denounces us valorously as trespassers, and then either dives ignominiously below or flees to some distant sage top. ❧ *William Leon Dawson (1923)*

No bird could be a more appropriate symbol of this atlas project than the splendid little Burrowing Owl. Under siege throughout the county, it tenaciously clings to shrinking parcels of grassland until the last possible moment before departing in hopes of finding another suitable spot that is still free from bulldozers. It must be remarked, no matter how regrettably, that the long-term future of the "Billy Owl" in Contra Costa County is at best bleak and at worst terminal.

Current status and distribution

The Burrowing Owl is still fairly common in East County where grasslands have been allowed to persist and appears to be most common in the sandy habitats just west of the low-lying true "delta." The species appears to be most numerous in the vicinity of the Byron Airport and Clifton Court Forebay, with additional highly precarious colonies still in existence around Knightsen. For unknown reasons, Jersey and Bethel Islands appear completely unoccupied. A small population is found around the Dougherty Valley east of San Ramon, though massive housing construction in recent years has left those birds in grave danger. An estimated 10 pairs or less are present on the Los Vaqueros watershed west of Bryon (B. Chilson, pers. comm.) and it seems likely that additional

pairs went undetected in the extensive grasslands south of Mt. Diablo and around the windfarms southeast of the mountain. A pair or two have managed to persist on private property on the western flank of Mt. Diablo.

Nesting Burrowing Owls require generously open, flat grasslands or disturbed areas with short vegetation. Around Byron the species is often found around the edges of agricultural fields and on levees and berms. Fence lines frequently host burrows because they offer a suitable perch.

Historical occurrence

Grinnell and Miller (1927) called the species "a fairly common resident in the drier, unsettled, interior parts of the region; most numerous in parts of Alameda, Contra Costa and Santa Clara Counties," suggesting that its overall status is likely similar currently.

Breeding and natural history

The amount of data gathered for the beleaguered Burrowing Owl is less substantial than its numbers merit, for a specific reason. Although each block in East County was covered fairly thoroughly, there was unfortunately little time available to be spent on any single species once it had already been confirmed. A pity, as this bird certainly deserves better.

The earliest record of a "pair" during the atlas was 26 March. Occupied nests were noted on five occasions spanning 30 April–16 June. The breeding season must begin earlier, however, as a set of eggs was collected from Brentwood on 25 Mar 1915 (MVZ #5953). Of 20 eggs sets in the possession of the MVZ, 19 were collected between early April and late May. Fledglings were noted four times between 22 May and 16 June, which is similar to results from Monterey County where the species was noted from late May to late June (Roberson and Tenney 1993).

Conservation

It is indeed unfortunate that the habitat needs of the Burrowing Owl perfectly match those of sprawling housing tracts and "power shopping centers." Although Burrowing Owls are tolerant of disturbances, the wholesale habitat destruction in their East County stronghold has become catastrophic in recent years and there is no end in sight. Mainly due to habitat destruction, the Burrowing Owl has been given Second Priority Status as a Californian Bird Species of Special Concern (Shuford and Gardali 2008).

BURROWING OWL

DOWNY WOODPECKER

LONG-EARED OWL • *Asio otus*

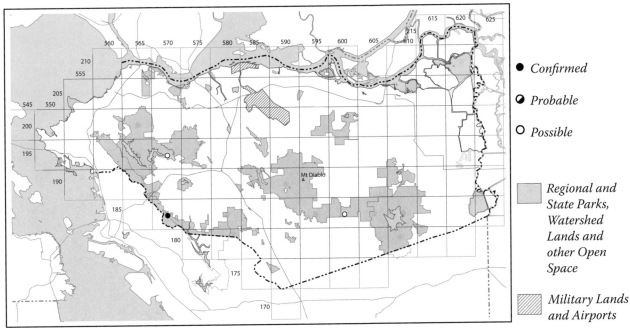

The Long-eared Owl just might be the least understood of all of Contra Costa County's breeding birds. However, there is little shame in that, as its mysterious ways are poorly understood throughout Northern California. Although there is little evidence for it, it is tempting to think that increased coverage of suitable habitats would prove these hermits to be more common than previously imagined.

Current status and distribution

The Long-eared Owl was detected only twice during the atlas project. A single bird was found in shady oak woodlands on Morgan Territory Rd. east of Mt. Diablo on 23 June 2002. The first and only nesting confirmation for the county was provided by the discovery of three fledglings near Moraga 8 July 2002. Unfortunately, breeding bird atlases aren't well suited for determining the true status of nocturnal species, particularly ones so notoriously secretive. During this project, it is doubtful that even 10% of suitable Long-eared Owl habitat was censused.

The habitat requirements of the Long-eared Owl were well-described by Grinnell and Miller (1944), "Typically, bottomlands grown to tall willows and cottonwoods; but also, west of Sierran divides, belts of live oaks, especially as paralleling stream courses. Adjacent open land productive of mice is requisite as also presence of old nests of crows, hawks or magpies for breeding purposes." Shuford (1993) summed up the primary nesting requirements in Marin County as short grass or sparse vegetation for foraging, sufficient small mammals for prey, and suitable nest and roost sites in forests or thickets adjacent to foraging sites. The Morgan Territory sighting was in a moist stand of coastal oak woodland adjacent to a fairly extensive patch of grassland.

Historical occurrence

Grinnell and Wythe (1927) considered the Long-eared Owl to be a sparse, local resident, particularly along the coast, including Alameda, Alameda County. Belding (1890) considered the species to be a rare resident in both Alameda and Contra Costa counties, but it is unclear what this assertion is based upon.

Breeding and natural history

Because breeding records of this elusive bird are scarce, it is difficult to construct a detailed nesting chronology. Of 16 egg sets from California at the MVZ, dates range from 17 March–21 May, with most collected in March and early April. The three sets from the Greater Bay Area were collected in early April. In Monterey County, a nest had young in early April. Another nest in adjacent San Benito County contained half grown young on 19 Apr 1964 (Roberson and Tenney 1993). In Marin County, nests with eggs have been found on 6 and 20 April and 3 May and a full-sized juvenile was discovered on 12 May (Shuford 1993).

Conservation

Long-eared Owl populations have suffered from the destruction of riparian and grassland habitats. The birds found during the atlas project, however, were found in moist oak woodlands, a truly abundant habitat in Contra Costa County. The species has been given Third Priority status on the most recent California Bird Species of Special Concern List (Shuford and Gardali 2008).

101

SHORT-EARED OWL • *Asio flammeus*

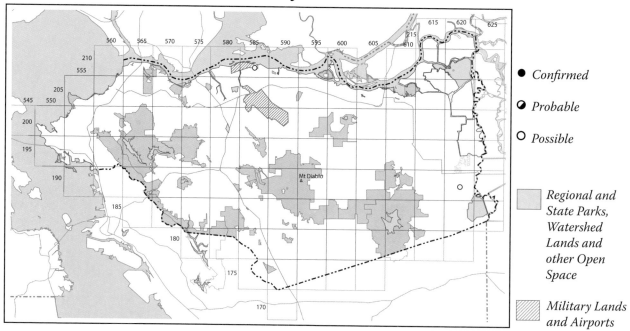

- ● *Confirmed*
- ◑ *Probable*
- ○ *Possible*

▨ *Regional and State Parks, Watershed Lands and other Open Space*

▨ *Military Lands and Airports*

The sight of a Short-eared Owl hunting over a grassy field like a giant, blunt-faced moth is an unforgettable but sadly rare sight in Contra Costa County. If the species does in fact still breed in the county, it is clearly one of our scarcest and most vulnerable breeding species with a future that looks very bleak indeed.

Current status and distribution

The only sightings of the Short-eared Owl during the atlas project pertained to single birds in the saline emergent wetlands at the Concord Naval Weapons Station 21 Apr 1999 and in grasslands near the east end of Camino Diablo in Byron 30 May 2002. The earlier date is of little use in ruling out a lingering winterer but the latter is strongly suggestive of breeding. A bird was noted at the same general location on 5 June 2004 (NAB notebooks).

Throughout its range, the Short-eared Owl nests in marshlands and grasslands with vegetation tall enough for concealment and nesting. The species has also been noted nesting in alfalfa fields but this has never been suspected here.

The Short-eared Owl is well known for nomadic habits, suddenly appearing when sufficient prey is available and then disappearing just as quickly when the food supply dries up. Since appropriate habitats were often checked only sporadically and generally not during the early morning and late evening when the species is most active, it is possible that birds were overlooked, though unlikely that very many escaped notice.

Historical occurrence

Grinnell and Wythe (1927) listed no nestings or even sightings from Contra Costa County. The first breeding season sighting was as recently as July 1970 at Concord (AFN 24: no. 5). The first confirmed breeding was not until 1979 at West Pittsburg when a nest with young was reported by a rancher (AB 33: no. 6). The species was also "apparently breeding" near Byron in 1980 (AB 35: no. 2).

Breeding and natural history

Because breeding Short-eared Owls are so scarce throughout the Greater Bay Area, firm nesting dates are hard to come by. Egg dates in southern California are said to be mostly late March and April (Eckert 1973) (Roberson and Tenney 1993) and would likely be slightly later here. Gill (1977) cited a nest with eggs on 24 April at the south end of San Francisco Bay but also found a nest with young in the same area on 15 April. A nest with young was reported during the San Mateo County atlas on 26 May (Sequoia Audubon Society 2001); another in Monterey County was found on 27 May (NAB notebooks). Fledglings have been noted at Livermore, Alameda County on 1 June, at Davis, Yolo County on 3 June and at Pt. Reyes, Marin County on 24 June (NAB notebooks).

Conservation

As is the case with many other species dependent upon grasslands and other open settings, the Short-eared Owl has suffered greatly from habitat destruction, apparently declining by more than 50% in California during the 20th century (DeSante and George 1994). This is particularly true in eastern Contra Costa County, where the destruction of suitable grasslands has been profound. Such drastic declines have led them to be designated as a Yellow List Species on Audubon's Watchlist 2002 and as a Third Priority California Bird Species of Special Concern (Shuford and Gardali 2008).

SHORT-EARED OWL

NORTHERN SAW-WHET OWL • *Aegolius acadicus*

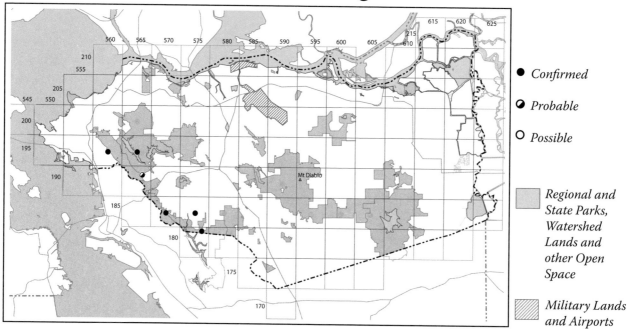

● *Confirmed*

◑ *Probable*

○ *Possible*

▨ *Regional and State Parks, Watershed Lands and other Open Space*

▨ *Military Lands and Airports*

The tiny Northern Saw-whet Owl has long presented a deep mystery to California ornithologists. Dawson (1923) knew of only a dozen or so records for the entire state and breeding was barely suspected. Even now, only a basic outline of its life history in Contra Costa County can be written.

Current status and distribution

A perfect example of how poorly suited breeding bird atlases are for determining the status of owls, atlasers reported the Northern Saw-whet Owl on just eight occasions. Confirmations were achieved in five blocks, all in a compact area of the Berkeley Hills, including Tilden Regional Park, San Pablo Res., Redwood Regional Park and Upper San Leandro Res. The confirmation in block 575-180 at Upper San Leandro Res. was within the confines of Alameda County.

Based upon habitat and historical sightings, the Northern Saw-whet Owl is thought to be an uncommon permanent resident of the moist forests of the Berkeley Hills. The species is completely absent elsewhere, even in the moistest pockets of the Diablo Range, except as a very rare wintering bird or migrant. Numerous historical records of "tooting" adults have been tallied at Redwood Regional Park, along Pinehurst Rd. near Moraga, at Lake Anza and Inspiration Point in Tilden Regional Park, and around the Bear Creek Rd. entrance to Briones Regional Park.

The Northern Saw-whet in Contra Costa County typically inhabits coastal oak woodlands, especially ones with California bay, redwood forests, and Monterey pine

stands. Such situations are invariably moist and generally appear to feature a fairly dense understory.

Historical occurrence

The Northern Saw-whet Owl had gone completely unrecorded in the East Bay through at least 1927, when the only known records for the Bay Area involved winter sightings from coastal counties (Grinnell and Wythe 1927). A long-dead adult of this species found just northeast of Redwood Peak 16 June 1940 might have been the first record for the county (Seibert 1942). It seems reasonable, based on records that began accumulating in the 1960s, that the species had been present all along but simply went overlooked. The first nest record for the county was confirmed on the western side of Briones Regional Park on 18 May 1996 when an adult, one fledged juvenile and two juveniles still in the nest cavity were found (J. Morlan, pers. comm.).

Breeding and natural history

Each of the confirmations achieved during the atlas project was based upon the presence of fledglings, with dates spanning 9–23 June. Several of these records involved birds nesting in artificial boxes on watershed lands, the data graciously supplied by the EBMUD.

The *San Mateo County Breeding Bird Atlas* (Sequoia Audubon Society 2001) provided a bounty of fledgling records with twenty-four records spanning 13 May–25 July, with most records in the second half of June through late July. In Sonoma County (Burridge 1995) a nest with young was reported as early as 7 April.

Conservation

The majority of suitable habitat for this species is within the confines of various regional parks and watersheds.

LESSER NIGHTHAWK

LESSER NIGHTHAWK • *Chordeiles acutipennis*

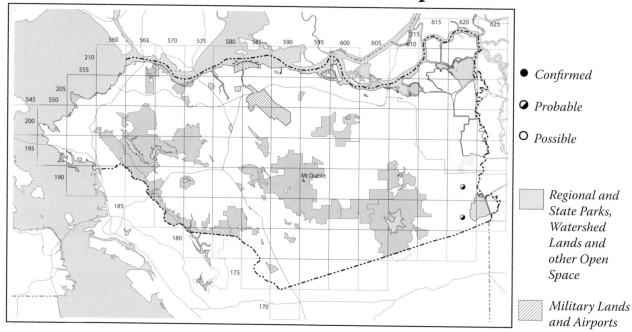

● *Confirmed*

◕ *Probable*

○ *Possible*

▨ *Regional and State Parks, Watershed Lands and other Open Space*

▨ *Military Lands and Airports*

Only recently discovered to be a (presumed) member of the county's breeding avifauna, the Lesser Nighthawk is clearly one of our scarcest and most vulnerable nesting birds since it prefers the same flat, open country that is so prized by developers.

Current status and distribution

The Lesser Nighthawk is one of the few species thought with near certainty to breed in the county that has never been confirmed doing so. The assumption of nesting is based solely on the species presence during the breeding season, year after year, in suitable habitat. The species is currently found only in the extreme southeastern portion of the county, specifically at Clifton Court Forebay and around the east end of Camino Diablo, both near Byron. The species has yet to be detected in other possibly suitable sites in East County such as Holland Tract, Jersey or Bethel islands, although it might possibly do so.

The only records obtained during the atlas project involved pairs in suitable breeding habitat 8 June 2000, 22 May 2001, and 2 June 2002.

The Lesser Nighthawk is most often found in desert washes and along wide, mostly dry cobbled streambeds in hills at lower elevations. In the Central Valley it also prefers open, rocky streambeds and seems particularly fond of disturbed areas around quarrying operations. Foraging sites in Contra Costa County feature open, flat, dry ground which is often grassy but may also be weedy and disturbed.

Historical occurrence

Grinnell and Wythe (1927) and Grinnell and Miller (1944) considered both the Lesser Nighthawk and the Common Nighthawk to be rare vagrants to the Bay Area but it appears likely that several of the records of Common Nighthawk were misidentified, particularly birds reported in April. A record of Lesser Nighthawk from Arroyo Mocho south of Livermore, Alameda County from 26 May 1929 (Gull 11: no. 6) is suggestive of nesting. There is suitable habitat there, but this is also a date that could suggest a migrating Common and, in any event, the species has apparently gone unrecorded there since. The first hint of nesting in Contra Costa County was not until 1995 when at least nine birds were present at Clifton Court Forebay on 7 July (Quail 42: no.1).

Breeding and natural history

It is unclear when the Lesser Nighthawk arrives in the county although it is likely in late March or early April. Breeding records are very scarce for the Greater Bay area. Six sets of eggs collected in Santa Clara County early in the 20th century spanned 4 June–1 July (Unglish 1929). Pickwell and Smith (1938) studied these same nighthawks and found nests from 22 April–12 July. Eggs were noted throughout May and June with young hatching in late June and July. Departure dates are also unclear, although Pickwell and Smith noted an adult and a juvenile still present on 13 September.

Conservation

The amount of habitat utilized by foraging and presumably breeding Lesser Nighthawks in eastern Contra County is quite small and, alas, the type of nearly perfectly flat terrain so prized by developers for subdivisions and shopping centers. Very little of it is currently afforded any type of protection.

COMMON POORWILL • *Phalaenoptilus nuttallii*

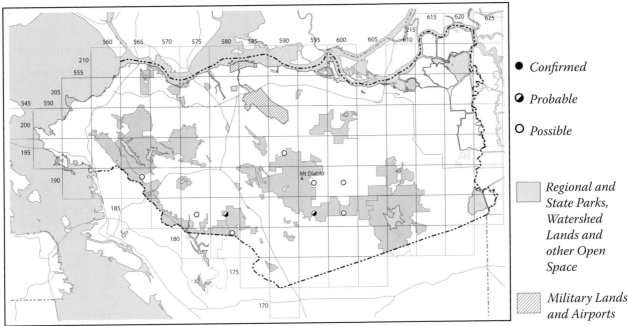

Legend:
- ● *Confirmed*
- ◑ *Probable*
- ○ *Possible*

Regional and State Parks, Watershed Lands and other Open Space

Military Lands and Airports

It is not a disturbing note, but rather the authentic voice of silence, the yearning of the bordering wilderness made vocal in appeal to the romantic spirit of youth.

⋅ William Leon Dawson (1923)

Current status and distribution

Often heard but rarely seen, the Common Poorwill is a fairly common resident of interior stands of chamise and mixed chaparral, as well as in coastal scrub. The Poorwill is also found around opening in drier woodlands of the Diablo Range, as in Mitchell Canyon on Mt. Diablo, where fire roads provide foraging opportunities. The species is likely quite local in the Berkeley Hills, although probably not to the extent that the map would indicate; the scarcity suggested by the map is likely a function of poor nocturnal coverage. The limited number of sightings in the Diablo Range was also due in great part to poor nighttime coverage; the species is probably present somewhere in nearly every Diablo Range block except for those composed almost exclusively of grasslands. The species is completely absent from suburban areas, the northern marshes, East County, and from coastal scrub around Richmond, although birds have been found in similarly fog-prone areas of the western Berkeley Hills.

The status of the Common Poorwill during winter is poorly understood. It is assumed, based upon a smattering of local sightings from Christmas Bird Counts as well as from data published from other counties, that at least a portion of the local population are permanent residents.

Historical occurrence

There has been no known change in the status and distribution of the Common Poorwill in Contra Costa County. The first known nest record for the county was a set of eggs collected from, of all places, a vineyard in Ygnacio Valley northwest of Mt. Diablo on 11 June 1920 (WFVZ #86941). An additional egg set was collected by Henry W. Carriger near St. Mary's College, Moraga 11 May 1934 (WFVZ #111069).

Breeding and natural history

The Common Poorwill, because it is nocturnal and because it occupies rugged habitats, was not confirmed breeding during the atlas project. Each of the records in the atlas database is based upon the presence of "singing" birds in suitable habitat during the breeding season. The dates, which span 24 April–19 July, are clearly more reflective of when atlasers were in the field than when the birds were present.

In Napa County, records spanned 6 March–3 September. A nest with young discovered on the latter date suggests that the breeding season likely extends to October (Napa-Solano Audubon Society 2003). Ten egg-sets at the MVZ from the lowlands of California were collected between 25 April–20 June.

Conservation

The vast majority of suitable poorwill habitat in the county is within protected parklands or watersheds; most unprotected habitat is still likely safe because it tends to be on rugged, steep slopes.

WHITE-THROATED SWIFT • *Aeronautes saxatalis*

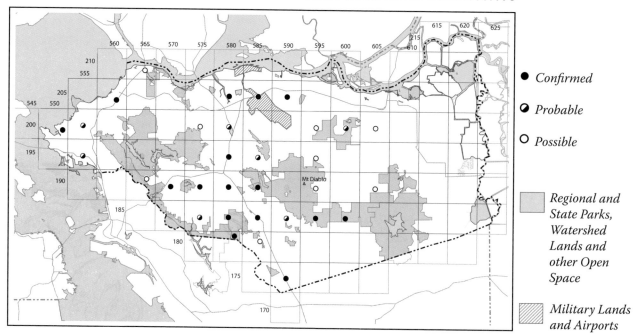

● *Confirmed*

◖ *Probable*

○ *Possible*

▦ *Regional and State Parks, Watershed Lands and other Open Space*

▨ *Military Lands and Airports*

The White-throated Swift is a chatty, acrobatic permanent resident of cliff faces and freeway overpasses. Almost constantly airborne in search of flying insects, the species seems to land only to sleep and nest. In winter it can be harder to find as it wanders long distances from roosts or, if the weather is too foul, never leaves its roost sites at all.

Current status and distribution

The White-throated Swift has historically nested in some of the few rocky cliff faces that occur in the county, mostly in the Diablo Range at and near Mt. Diablo State Park. There are no known nest sites in the Berkeley Hills or in East County. In recent decades the species has managed to adapt to drainage holes beneath freeway overpasses, particularly along the Interstate 680 corridor, but also locally in West County and it now seems likely that more pairs breed in Contra Costa County in these situations than in natural cliff formations. It should also be noted that the species only seems to nest where the freeway passes over a surface street rather than vice versa, perhaps due to heavy traffic beneath the nest site, which could pose a serious hazard to birds entering and leaving the nest. Most of these colonies have just two to ten pairs each, although the Interstate 680/Highway 24 interchange, which offers more nest sites, may have as many as fifty pairs.

Historical occurrence

By 1927 the White-throated Swift was thought to be established in the Bay Area only at Mt. Diablo (Grinnell and Wythe 1927), where eggs were collected 6 June 1878 (*fide* W. Bousman) and 4 June 1921 (MVZ #1847).

However, it is likely that it occurred in other remote spots as well.

Breeding and natural history

The use of the possible, probable and observed breeding codes for the White-throated Swift, as with other highly mobile species, would appear to have been used inconsistently during the atlas project. Some of the possibles and probables likely should have been termed observed when the birds were not noted near suitable nest sites.

Courtship by the White-throated Swift was noted as early as 8 March. Active nests—contents unknown for any of them—were detected on nineteen occasions spanning 30 March–8 July. The early and late dates discovered during the atlas each surpass those known to Bent (1940), who noted that most California nests were found in the latter half of May. Grinnell and Wythe (1927), however, note nestlings on Mt. Diablo as late as 5 July. Since each of our confirmations was based exclusively upon adults entering presumed nest sites, it is impossible to say with certainly that birds were nesting on every occasion.

Conservation

The White-throated Swift has eagerly adapted to human settlements in recent decades, greatly increasing suitable nesting opportunities. Despite this, the species is said to have suffered a significant long-term decline throughout the west, quite possibly due to a decrease in flying insects due to pesticide use and habitat destruction. These declines have led them to be placed on Audubon's Watchlist 2002 as a yellow list species.

BLACK-CHINNED HUMMINGBIRD • *Archilochus alexandri*

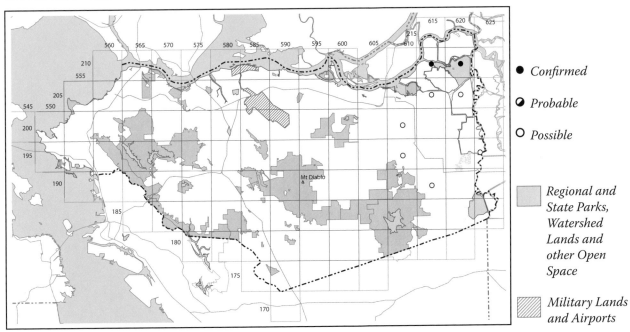

It is tempting to think of the Black-chinned Hummingbird as the Central Valley replacement to the usually much more widespread Anna's Hummingbird, except that the atlas project seems to have revealed a situation that is more complicated than that.

Current status and distribution

The Black-chinned Hummingbird is apparently a fairly common resident of the Delta portion of Contra Costa County. A limited number of sightings seem to suggest that local breeders are truly partial to valley foothill riparian habitats. An informal survey on a local "chatline," however, would seem to indicate that this hummingbird frequently nests in suburban neighborhoods in the Central Valley, particularly in the Sacramento Valley. Much of East County suburbia is of relatively recent vintage with a correspondingly young flora so perhaps the population will increase as neighborhoods mature.

Historical occurrence

Grinnell and Wythe (1927) were unaware of any nests or even sightings from Contra Costa County. Grinnell and Miller (1944) also make no mention of Contra Costa County sightings but do state that the species was most common in the San Diegan district and in portions of the Sacramento and San Joaquin valleys. In light of this, in combination with its current status in East County, it may be presumed that the species was present all along east of the Diablo Range but was simply not noted.

Breeding and natural history

The Black-chinned Hummingbird was confirmed breeding on just two occasions during the atlas proj-

ect. Occupied nests were found on 21 May and 3 June, each time on Bethel Island in the northeast corner of the county. The San Diego County Breeding Bird Atlas (Unitt 2004) documented egg-laying from late April to early July. In Santa Barbara County, the nesting season is thought to stretch from 15 April–30 June, with a peak of activity 5–10 May (Pitelka 1951).

Conservation

The Black-chinned Hummingbird, like many other species of hummingbird, has increased with the aid of feeders and exotic plantings that provide high quality food sources, often in situations with no suitable native habitats (Baltosser and Russell 2000).

ANNA'S HUMMINGBIRD • *Calypte anna*

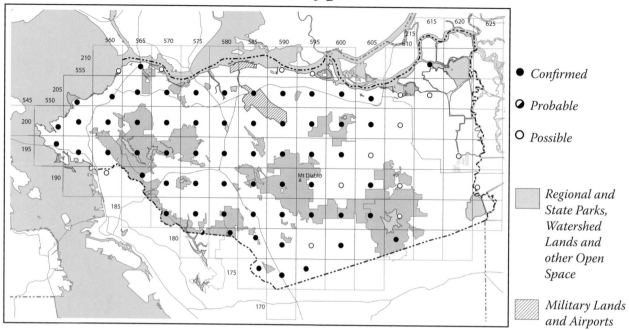

The Anna Hummer, Hyperion of the Golden West, is the California hummer par excellence. And while we may not endure to match his beauties against the flaming splendors of certain tropical species, we are well content that such a treasure should be in our portion.

❧ William Leon Dawson (1923)

Truly one of the marvels of our local birds, the Anna's Hummingbird is a model of toughness and resourcefulness. At only four inches in length, the species is only a quarter-inch larger than Allen's and Black-chinned Hummingbirds, our two smallest breeding birds, so one can only be astonished the first time one sees a territorial male Anna's zip up into the sky to harass passing Red-tailed Hawks and Golden Eagles.

Current status and distribution

The Anna's Hummingbird is a common and widespread nester in the county, and, like many species, it is rare or absent in East County. The species was confirmed in 60 blocks, nearly every block in which it was detected. The cluster of "possible" records east and southeast of Mt. Diablo is surely more indicative of light coverage and bad luck—it almost certainly nests in each of those blocks. In the Richmond area, in the center of the county, and in the Diablo Range, the species is far and away the most common hummingbird and, except in rare instances, the only one present in winter. The species commonly occurs in oak and riparian woodlands, evergreen woodlands (especially around the edges), chaparral, eucalyptus groves, and, most notably, in urban and suburban settings with their attendant exotic flowering plants and feeders. The species is less common in moister forested areas of the Berkeley Hills, where the Allen's Hummingbird is widespread and in arid East County, where the Black-chinned Hummingbird is more common.

The atlas project did little to illuminate the status of the Anna's Hummingbird in East County and as of 2002 all we can dare state with certainty is that it is uncommon and usually found around introduced stands of eucalyptus. In fact, most of East County seems to be unoccupied by any types of hummingbird.

Historical occurrence

Grinnell and Wythe (1927) considered the Anna's Hummingbird to be a common resident throughout the East Bay area and thus its distribution seems little changed since the beginning of local record keeping. DeSante and George (1994), however, state that Anna's populations in California as a whole increased 50% in the 20th century, mainly due to flower gardens and feeders. Exotic urban plantings, (which unlike our native plants often bloom in winter) in combination with feeders, allow large numbers of birds to subsist through winters that would normally be quite lean.

Breeding and natural history

Anna's Hummingbirds can begin nesting as early as December, just as the rainy season begins in the East Bay. The atlas, however, failed to prove this for the obvious reason that nobody is atlasing in December. The atlas database contains ninety-six confirmations, the earliest being 21 January. Twenty-eight records of adults carrying nest material or building nests were amassed 21 January–5 June. Twenty-six occupied nests (contents unknown) were found 14 February–24 June and nests with young were confirmed ten times 24 April–25 June. Fledglings were noted twenty-two times between 16 March and 6 July. The later dates, listed above, likely represent second or even third broods.

Conservation

Because the Anna's Hummingbird is so well suited to both native and exotic habitats (and because of the widespread placement of feeders), it appears poised to remain one of Contra Costa County's most common and widespread breeding birds, continuing development aside.

ANNA'S HUMMINGBIRD

Allen's Hummingbird • *Selasphorus sasin*

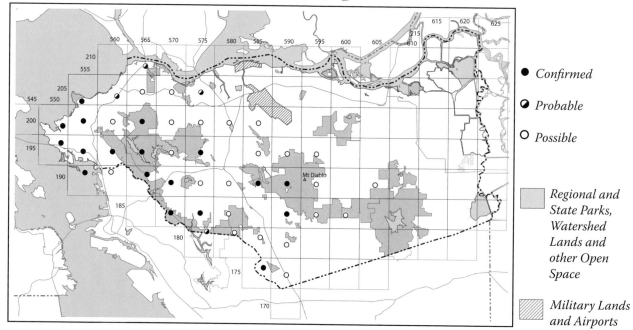

The dazzling Allen's Hummingbird, a true avian jewel, combines peculiar zipping calls, distinctive courtship displays and fascinating migration habits, to be one of Contra Costa County's most compelling breeding birds.

Current status and distribution

The Allen's Hummingbird is a common breeding bird in the Berkeley Hills and, at some locations, may be more numerous than even the ubiquitous Anna's Hummingbird. The species is also present on the Bay plain around Richmond and locally in residential neighborhoods along the Interstate 680 corridor. In the Diablo Range the species appears to breed sparingly in some of the moist canyons on Mt. Diablo itself but is absent from more arid sites to the east such as Black Diamond Mines Regional Park. The species is apparently completely absent as a breeder from residential areas around Pittsburg and Antioch and from the entire Central Valley portion of the county.

The Allen's Hummingbird is rather easily found during the breeding season in or around moist coastal oak woodlands, redwood forests, riparian woodlands, moist coastal scrub, stands of introduced eucalyptus, and, locally, in suburban gardens.

Historical occurrence

The overall status of Allen's Hummingbirds in Contra Costa County has likely little changed since Grinnell and Wythe (1927), with the possible exception of slight range expansions made possible by the widespread planting of eucalyptus.

Breeding and natural history

The earliest recorded Allen's Hummingbird during the atlas project was 19 January. It doubtless would have been earlier had more atlasers been in the field in January as male Allen's Hummingbirds, our earliest arriving migrant breeder, routinely appear before the second week of the new year to begin setting up territories. The earliest of eight records of a female carrying nest material was 28 January, the latest 30 May. Four occupied nests (contents unknown) were detected 4 April to 31 May and a nest with eggs was found 21 April. Nests with young were recorded three times between 18 April and 15 May; adults carrying food or feeding young were found four times between 8 April and 3 July; fledglings were noted on four occasions between 25 April and 30 May. The Allen's Hummingbird routinely double broods, as indicated by the carrying of nest material in late May and the feeding of young on the late date of 3 July.

The movements of the Allen's Hummingbird are complex, fascinating and unique. Phillips (1975) states that the nominate, northern race of Allen's Hummingbird (the one that breeds locally) is the only North American landbird to migrate south in appreciable numbers during spring (because they play no role in the nesting process, adult males can depart during May!). The vast majority of adult males depart California by early July and it seems that the species is completely absent from California by the beginning of August. Both adult and immature females are thought to have dispersed by late July, leaving only immature males to linger into August (Phillips 1975).

The status of the Allen's Hummingbird is, not surprisingly, complicated by the extremely similar Rufous Hummingbird, which generally migrates later both in spring and fall. Although records of single birds in late May and much of June can likely be attributed to the Allen's Hummingbird with some certainty, by July both are likely common. Because of this overlap, some atlas records of "possible" in March through April and again in July may well refer to Rufous Hummingbirds.

Conservation

Even though the local Allen's Hummingbird population appears healthy, the species was designated a Yellow List Species on the Audubon Watchlist 2002. Prime considerations include a restricted breeding and wintering range that makes it vulnerable to natural disasters, disease, and habitat destruction. Locally, however, it seems likely that the Allen's Hummingbird has probably increased in numbers thanks to feeders and, especially, eucalyptus plantings.

WHITE-THROATED SWIFT

BELTED KINGFISHER • *Ceryle alcyon*

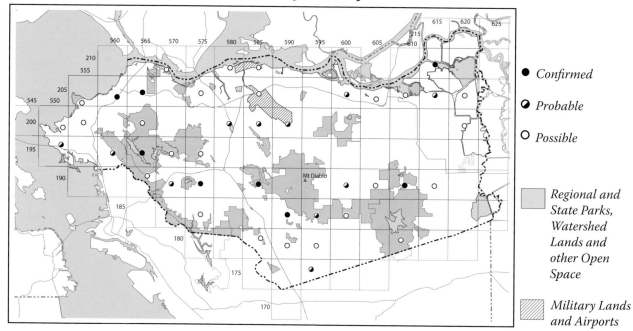

Confirmed

Probable

Possible

Regional and
State Parks,
Watershed
Lands and
other Open
Space

Military Lands
and Airports

The Belted Kingfisher, with a raucous rattle and perilous plunge dives, is an uncommon member of the avifauna of Contra Costa County. Although its boisterousness renders it easily detectable, strict habitat needs dictate an unavoidable scarcity as a breeding bird.

Current status and distribution

The Belted Kingfisher is a fairly rare, widely spaced breeder along freshwater streams and sloughs, particularly in Central and East counties. The species is apparently least common in the arid Diablo Range where most streams have dried up by early summer. Even though it is likely that local breeding birds are permanent residents the population is bolstered from fall through spring by birds from the north.

In addition to clear, calm water for fishing, the Belted Kingfisher is a strict cavity nester that virtually always nests in steep dirt banks, a scarce commodity indeed in a county where most of the streams have been channelized and cemented.

Historical occurrence

Grinnell and Wythe (1927) were unaware of any breeding records for the East Bay, instead citing a handful of fall records pertaining to post-breeding wanderers. The first East Bay nest record, apparently unknown to Grinnell and Wythe, occurred 10 Apr 1910 when a set of eggs was collected from Alameda County (WFVZ #46610). This record hints at the fact that the interior of the East Bay was monitored only rarely, particularly in comparison with the Bay plain, and that Contra Costa County breeding birds would likely have gone unde-

tected. It is unclear when the first nest for Contra Costa County was confirmed.

Breeding and natural history

The Belted Kingfisher was confirmed breeding just eight times during the atlas project. Three occupied nests were discovered 11 May–23 June. Adults were noted carrying food on three occasions from 31 May–17 June. A nest with young was detected 4 August and an adult was seen feeding young 10 June. The breeding season in Contra Costa County is almost certainly a lengthier affair than atlas data would suggest as the San Mateo atlas project found an occupied nest on 24 April (Sequoia Audubon Society 2001) and the Sonoma atlas detected a nest with young as late as 13 August (Burridge 1995).

Conservation

Although probably never common, at least since European colonization, nesting opportunities must have decreased with the degradation and destruction of stream banks. Restoration of such habitats would certainly improve the situation.

Nuttall's Woodpecker

ACORN WOODPECKER • *Melanerpes formicivorus*

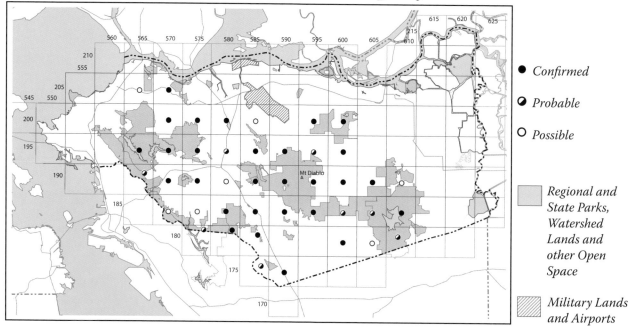

Confirmed

Probable

Possible

Regional and State Parks, Watershed Lands and other Open Space

Military Lands and Airports

As aptly-named as any of our breeding birds, the Acorn Woodpecker is inevitably found in the company of various species of oak, particularly during the breeding season. Its comical appearance and fascinating lifestyle makes them a favorite amongst bird devotees.

Current status and distribution

The range of the Acorn Woodpecker in Contra Costa County matches closely both the extent of the Coast Range and the county's oak woodlands. The species is locally fairly common west of the Interstate 680 corridor where open oak situations exist but reaches maximum abundance in the blue oak woodlands and valley oak savannahs of the Diablo Range, where it can be quite common. The species is completely absent from the Bay plain around Richmond and from the extreme western edge of the Berkeley hills. Because this fog-prone leading edge of hills is so narrow, this distribution is barely perceptible on the atlas map. The species is generally absent from the mostly urban Interstate 680 corridor (although they do persist locally in older neighborhoods where large oaks have avoided the bulldozer) but, again, this corridor is so narrow that it isn't reflected in the atlas map. The area along the river plain around Pittsburg and Antioch contains little or no suitable habitat and is thus unoccupied. This absence continues into the eastern portion of the county where only a small amount of narrow riparian habitats featuring large valley oaks is extant. It is unknown if oaks ever grew in significant enough stands to support Acorn Woodpeckers in that area.

Historical occurrence

Grinnell and Wythe (1927) considered the "California Acorn-storing Woodpecker" to be common in each of the Bay counties except San Francisco, a situation that seems little changed.

Breeding and natural history

The Acorn Woodpecker was noted building nests on three occasions 9–20 May. Fourteen occupied nests (contents unknown) were tallied 12 April–6 July; nests with young detected three times 27 May–22 July. Adults carrying food were recorded 3 April–17 June. Because adults carry acorns throughout the year, this code was almost certainly used inappropriately. Still, it is probable that birds were breeding on those occasions. Fledglings were found four times 30 May–16 August.

The Acorn Woodpeckers is known to re-nest in some autumns. This apparently happens only in 20% of years and usually occurs in years of large acorn crops following a spring of poor reproductive success (Koenig and others 1995). If this phenomenon occurred during the atlas project, it was missed because efforts had essentially wrapped up by mid-August.

Conservation

Koenig and others (1995) state that poor regeneration of oaks in California will likely affect populations in the future. Additional threats include the removal of granary trees, particularly in residential areas, and the ever-aggressive European Starling. Grinnell and Miller (1944) felt that local range reductions in the state caused by the removal of old oaks were offset by suburban plantings of oaks as well as exotic conifers that at least partly provide substitute food for acorns.

ACORN WOODPECKER

NUTTALL'S WOODPECKER • *Picoides nuttallii*

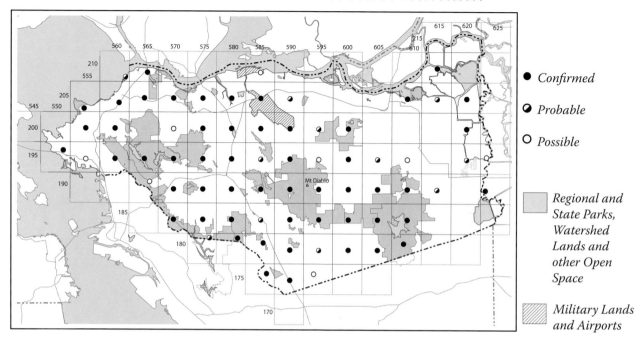

- ● Confirmed
- ◑ Probable
- ○ Possible

▨ Regional and State Parks, Watershed Lands and other Open Space

▨ Military Lands and Airports

Although unimpressive in melody or volume, no sound is more characteristic of California's oak woodlands than the rattle of the Nuttall's Woodpecker. And there is plenty of opportunity to hear it because this ladder-backed bird is the most common and widespread of the county's woodpeckers.

Current status and distribution

The Nuttall's Woodpecker is present throughout the county's woodlands, especially when oaks are present. Preferred habitats include riparian corridors, valley and blue oak woodlands and, somewhat locally, residential settings, particularly in established neighborhoods with mature trees. Nuttall's populations become healthiest in the Diablo Range where sunny, open woodlands abound. On the western side of the Berkeley Hills, where shady, moist woodlands are predominant, the Nuttall's Woodpecker is correspondingly rare but as habitats open up to the east the species quickly becomes conspicuous, as at Briones and Las Trampas Regional Parks. In East County the species was detected sparingly in willow brambles and around homesteads, with but a couple of pairs detected in any given location. In West County, where oaks are found only in reduced remnant patches, nesting birds were discovered in the extensive eucalyptus monoculture of Pt. Pinole Regional Shoreline. The Nuttall's Woodpecker went undetected only in suburban and industrial areas around Pittsburg and Antioch, from recently developed communities around Brentwood, and from nearly tree-less areas in the southeast portion of the county.

Historical occurrence

Considered "resident in small numbers only" by Grinnell and Wythe (1927), the Nuttall's Woodpecker is now the most numerous breeding woodpecker in the oak belt. The first known nest record for Contra Costa County is a set of eggs collected on Mt. Diablo 29 May 1880 (WVZ #8956).

Breeding and natural history

Nest-building was reported just four times during the atlas project, with dates spanning 3 April–2 June. Twelve occupied nests (contents unknown) were detected 12 April–4 July; nests with young were found fourteen times 3 May–3 June. Adults carrying food were found twenty-five times 14 April–2 July, with the majority of records in May. Sixteen sightings of fledglings spanned 12 May–3 July.

Conservation

Because of the limited range of the Nuttall's Woodpecker (almost completely within California), low density, and preference for oak and riparian woodlands, it was named a Red List Species on Audubon's Watchlist 2002.

DOWNY WOODPECKER • *Picoides pubescens*

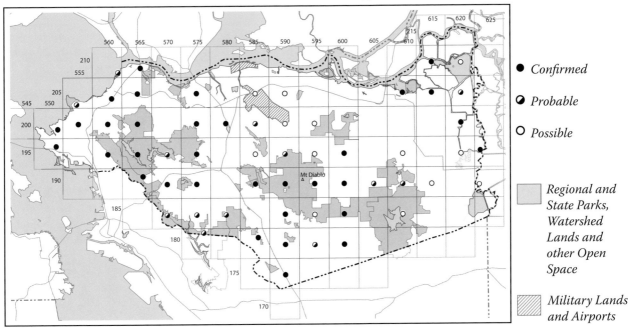

The diminutive Downy Woodpecker was known to Grinnell and Miller (1944) as the "Willow Downy Woodpecker," a name that aptly describes the habitat preferences of this active little bird.

Current status and distribution

The Downy Woodpecker is a rather sedentary resident of lightly wooded situations throughout the county, reaching maximum abundance in the willow clumps and narrow riparian strips of East County. In the Coast Range the species replaces the forest-dwelling Hairy Woodpecker around forest edges and especially in riparian habitats, such as around Jewel Lake in Tilden Park. Central County suburbs, particularly those with more mature trees, are lightly occupied.

In Contra Costa County, as elsewhere, the Downy Woodpecker is primarily present in open, sunny riparian situations that feature willows and other "soft" trees. The species is also found somewhat more locally in orchards and in residential settings where woodpeckers tend to be scarce during the breeding season. It is far less common in oak woodlands and generally completely absent from the denser, moister forests of the Berkeley Hills except where there are conspicuous clearings, as around ponds.

In East County, the species maintains a common presence wherever willows have been allowed to thrive, and along the perilously narrow riparian corridor along Marsh Creek. In the grasslands north and south of Mt. Diablo it occupies similarly marginal riparian strips. In urban settings, particularly in Central County, the Downy Woodpecker may be the most common breeding woodpecker.

Historical occurrence

The status and distribution of the Downy Woodpecker has changed little since the beginning of the 20th century.

Breeding and Natural History

Occupied nests (contents unknown) were found on four occasions 5 May–5 June; nine nests with young were detected 6 May–2 June, suggesting that most of the occupied nests probably also contained young. Adults were seen carrying food on eleven occasions 6 May–19 June. Ten records of fledglings ranged from 23 May to 4 July with an additional late record from 11 August.

Conservation

Because the Downy Woodpecker has adapted, at least locally, to residential neighborhoods and because the species may actually benefit from forest thinning, there is currently very little concern for the long-term future of the species in Contra Costa County.

119

HAIRY WOODPECKER • *Picoides villosus*

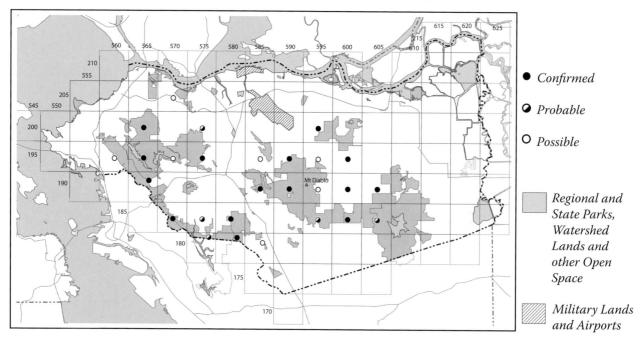

Confirmed

Probable

Possible

Regional and State Parks, Watershed Lands and other Open Space

Military Lands and Airports

Except for its loud calls and resounding drumming, the Hairy Woodpecker is a retiring member of the local hardwood community, often going undetected in vast amounts of seemingly appropriate habitat.

Current status and distribution

The Hairy Woodpecker is wedded to the hardwood forests of the Coast Range, although there is nowhere it can be said to be common. The species is distributed thinly but evenly across shady coastal oak woodlands in the Berkeley Hills, particularly in association with redwoods. The species is most readily detected, however, in large stands of introduced Monterey pines, most notably around Inspiration Point in Tilden Park and around Sibley and Redwood Regional Parks just to the south. East of the Interstate 680 corridor in the Diablo Range the species is present but widely spaced in oak-gray pine woodlands. The range of the Hairy Woodpecker seems to overlap only slightly with the closely related Downy Woodpecker.

Although often confused with the Downy Woodpecker, the Hairy Woodpecker has never been reliably reported in Contra Costa County away from areas of permanent residence in the Coast Range. The species is completely absent from the Bay plain at Richmond, from the shores of north Pittsburg and Antioch and from the entirety of East County. Surprisingly, there are even very few records from established neighborhoods in Central County.

Historical occurrence

Because Grinnell and Wythe (1927) and local sightings columns offer little guidance, it must be assumed that the status of the Hairy Woodpecker has changed little in the past century, although timber harvesting, particularly in the late 19th century, may have diminished populations somewhat.

Breeding and natural history

Because the Hairy Woodpecker population of the East Bay is thought to be nearly exclusively sedentary, it seems likely that each sighting, particularly of pairs, pertains to true breeding birds in each of the 27 blocks in which it was found. Occupied nests were noted 21 April and 10 May; one with certain young was found 21 May. Five records of adults carrying food were tallied 16 May through 13 June. Fledglings were recorded seven times 31 May–6 July.

Conservation

Hairy Woodpecker populations have apparently held their own in Contra Costa County as well as in other Bay Area counties. Forest fragmentation is a concern, however, as is competition with nest hole nabbing European Starlings. The tenuous health of the Monterey pine stands in the Berkeley Hills may pose long-term problems.

NORTHERN FLICKER • *Colaptes auratus*

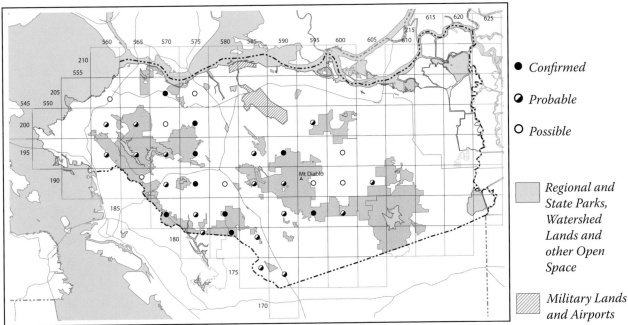

The Northern Flicker is one of our most familiar yet most misunderstood breeding birds. The perception of commonness long held by the birding community seems to have been based on the species winter status, when it is indeed quite numerous throughout the county. The relative scarcity of the species during the breeding season is surprising as the Northern Flicker is a bona fide habitat generalist, often found eating berries, flycatching and even foraging on the ground.

Current status and distribution

The Northern Flicker was confirmed breeding in just 8 blocks in the Coast Range and was thought to probably breed in numerous others. The species is not known to breed in either West or East counties. Many records of single birds in March and April, likely either wintering birds or migrants, have been stricken from the database. Birds detected in May are more problematic but more lenience was given to birds within the Coast Range as opposed to birds in less suitable habitats elsewhere.

The Northern Flicker is fond of extensive stands of open woodlands that feature numerous dead or dying trees as well as open ground or grasslands for foraging. A dearth of such situations may explain its unexpected scarcity as a breeding bird in the county. The species shuns dense forests with thick undergrowth as well as very open blue oak and valley oak woodlands.

Historical occurrence

Grinnell and Wythe (1927) considered the Northern Flicker to be a common resident almost throughout the Bay Area. It is unclear if this was the case in Contra Costa County, specifically.

Breeding and natural history

The atlas database contains records of "possibles" from as early as atlasers were in the field to the end of the season. It is less than clear how many of these birds were wintering birds or post-breeding wanderers. Many records of single birds early in the breeding season, particularly away from the Coast Range, have been removed from the maps. Twenty-three records of pairs were tallied between 21 February and 21 July. A meager total of just nine confirmations were obtained during the atlas project: three occupied nests were found 18 May, 23 May and 6 July; nests with young were recorded 12 May and 16 June; and fledglings were noted 15 and 17 July. In Monterey County, where the species breeds more commonly, occupied nests were mostly found in May. Nests with young were detected 7 May–19 June and dependent young 28 May–27 July (Roberson and Tenney 1993).

Conservation

Possible or probable causes for the unexpectedly low numbers of breeding flickers in Contra Costa County include the removal of dead and dying trees and competition for nest holes from European Starlings. However, these factors exist, of course, in places where flickers are more common.

PILEATED WOODPECKER • *Dryocopus pileatus*

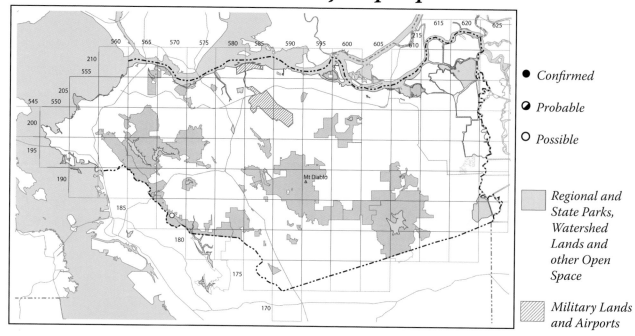

Confirmed

Probable

Possible

Regional and State Parks, Watershed Lands and other Open Space

Military Lands and Airports

The Pileated Woodpecker, once known as the "Logcock", is one of Contra Costa County's most mysterious birds. This astonishing woodpecker has a fondness for large hardwood trees covering extensive areas, a rare combination in the East Bay. As should be expected, the species is quite rare here and is reported only sporadically.

Current status and distribution

There were but two records of this retiring woodpecker during the atlas project although there were additional second-hand reports. In 2001 a male was reported at Redwood Regional Park in the vicinity of the Skyline Gate on 29 April and 21 May. There were additional reports just to the south around Joaquin Miller Park, Alameda County. Since completion of the atlas, there have been numerous records from the immediate vicinity, as well as several records from the Pinehurst Rd. area just to the east. This combination suggests that there is a tiny resident population that is likely breeding. The entire area is heavily wooded with oaks, madrones and, in shady canyon bottoms, a relict population of redwoods. Together they form what appears to be fine Pileated Woodpecker habitat but, alas, the total acreage is not large and is probably insufficient for a healthy population of a bird that requires vast parcels of habitat.

Historical occurrence

The earliest known record was "near" Mt. Diablo, Contra Costa County (Grinnell and Miller 1944). Grinnell and Wythe (1927) state that the bird was "taken" prior to 1870, indicating its possible former presence, although perhaps only casually. The habitat on and around Mt. Diablo doesn't appear terribly suitable for the species

but it was reported there again 31 Aug 1975 (Northern California Rare Bird Alert 1975), 22 May 1983 (Quail 7-8 1983), 5-11 June 1988 (AB 42: no. 5) and 7 May 1989 (AB 43: no. 3). Although all of these birds could be discounted as migrants or post-breeding wanderers, the date of the June record from Curry Canyon is particularly suggestive of breeding.

The rest of the records from Contra Costa County have come from more likely locations around Redwood Regional Park and the hamlet of Canyon, just to the east. These occurrences have been extremely erratic, with years passing between sightings.

Breeding and natural history

As virtually no nesting information has been obtained locally, data collected by other Northern California counties must be used to sketch a chronology. In Marin County, a nest with eggs was found as early as 10 April (Shuford 1993). Occupied nests in Napa County were found on 26 April and 1 May (Napa-Solano Audubon Society 2003). Nests with young in various local counties have been detected on 3 and 19 June and 7 July. Records of fledglings range from 28 May through 15 August.

Conservation

Because Contra Costa County has probably never offered ideal Pileated Woodpecker habitat in any significant quantities, and because the small amount of serviceable habitat that does exist is already under the protection of either the EBRPD or EBMUD, it seems little can be done to encourage the establishment of a viable population of this magnificent woodpecker.

OLIVE-SIDED FLYCATCHER • *Contopus cooperi*

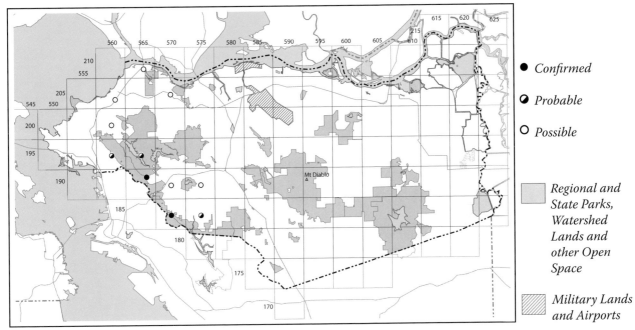

The well-known "quick-three-beers" song of the Olive-sided Flycatcher adds a bit of a montane feel to the moist woodlands of the Berkeley Hills although, as it turns out, only at a handful of locations.

Current status and distribution

Although the Olive-sided Flycatcher has long been thought to be a scarce and local breeding bird, few would have guessed the species to be as rare as it was during the atlas. The question of how many blocks the species might have actually bred in is complex and probably not answerable to a satisfactory level. Although the species was recorded in May or June in 15 blocks, it is far more than likely that at least some of these were migrants, as the Olive-sided Flycatcher is well known to migrate locally through early June. A few reports may have pertained to misidentified Western Wood-Pewees. Based on dates noted (usually May) and locations, many of these records do not appear on the map. In any event, the species is apparently present in very low densities exclusively within a narrow belt of the fog-shrouded Berkeley Hills between Tilden and Redwood Regional Parks.

In Contra Costa County, nesting Olive-sided Flycatchers favor open coastal oak woodlands with openings for foraging and tall trees, often redwoods, Monterey pines or other planted conifers, which offer commanding views. Moistness or cool temperatures may play a factor in choice of nest sites as similar habitats remain unoccupied just slightly inland.

Historical occurrence

The historical status of the Olive-sided Flycatcher in Contra Costa County is somewhat muddled. For the Bay Area as a whole, Grinnell and Wythe (1927) considered the species a "summer resident in small numbers and is restricted to heavily forested areas of redwood, spruce or pine, or, locally, to certain planted groves of pine, cypress and eucalyptus." It was in such planted groves that nests were first detected in Berkeley in 1920 (Dixon 1920). It isn't clear whether or not the species was already breeding in native forests of the East Bay, as they did elsewhere, before the Berkeley sighting.

Breeding and natural history

The earliest Olive-sided Flycatcher detected during the atlas project was 24 April, probably a typical arrival date. The atlas database contains just eight probable records, seven of them based on males singing at least 7 days apart. The lone confirmation was an adult carrying nest material 14 May 1998. The San Mateo County Atlas (Sequoia Audubon Society 2001) was particularly helpful with constructing a nesting chronology. Atlasers there noted nest building on six occasions between 29 April and 31 May, with an additional record from 17 June. Occupied nests were noted six times from 6 May–7 July. Nests with young were tallied six times 16 June–22 July, adults carrying food on another eight occasions 21 June–22 July. An additional early record of an adult toting food was noted 19 May. Fledglings and adults feeding young were detected twelve times between 10 June and 20 July. The Sonoma County atlas (Burridge 1995) found an occupied nest as late as 27 July.

Conservation

Because of declines in virtually the entirety of its breeding range, the Olive-sided Flycatcher has been given Second Priority status as a California Bird Species of Special Concern (Shuford and Gardali 2008). Breeding Bird Survey analyses have revealed a range wide decline of 3.3% annually between 1966 and 2001 with particularly pronounced declines in western North America (Audubon's Watchlist 2002). It is suspected that destruction of its tropical wintering grounds has played a significant role in this decline (Altman and Sallabanks 2000).

OLIVE-SIDED FLYCATCHER

WESTERN WOOD-PEWEE • *Contopus sordidulus*

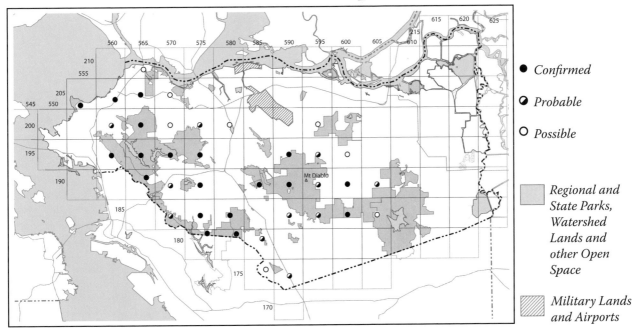

Confirmed

Probable

Possible

Regional and State Parks, Watershed Lands and other Open Space

Military Lands and Airports

Not large, nor colorful and certainly not terribly musically inclined, the Western Wood-Pewee might be seen as more of a sentry over the county's woodlands, spending much of its time on the uppermost branches of stately trees, in constant search of the flying insects it is dependent upon.

Current status and distribution

As tied to native woodlands as nearly any of Contra Costa County's breeding species, the Western Wood-Pewee is a fairly common summer resident of forested areas throughout the Coast Range, showing no pronounced center of abundance. It is almost completely absent elsewhere. One of our latest spring arrivals, the Western Wood-Pewee typically appears during the last week of April. A report during the atlas from 8 April was particularly early, although not unprecedented as one was found on Mt. Diablo on 4 April 1990 (AB 44: no. 3). Migrant wood-pewees on their way to northern breeding grounds are often detected through the first week of June, compelling caution as to which records to include on the atlas map.

The Western Wood-Pewee in Contra Costa County is most often found in coastal oak woodlands and especially in riparian settings, most often when adjacent to hillside oak woodlands, although it is occasionally found in riparian corridors well away from such hillsides. Wood-Pewees shun the interior of dense forests such as redwood, although the species is often found around the edges. No breeding wood-pewees were detected in even the oldest wooded neighborhoods in central county and, not surprisingly, the species was absent from the grasslands north and south of Mt. Diablo and the entirety of East County.

Historical occurrence

Three eggs collected from a nest in Danville 10 July 1898 provided the first known nest record for Contra Costa County (WFVZ #69849). Based upon sources from the late 19th and early 20th centuries it would seem that little about the status and distribution of the Western Wood-Pewee has changed in the past century.

Breeding and natural history

The *Monterey County Breeding Bird Atlas* (Roberson and Tenney 1993) achieved a majority of confirmations based upon nest-building activities, presumably because the bulk of atlasing activity occurs in May and early June. In this atlas, however, adults were noted nest-building on just two occasions: 9 May and 1 June. An additional report from 11 July is so late as to be suspect and could possibly have been carrying food rather than nest material. Nine occupied nests were found 17 May–9 July; the earliest of the nests in which young were detected was 30 May. Adults carrying food were tallied on five occasions 8 June–4 July. Ten records of fledglings spanned 8 June–9 August.

Conservation

The Western Wood-Pewee is vulnerable to loss of habitat on southern wintering grounds and has shown declines within its breeding range. Published breeding bird atlases from the Bay Area, however, point out no significant status or distribution changes. The future of the species in Contra Costa County appears bright with the stipulation that its wintering grounds must be protected.

PACIFIC-SLOPE FLYCATCHER • *Empidonax difficilis*

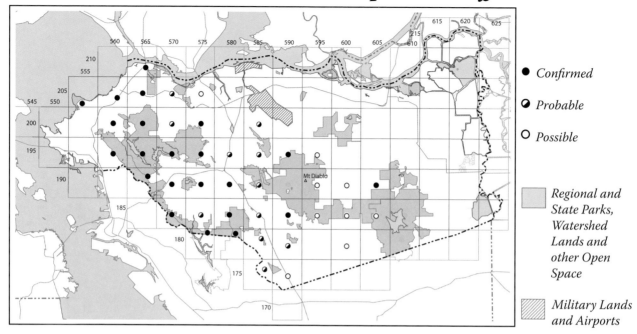

Confirmed

Probable

Possible

Regional and State Parks, Watershed Lands and other Open Space

Military Lands and Airports

This "gnat king," our only breeding representative of the Empidonax family of small flycatchers, was long known as the Western Flycatcher until its somewhat controversial recent "split" from the Cordilleran Flycatcher which breeds east of the Sierra divide.

Current status and distribution

The Pacific-slope Flycatcher is a fairly common and locally common summer resident of the humid forests of the Berkeley Hills. The species is less common in the significantly drier Diablo Range, where it is almost exclusively found in the shadier canyon bottoms, as in Mitchell and Pine canyons on Mt. Diablo and along Morgan Territory Rd. The majority of the eastern Diablo Range is too dry and open to suit this species. In West County, where there is very little in the way of true forest, Pt. Pinole Regional Shoreline is the only known nesting site. Modest numbers are present in shady riparian corridors in Central County, particularly around older, more established residential settings, as at Danville and Alamo. In the Central Valley portion of the county the species is known only as a spring and fall migrant.

In Contra Costa County, the Pacific-slope Flycatcher prefers moist, shady coastal oak woodlands, forests of redwood, Monterey pine and eucalyptus, and montane riparian habitats. In the Diablo Range it is found almost exclusively along stream courses in canyon bottoms. West of the Interstate 680 corridor, as around Bear Valley north of Lafayette, the species nests locally in narrow but dense riparian corridors within broader valleys but such situations are relatively scarce.

Historical occurrence

There is no indication that the status of the Pacific-slope Flycatcher changed during the 20th century.

Breeding and natural history

The earliest arriving Pacific-slope Flycatcher detected during the atlas was on 20 March, a typical arrival date for the county; the first pair was recorded 8 April. The carrying of nest material and/or actual nest building was noted on three disparate dates: 18 April, 15 May and 18 June. The latter date, if correct, is particularly late. Occupied nests, probably with eggs, were found 22 and 24 May though earlier eggs must have been missed since three eggs sets taken in the county and in the possession of the MVZ were collected between 1–10 May. Seven nests containing young were tallied between 20 May and 20 June. Adults carrying food were recorded ten times from 27 April–9 August. Fledglings were found an additional seven times spanning 20 June–9 July.

Conservation

Since most suitable nesting sites are within the confines of parks and watersheds, there appear to be no immediate threats to local Pacific-slope Flycatcher populations.

BLACK PHOEBE • *Sayornis nigricans*

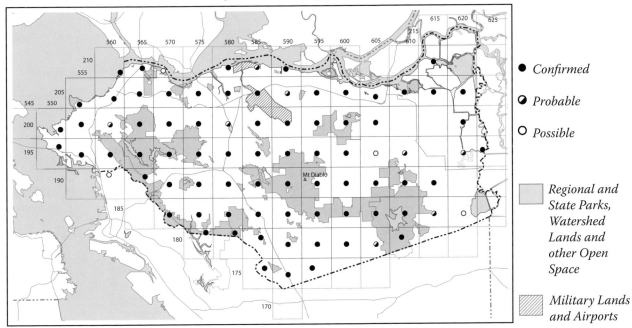

● *Confirmed*

◐ *Probable*

○ *Possible*

▨ *Regional and State Parks, Watershed Lands and other Open Space*

▨ *Military Lands and Airports*

The Black Phoebe is a charismatic and conspicuous permanent resident in open areas throughout the county and does more than its share to liven up avifaunally impoverished residential settings.

Current status and distribution

The Black Phoebe is found in urban and rural areas throughout the county and is absent only from heavily forested areas. And even forests are vulnerable to becoming suitable phoebe habitat due to alteration by humans. For example, much of Morgan Territory Rd. winds through dense coastal oak woodlands that would be completely unsuitable were it not for the road cuts, culverts and bridges that have allowed the species to become fairly common.

Nest sites are most often characterized by some kind of water, be it a creek, canal or pond, with nearby structures suitable for accommodating its mud nests. Especially common are nests placed underneath bridges over small creeks. Open-ended drainage pipes are also prized when present. Being the industrious species that it is, the species was even noted on several occasions carrying food through sewer gratings to nests under the street! Although the Black Phoebe will occasionally nest in mud banks, as it must have done during pre-settlement times, the vast majority of nests are on unnatural substrates.

Historical occurrence

Based on Grinnell and Wythe (1927), the status of the Black Phoebe seems little changed locally, even though it seems likely that it has increased from historic times with the aid of manmade substrates for nest placement.

Breeding and natural history

Over 300 Black Phoebe records were amassed during the atlas project, including 107 confirmations. Pairs were detected as early as late February but earlier pairings could easily have been overlooked as atlasers spent very little time in the field so early in the year. Twenty reports of adults carrying nest material or building a nest ranged from 15 March–3 May. A report from 11 June is suggestive of a second brood (as are the later dates cited below). Thirty-five occupied nests (contents unknown) were found 9 March–12 June. Adults carrying food were noted on twelve occasions, 26 April–20 June, with an additional very early report from 7 March. Young on the nest were found nineteen times, spanning 17 April–4 July. Fledglings were detected as early as 1 May and as late as 3 July with a total of seventeen records.

Conservation

With a confirmation in 68 blocks, the Black Phoebe is easily one of our most widespread breeders and is likely far more common than in pre-settlement days.

SAY'S PHOEBE • *Sayornis saya*

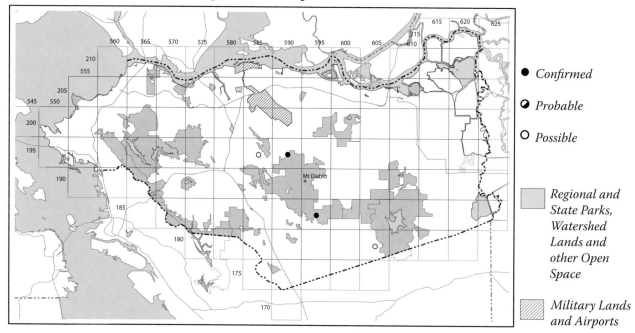

Confirmed

Probable

Possible

Regional and State Parks, Watershed Lands and other Open Space

Military Lands and Airports

A gentle melancholy possesses the soul of all pewees, and Sayornis sayus is the most desponding of the lot. It is impossible to guess what ancestral hardship could have stamped itself so indelibly upon any creature with wings.

🖎 *William Leon Dawson (1923)*

Current status and distribution

The Say's Phoebe, with its modest plumage and mournful whistle, resides sparingly in arid portions of the county. Although the species winters commonly throughout much of Northern California, Mt. Diablo generally represents the current northwestern boundary of their California breeding range. A 2007 nest record from near Vallejo, Solano County represents a significant range extension but it remains to be seen whether this was an isolated event (NAB 61: no. 4). There is precedence for such extralimital nesting. A pair nested near Novato, Marin County, in 1976 (Shuford 1993).

Two confirmations were made during the atlas project: a pair was noted feeding young near Blackhawk on the south flank of Mt. Diablo on 22 June 2001 and young were noted in the nest in Clayton on 20 Apr 2002. The latter nest was in a restroom at a crowded city park! Additional records suggestive of breeding include birds around Lime Ridge on the western flank of Mt. Diablo on both 13 May 2000 and 19 June 2002, and a single bird along the south end of Morgan Territory Rd. on 22 June 2002.

Suitable habitat for nesting Say's Phoebes features extensive amounts of open grasslands in the arid interior, with either a cliff face or a building for nest placement. It would seem that a significant amount of suitable habitat is unoccupied in Contra Costa County.

Historical occurrence

Historically, the Say's Phoebe was recorded breeding in 1936 at St. Mary's College near Moraga (Gull 18: no. 6) but this is the only known nest record from the western half of the county. Nest records since then have come from arid areas in the Diablo Range such as Black Diamond Mines Regional Park, Pine Canyon on Mt. Diablo, and around the area now occupied by Los Vaqueros Reservoir.

Breeding and natural history

The atlas database contains just six records of the Say's Phoebe, three of them confirmations. A nest with young was noted 20 April and those same young were out of the nest by 24 April. An adult feeding young from a second or even third brood was noted on the much later date of 22 June. In Monterey County, a nest with young was detected on 15 March, indicating that eggs were laid before 1 March. Later records, probably representing second or even third broods, included nest building on 25 May, occupied nests 14 April–14 June, and fledglings 13 May–14 June (Roberson and Tenney 1993).

Conservation

Significant amounts of apparently suitable habitat exist but remain unoccupied in the Diablo Range, an area at the very periphery of this species current range. Except for the protection of open habitats that may one day be occupied by nesting phoebes, most of which is already protected with park and watershed lands, there is little that can be done to encourage an increase in breeding pairs.

ASH-THROATED FLYCATCHER • *Myiarchus cinerascens*

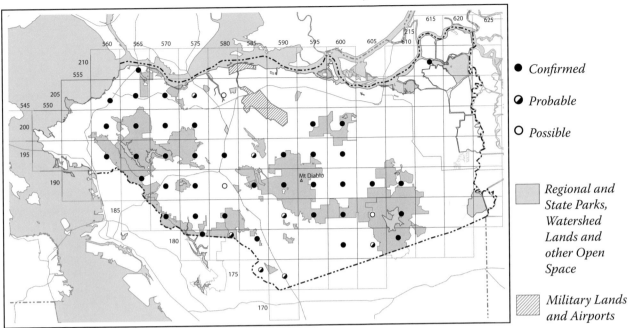

Confirmed

Probable

Possible

Regional and State Parks, Watershed Lands and other Open Space

Military Lands and Airports

Rather like the woodland answer to the Western Kingbird, the understated Ash-throated Flycatcher is unique for being our only cavity nesting member of the family Tyrannidae.

Current status and distribution

The Ash-throated Flycatcher is present almost exclusively in the Coast Range. Although it is unclear from the map, the species is far more numerous in the more arid, open woodlands of the Diablo Range than in the moist, often densely forested Berkeley Hills. The lone confirmation away from the Coast Range was at Piper Slough at the north end of Bethel Island. The Ash-throated Flycatcher is completely absent from the Richmond area, the marshes north of Concord and Pittsburg, the entirety of East County with the exception of Piper Slough, and from suburban settings in general. Although common in wooded areas throughout the Diablo Range, the species appears to be particularly abundant in the scrubby blue oak gray pine woodlands and valley oak savannah on the eastern flank. It is also found in riparian habitats, relatively open coastal oak woodlands, and in mixed chaparral. The species is completely absent from the closed canopy forests of the Berkeley Hills.

Historical occurrence

Grinnell and Wythe (1927) categorized the Ash-throated Flycatcher as a common summer resident locally, an apt description of its current status.

Breeding and natural history

The earliest arrival date for Ash-throated Flycatcher during the atlas project was 1 April with the majority of breeders seeming to arrive about the third week of that month. By late April most sightings pertain to pairs. Ten records of nest building ranged from 27 April–17 June, three occupied nests were detected 30 May–14 June, nine reports of adults feeding young in the nest spanned 18 June–22 July and fledglings were noted 8 June–7 July. Three egg sets in the possession of the MVZ span 16 May–2 June 2.

Conservation

Ash-throated Flycatcher populations are thought to be healthy locally and throughout most of their range. Although habitat destruction has likely been costly, forest fragmentation in the Berkeley Hills, as well as the relatively recent availability of widespread artificial nest sites, has likely provided fair compensation.

WESTERN KINGBIRD • *Tyrannus verticalis*

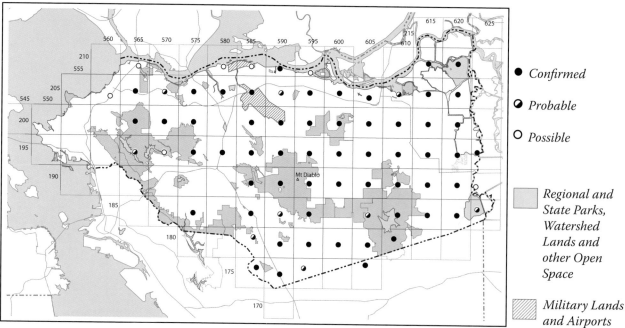

Himself a lover of the open country, he has become the presiding genius of all properly conducted ranches. Guest he is not, host rather; and before you have had time to shut off the motor and clap on the brakes, this bird bustles forth from the eucalyptus row and hovers over you with noisy effusiveness.

🐦 *William Leon Dawson (1923)*

The Western Kingbird is a regal summer resident of open habitats throughout much of the county and though not terribly abundant numerically, its preference for obvious perches in open habitats makes it one of our more conspicuous breeding birds.

Current status and distribution

The Western Kingbird is most common in the eastern portion of the county where it may be found around virtually every homestead and windbreak available, though native habitat is still utilized where it has been allowed to survive. While the atlas map appears to show a solid distribution well into the western half of the county, it belies the fact that in the western portions of the Coast Range it is far less common than in drier areas to the east. Where open grassland continues to hold sway, for example around Crockett and Bear Creek, the species can be somewhat common and gradually becomes more common as one heads east. The species is somewhat local along the hilly fringes of the San Ramon Valley. To the north and south of Mt. Diablo, where the oaks yield to extensive grasslands, the species becomes rather common, as around the Concord Naval Weapons Station, where it is often found in small clumps of introduced

eucalyptus. On Mt. Diablo itself the Western Kingbird is somewhat local though it becomes more prevalent in the open valley oak savannah just east of the mountain. The species is found somewhat sparingly along the Highway 4 corridor in Pittsburg and Antioch before reaching maximum abundance in the Delta area.

The Western Kingbird is widely found in grassland, open oak savannahs, riparian woodlands (generally when adjacent to open grasslands), and agricultural fields, so long as there are suitable perches for foraging and trees for nesting. And even trees aren't a necessity, as the species readily utilizes telephone poles for nesting.

Historical occurrence

Grinnell and Wythe (1927) are uncharacteristically vague about the status of the Western Kingbird. They label it a summer resident, though common only locally and in the interior, but cite no specific nesting. Further, the only East Bay stations of occurrence mentioned are Hayward and Berkeley, neither of which is in the interior. Grinnell and Miller (1944), however, indicate that the entire Central Valley was occupied by the Western Kingbird, so its presence in east Contra Costa County may be presumed.

Historic information is scarce but it seems more than likely that the Western Kingbird once bred widely in the San Ramon Valley and around Lafayette and Orinda, areas where residential neighborhoods have matured into almost forest-like settings in some areas. Such losses have been offset to at least some extent by tree plantings in formerly unbroken grasslands, particularly south of Mt. Diablo and in the southeast corner of the county.

Breeding and natural history

The earliest noted spring arrival was 26 March, although the first kingbirds usually appear closer to mid-March in East County. The first noted pairs were recorded shortly thereafter, as early as 31 March. Adults either carrying nest material or actually in the process of nest-building were noted on twenty occasions 5 April–5 June. Twenty-four records of adults either carrying food or feeding young ranged from 3 May to 4 August. Nests with young were found seven times between 6 June and 9 July. Fledged young were tallied twelve times between 5 May and 18 July. June and July records of nests with young or fledglings hint strongly at second broods.

Conservation

With fifty-five confirmations, the Western Kingbird is one of our more widespread nesting birds. It should be noted, however, that its preference for conspicuous nest sites also makes it one of our easiest birds to confirm. It will remain to be seen what effects current and future large scale developments in East County will have on kingbird populations. Without open space preserves amongst the sprawl it seems unlikely that kingbird numbers can do anything but decline.

WESTERN KINGBIRD

LOGGERHEAD SHRIKE • *Lanius ludovicianus*

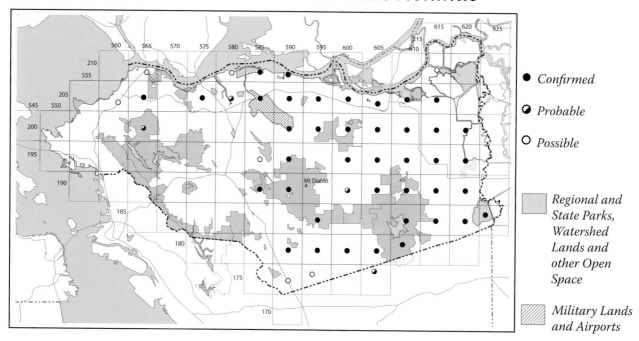

Confirmed

Probable

Possible

Regional and State Parks, Watershed Lands and other Open Space

Military Lands and Airports

Loggerhead Shrike, Butcher-bird, know it as you will, but the Loggerhead Shrike successfully fills an ecological niche and would scarcely be noticed were it not for its bold and somewhat grotesque habit of storing its small prey on conspicuous thorns and barbs, on standby for when hunger arrives.

Current status and distribution

A quintessential bird of open habitats, the Loggerhead Shrike remains, despite recent habitat contractions, fairly common and conspicuous on telephone wires and fences in the grasslands of Central County and the agricultural fields of East County. Occupied habitats include open grasslands, valley and blue oak savannah (which occurs primarily on the east slope of the Diablo Range) and open agricultural areas that have suitable perches and isolated shrubbery or trees for nest concealment. Forested habitats of any density are unsuitable.

During the atlas, the species was absent from the westernmost portion of the county around Richmond but was found to be probable and confirmed in one block each around Hercules where grasslands begin to become more prevalent. The entire northern border of the county from Pt. Costa east to San Joaquin County is occupied although the number of pairs east to Antioch tends to be small as the habitat is rarely extensive. The hills around Las Trampas Regional Park west of Danville do feature parched savannah, but that area was unoccupied during the atlas project. Just east of the Interstate 680 suburban corridor near Blackhawk the species is fairly common in both open grassland and savannah. This area has hosted wholesale development in recent years, which has accel-

erated since the atlas project was completed, almost certainly resulting in fewer nesting shrikes. The Loggerhead Shrike tends to be most numerous in the open fields of East County, an area where the pace of development is nothing short of frantic, causing justifiable concern for its future there.

Historical occurrence

Considered an abundant resident in much of Alameda and Contra Costa counties by Grinnell and Wythe (1927), it would appear that little has changed locally though undoubtedly there have been some local losses of breeding acreage. Two sets of eggs collected at Oakley 16 Apr 1918 (WFVZ #36530, 36531) provided the first known nest records for the county.

Breeding and natural history

The Loggerhead Shrike is a permanent, rather sedentary, resident in Contra Costa County, with winter numbers clearly bolstered by birds from the north. The species was confirmed nesting on fifty-two occasions during the atlas project: adults were seen building nests five times during the startlingly narrow window of 29 March–2 April; 7 occupied nests were observed 30 March–27 April with an additional late record of 31 May; adults were found carrying food twelve times between 5 May and 16 June; eight adults were seen feeding young with dates spanning 21 April–22 July; and nineteen records of fledglings fell between 5 May–10 August. A report of a fledgling 14 April, if identified correctly, was particularly early. Five egg sets at the MVZ were all taken between 29 April and 22 May.

Conservation

The Loggerhead Shrike is a California Species of Special Concern and has been given a Second Priority ranking (Shuford and Gardali 2008). Despite being confirmed in 39 blocks, there is concern locally as well. The wholesale development of the grasslands, most notably in the Dougherty Valley and in East County, has usurped significant amounts of occupied habitat in recent years and is expected to continue for the foreseeable future.

LOGGERHEAD SHRIKE

CASSIN'S VIREO • *Vireo cassinii*

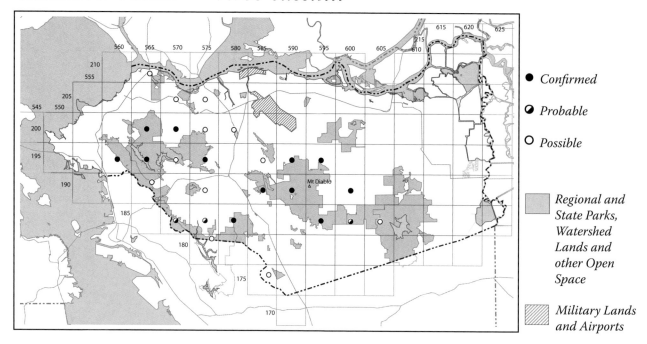

By far the least common of Contra Costa County's three species of breeding vireos, the curious "song" of the Cassin's Vireo is heard only locally in Contra Costa County's woodlands. What precludes this vireo from nesting in seemingly suitable habitats is unknown.

Current status and distribution

Nesting Cassin's Vireos are present in widely scattered areas of the Coast Range. During the atlas the species was confirmed in a nearly equal number of blocks in the Berkeley Hills and the Diablo Range. Despite confirmed or likely breeding in a high number of blocks, the species is not thought to be common anywhere in the county and it is unlikely that very many blocks, if any, had more than a handful of breeding pairs.

Preferred breeding habitat for the Cassin's Vireo is usually met at the edge of a relatively open-canopy forest, primarily composed of oaks but often with an added component of bay, maple or pine. The forest edge is often at the edge of a stream but the water may be coincidental as the species is frequently found at the edges of road cuts.

Historical occurrence

Grinnell and Wythe (1927) considered the Cassin's Vireo to be a sparse transient and summer resident, citing a nest record from San Pablo Creek, Contra Costa County. Numerous summer sightings and reports of nests are contained in various Audubon newsletters for the ensuing decades so it seems odd that American Birds chose to report that nesting was confirmed in Contra Costa County (at Briones Regional Park and Morgan Territory Rd.) in 1982 (AB 36: no. 6).

Breeding and natural history

The Cassin's Vireo was believed to nest in 25 blocks during the atlas period, a high total that came as a bit of a surprise. Eleven of these records, however, were "possibles" based upon singing males in suitable habitat during the breeding season and it is possible that a few of these were migrants rather than breeding birds. The earliest Cassin's arrived on territory 15 March with most first arrivals noted in April. This likely has much to do with the amount of atlasing done in April as opposed to March. The species was confirmed breeding in 11 blocks. Adults were seen carrying nest material on 2 and 4 May and nest-building 11 May. Occupied nests (contents unknown) were detected 16 May–11 June; a single nest with young was recorded 1 July. A record of a fledgling was tallied 29 June.

Conservation

Except for its susceptibility to parasitism by Brown-headed Cowbirds, very little concern has been expressed for the long-term future of this species, mainly because it seems to adapt well to various forestry methods.

HUTTON'S VIREO • *Vireo huttoni*

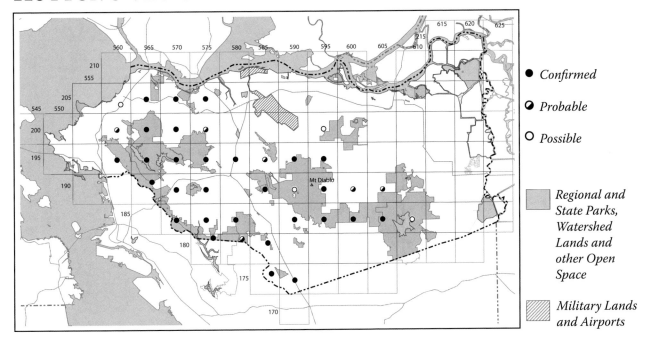

Confirmed ●
Probable ◓
Possible ○

Regional and State Parks, Watershed Lands and other Open Space

Military Lands and Airports

At once the least musical and patterned of our three breeding vireos, the Hutton's Vireo is a permanent resident of the county's woodlands. Bearing an almost uncanny resemblance to the Ruby-crowned Kinglet (which breeds nowhere near Contra Costa County), its dull, monotonous song often reveals its presence long before it is seen.

Current status and distribution

The Hutton's Vireo is a fairly common, sedentary resident of woodlands throughout the Coast Range. Because the species is so sedentary, it is almost certain that it bred in each of the blocks in which it was recorded, making the atlas map a very accurate representation of its current range. The species is absent only from the densest forests of the Berkeley Hills but is otherwise spread evenly through fairly dense coastal oak woodlands. In the Diablo Range it is relegated to shady, well-wooded hillsides and canyon bottoms.

The Hutton's Vireo is thought to be a very scarce migrant to the Richmond area—but isn't known to nest—and has never been recorded in the Central Valley portion of the county.

Historical occurrence

Four eggs taken from a nest at Danville 16 Apr 1897 (WFVZ #69857) provided the first known nesting confirmation for the county. There is nothing to indicate that the status and distribution of the Hutton's Vireo has changed in the past century.

Breeding and natural history

The Hutton's Vireo was detected in 39 blocks and confirmed breeding in 29 of them. Because of the extremely sedentary nature of the species, it almost surely bred in each of them. Males begin to sing their monotonous songs by early February. Ten records of adults either carrying nest material or nest building spanned 17 March–16 May. The San Mateo atlas recorded the carrying of nest building as early as 4 March (Sequoia Audubon Society 2001). Nests proved hard to find but one was occupied (contents unknown) 27 April and nests with young were discovered on 27 April and 17 May. Adults carrying food were noted nine times as early as 16 April and as late as 10 June and adults in the process of feeding the young were tallied nine times between 3 May and 12 July. Fledglings were detected nine times with dates spanning 16 May–23 August with an additional, very early report from 22 April. The San Mateo atlas cites a very late fledgling record from 27 September (Sequoia Audubon Society 2001).

Conservation

Because the vast majority of Hutton's Vireo habitat in Contra Costa County is protected by state and regional parks as well as watershed lands, there appear to be no significant imminent threats.

WARBLING VIREO • *Vireo gilvus*

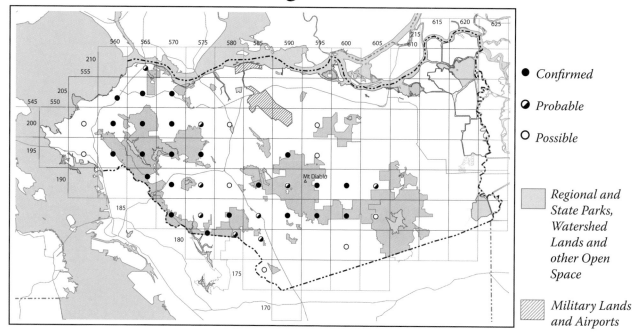

Fresh as apples and as sweet as apple blossoms comes that dear, homely song from the willows.

    🍂 *William Leon Dawson (1923)*

Although dull of plumage in the grandest vireo tradition, the Warbling Vireo is one of the more aptly named members of the local avifauna. A spring outing in preferred canyon bottom habitats will undoubtedly afford dozens of opportunities for hearing the cheerful song of one of the county's most abundant breeding neotropical songbirds.

Current status and distribution

The Warbling Vireo is one of the most common breeding passerines in wooded situations throughout the Berkeley Hills and Diablo Range but is completely absent from the western and eastern portions of the county. The species is most commonly found in wooded canyon bottoms where it inhabits coastal oak woodlands, particularly those with a strong component of Coast Live Oak and California bay, as well as montane and valley foothill riparian. Preferred habitats are most extensive in the moist Berkeley Hills. In the Diablo Range, the Warbling Vireo habitat is generally restricted to moist, shady canyon bottoms, mostly around Mt. Diablo and Morgan Territory Rd.

Historical occurrence

There has apparently been little change since 1927, when Grinnell and Wythe noted the species as abundant summer residents throughout the Bay area.

Breeding and natural history

The first arrival of the Warbling Vireo from the wintering grounds during the atlas project was noted 20 March, though the species is known to arrive even earlier. The first pair was noted 1 April. The species was confirmed thirty-one times in 21 blocks. Six records of adults carrying nest material or nest building spanned 21 April–30 May. Adults on occupied nests (contents unknown) were detected five times from 28 April through 21 June; a nest with eggs seen was found 1 June. Just two nests with young were recorded, one on 6 June and the other 8 July. Adults were seen carrying food on five occasions from 8 May–17 June. Young out of the nest were tallied twelve times 15 May–6 July.

Conservation

As elsewhere, significant losses have certainly occurred with the degradation and destruction of riparian habitats. In addition, many observers have commented upon the susceptibility of the Warbling Vireo to the parasitic Brown-headed Cowbird.

STELLER'S JAY • *Cyanocitta stelleri*

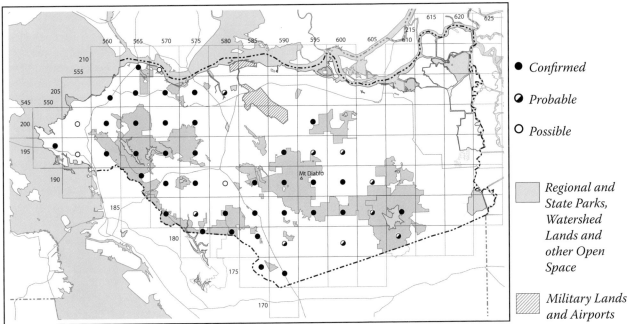

Legend:
● *Confirmed*
◑ *Probable*
○ *Possible*

▨ *Regional and State Parks, Watershed Lands and other Open Space*

▨ *Military Lands and Airports*

This pugnacious, crested corvid is a common permanent resident of forested areas throughout the central half of the county. Although commonly associated with dense, shady forests it is, in truth, most common near the open edges of such habitats where it may share space with Western Scrub-Jays. Despite its fiery demeanor, it is the scrub-jay that maintains dominance in such situations.

Current status and distribution

In Contra Costa County, the Steller's Jay is present in forested areas throughout the Coast Range. The species is quite widespread in the moist, fog-shrouded Berkeley Hills and is usually absent only from occasional patches of grassland. This ubiquitousness continues east to about Lafayette Res. but thereafter its distribution becomes patchier as the climate becomes more arid and the habitats more open. In the Diablo Range, its range is essentially restricted to shady canyons such as Pine and Mitchell on Mt. Diablo, Morgan Territory Rd. and vicinity. This essentially represents the eastern stronghold, however, a few birds are present as far east as Round Valley. Moderate populations persist in wooded portions of residential Lafayette, Orinda and Moraga and smaller numbers are present quite locally in "mature" neighborhoods around Alamo and Danville. Habitat needs dictate that the species is absent from the entirety of East County, from the river plain around Pittsburg and Antioch, from the open grasslands south of Mt. Diablo, and, with one notable exception, from the urban and industrial areas around Richmond.

This exception was in block 550-195 where a fledgling was noted on 8 July 2001. This small group near Miller/ Knox Regional Shoreline at Pt. Richmond was believed to have been present since an "invasion" during the winter of 1998–1999 that brought the species to normally unoccupied locations throughout much of Northern California.

The Steller's Jay inhabits coastal woodlands, forests of redwood, Monterey pine and eucalyptus, and shady riparian corridors. Riparian corridors are most often occupied when contiguous with other types of forest or woodland, most often in canyon bottoms. The species typically inhabits forest openings rather than the depths of the forest. Oaks are nearly always a common component wherever this jay is found.

Historical occurrence

The status of the Steller's Jay in Contra Costa County seems little changed since the time of Grinnell and Wythe (1927), who stated that "local colonies" were present in the Berkeley Hills and at Mt. Diablo. Belding (1890) considered the species to be a rare resident of Alameda and Contra Costa counties yet a 1943 paper stated that the species was first detected in the East Bay area at Woolsey Canyon, Alameda County in 1910, becoming established in Strawberry Canyon in 1915 (Allen 1943)

Breeding and natural history

The Steller's Jays were confirmed breeding in 35 atlas blocks, with a total of fifty-five confirmed records in the database. Pairs seem to remain on territory throughout the year in coastal California (Greene and others 1998) and were noted as early as atlasers began fieldwork. Because Steller's Jay nests are often difficult to find, the

137

species was recorded carrying nest material on twelve occasions from 11 March–7 May but actually seen nest-building just four times from 28 March–3 May. Just one bird, on 10 April, was seen occupying a nest. Nests with noisy young were found three times with dates spanning 29 May–4 July. Adults were seen carrying food on four instances between 14 May and 25 June. Fledglings at various stages of development were noted on thirty occasions 19 May–4 August, with most records falling into a window between late May and late June. The Steller's Jay is not known to double brood so some of these later dates likely refer to re-nesting attempts (Greene and others 1998).

Conservation

The future of the Steller's Jay in Contra Costa appears secure as most of its current range is locked up in regional parks and watershed lands.

WESTERN SCRUB-JAY

WESTERN SCRUB-JAY • *Aphelocoma californica*

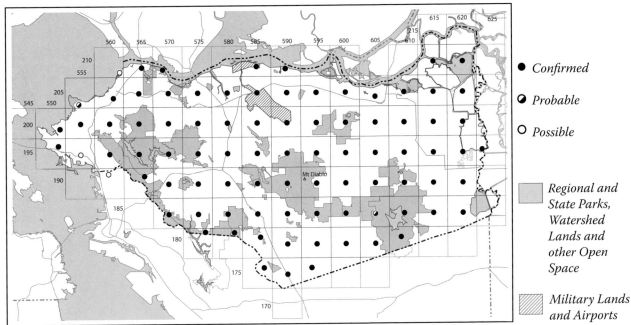

Confirmed

Probable

Possible

Regional and State Parks, Watershed Lands and other Open Space

Military Lands and Airports

The Western Scrub-Jay, the avian equivalent of the neighborhood bully, is far and away one of our most successful native birds. This "Blue Jay" is a widespread, common and conspicuous component of wilderness and garden settings alike, monopolizing food sources in both wild areas and feeding trays and never hesitant to rob and consume eggs from the nests of other birds.

Current status and distribution

The Western Scrub-Jay inhabits a tremendous variety of wooded habitats in Contra Costa County: open coastal oak woodlands, blue oak and valley oak woodlands; riparian corridors, particularly when adjacent to oak woodlands or chaparral; stands of mixed chaparral; eucalyptus groves that include a shrubby understory; suburban neighborhoods and city parks; and, in East County, even around ranch houses with just a smattering of trees and shrubs. The only habitats unoccupied by this versatile corvid are marshland, extensive parcels of grassland, and dense, unbroken forest. The exceptions never occur in large enough parcels to be reflected in the atlas map, which shows the species to be present in every block. Near the edges of the densely forested hillsides and canyon bottoms of the Coast Ranges the scrub-jay comes into contact with its crested counterpart, the Steller's Jay, and in such situations nearly always hold sway.

Historical occurrence

Grinnell and Wythe (1927) considered the "Northwestern California Jay" to be an abundant permanent resident, particularly in the oak belts.

Breeding and natural history

The atlas database contains 405 records of the Western Scrub-Jay and includes 158 confirmations, thus giving it the honor of having the most total records and the most confirmations of any bird during the atlas, narrowly beating out Mourning Dove, House Finch and, thankfully, European Starling. Much of this is due to the gregariousness of the adults and fledglings rather than true numbers and it is likely that each of those three actually outnumbers the scrub-jay in the county.

Pairs of Western Scrub-Jays remain together on territories that they aggressively defend year-round (Curry and others 2002) and thus pairs were noted as early in the season as atlasing began. Courtship was noted on four occasions between 13 March and 24 April. Thirty-one confirmations based upon adults carrying nest material were gathered between 3 March and 5 June with the overwhelmingly majority in March and April. Adults were found on occupied nests just twice, each on 5 April. Four sighting of nests with young ranged from only 21–29 May. Of ten egg sets at the MVZ that were collected in the county, the dates span 30 March–13 May. Adults were noted carrying food on fourteen occasions 28 April–26 June. Caution is warranted in this situation as these jays carry acorns throughout the year that are not used to feed young. Recently fledged young, some being actively fed by adults and some not, proved easy to detect and were tallied 106 times with dates spanning 5 May–11 July with very late reports from 16 August and 5 September. Late nestings likely represent re-nesting attempts, as the species is unknown to double-brood

(Curry and others 2002). Because little atlasing takes place after early August, it is unclear how commonly such late nesting takes place. However, the egg of a nestling found in San Mateo County in 1987 was thought to have been laid about 8 September. It is suggested that a heavy acorn crop that season may have been responsible (Curry and others 2002).

Conservation

It seems likely that the Western Scrub-Jay is now even more common than historically due to forest fragmentation and the building of ranch houses and windbreaks in what was formerly unsuitable grassland.

YELLOW-BILLED MAGPIE

Yellow-billed Magpie • *Pica nuttalli*

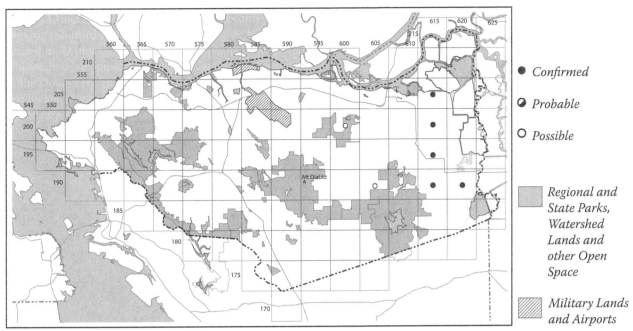

● Confirmed

◕ Probable

○ Possible

▨ Regional and State Parks, Watershed Lands and other Open Space

▨ Military Lands and Airports

The Yellow-billed Magpie, a bona fide California endemic, has always been an enigmatic bird in Contra Costa County. Despite nearby source populations and abundant habitat that is apparently similar to nearby occupied areas in the Central Valley or in adjacent southeastern Alameda County, it wasn't until 1994 that the species was finally confirmed nesting.

Current status and distribution

Despite a recent increase of breeding pairs in the county, the magpie remains quite local with a range restricted to East County. All known nest sites have been within a narrow band that extends from southern Bethel Island in the north to Byron in the south. Significant acreages of fields and orchards exist to the west of this band and extensive grasslands persist to the east yet the species is absent in either direction. Each of the nests found thus far has been in clumps of introduced eucalyptus adjacent to open grassland and/or agricultural lands, although a pair near Byron was found building a nest in a row of exotic conifers adjacent to a school playground.

Historical occurrence

The Yellow-billed Magpie was unknown to Grinnell and Wythe (1927) or Grinnell and Miller (1944) as having occurred in Contra Costa County. Grinnell and Wythe state that in the mid-19th century the species was "a more or less common resident" from the Golden Gate south to San Jose, areas where it is now found only as a rare post-breeding dispersant. Still, it seems possible that the species also occurred in western or central Contra Costa County when fields or pastures remained prevalent and simply went unrecorded. After the first county record at San Pablo Ridge 7 June 1959 (AFN 13: no. 5), the species was found sporadically over the next half-century, with at least twenty records from widely-spaced locations throughout the county. Most were post-breeding dispersants or wintering birds. The first nesting confirmation finally came in 1994 along Delta Rd. in Knightsen, to this day the most reliable spot in the county for magpies (Quail 40: no. 11).

Breeding and natural history

The Yellow-billed Magpie in Contra Costa County is thought to be a permanent and fairly sedentary resident though it may be slightly more widespread in winter and there is some evidence of post-breeding dispersal. Because the species is sedentary it is assumed that it likely nested in each of the 7 blocks in which it was detected. Because the species is so scarce in the county, accumulated data is rather meager. Adults were seen building nests 17 March and 7 June and one was noted carrying nest material 7 April. In central coastal California nest building can begin in late January and by the middle of February nearly all nesting pairs have begun this activity (Verbeek 1973). On average, egg laying begins during the first week of April (Reynolds 1995). The 7 June record of carrying nest material is assumed to refer to a re-nesting attempt, as the species is unknown to double brood (Reynolds 1995). Adults were on nests (contents unknown) 26 March–16 June. If more time was spent among the county's few breeding magpies, fledglings would likely have been noted deep into July (Verbeek 1973).

141

Conservation

As to the future of the Yellow-billed Magpie in Contra Costa County it is entirely possible that the species will increase in numbers and occupy vacant habitats that appear ideal. Unfortunately, it seems equally likely that this is but a temporary expansion at the very edge of its range and the species will again recede. As of 2002 it seems doubtful that there are more than 25 nesting pairs in the county.

Yellow-billed Magpie populations have disappeared from some parts of its historical range, most likely in response to urban sprawl or conversion to agriculture, leading Audubon's Watchlist 2002 to designate them a Yellow List Species.

BLACK-THROATED GRAY WARBLER

AMERICAN CROW • *Corvus brachyrhynchos*

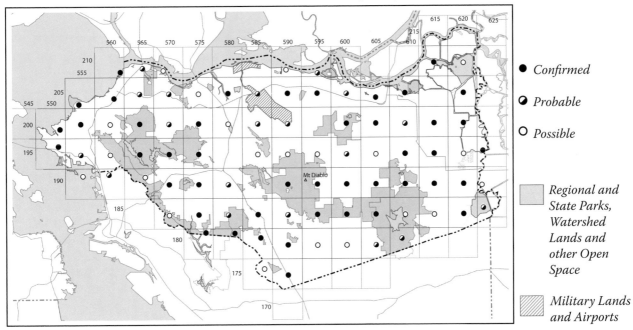

● *Confirmed*

◔ *Probable*

○ *Possible*

▨ *Regional and State Parks, Watershed Lands and other Open Space*

▨ *Military Lands and Airports*

Referred to by Dawson (1923) as "notorious mischief-makers," the common American Crow is an entertaining presence throughout open areas and around human settlements across the county, supremely suited for taking advantage of human alterations of the landscape.

Current status and distribution

The American Crow occurs as a nesting bird throughout the county, but it can be surprisingly local in "wilder" situations away from human settlement. When the species does nest in native habitats, it is often at sites immediately adjacent to altered habitats such as agricultural fields or stables. In Contra Costa County it clearly reaches maximum abundance around the orchards and fields of East County where it is among the most common of nesting birds. The species is also commonly found in urban and suburban settings in the western and central portions of the county.

Historical occurrence

Belding (1890) states that none had been seen for several years in the region, though the species had formerly bred at Berkeley. Grinnell and Wythe (1927), probably alluding to Belding, state "curiously we find no recent records of crows for the Alameda County shores, though in 1872 they nested commonly in the oaks on campus." Grinnell and Miller (1944) felt that crow populations had remained constant "this despite, on the one hand, general human belligerence toward this bird, expressed sporadically in crow shoots and even bombings of winter roosts, and on the other hand increase of suitable habitat in some agricultural areas". Shuford (1993) noted that

American Crows are likely now far more numerous than historically, primarily due to the boon in agriculture during the 20th century, and this is almost certainly true in Contra Costa County.

Breeding and natural history

Adults carrying nest material or nest building were recorded thirty-four times between 2 March and 23 May, the vast majority of records falling in March and early April. Seven occupied nests were detected 25 March–8 May. A nest with young was found 21 May. Adults carrying food and feeding young were tallied on thirteen occasions 27 April–28 June; an additional report from 27 March has been disregarded. Fledglings were found thirty times between 15 May and 11 August, the bulk of them from June.

Conservation

Few species have taken better advantage of man's alteration of the landscape than the common American Crow and few seem better suited for continued success in the 21st century.

COMMON RAVEN • *Corvus corax*

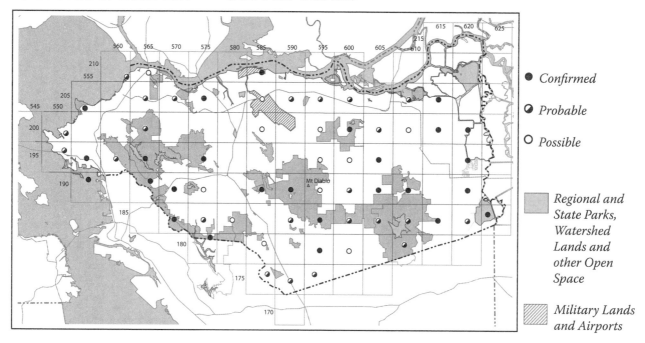

The Common Raven has been described in many ways, nearly always negatively. No less a towering figure than Dawson (1923) himself was unable to restrain himself, referring to the raven as the "... self-contained black angel and villain of nature's plot." Although this is hyperbolic to be sure, the recent spread of the Common Raven is indeed a threat to the well being of several vulnerable local species, particularly the Black-necked Stilt and the American Avocet.

Current status and distribution

One of the more surprising revelations of the atlas project was the discovery that the Common Raven has become a widespread, if generally uncommon, breeder throughout nearly the entirety of the county. The species was seen throughout the county with the only noticeable gap occurring in urban areas along the Interstate 680 corridor. Nesting confirmations were obtained from throughout the county. The species was perhaps most common (or easiest to find) in the Central Valley, an area where it was detected only rarely just 20 years ago.

The Common Raven forages in open habitats, particularly grasslands, and may fly great distances to reach them. Its wide foraging territories likely resulted in reports of possible or probable breeding from blocks in which the species didn't actually breed.

Historical occurrence

The Common Raven was unknown to Belding (1890) or Grinnell and Wythe (1927) as occurring in the East Bay. The following charming account is thought to be the first record for the East Bay: "Mr. Dyer asked for sugges-

tions as to the identity of a large black bird with pointed wings which flew slowly and steadily across his view in Piedmont on Nov 21. The bird was high in the air and, soaring in a wide circle, it disappeared. Its call was "kruk, kruk." The several members who ventured opinions were inclined toward the Raven as the identity of Mr. Dyer's bird, a stranger in our region" (Grinnell H 1935). In 1976 pairs were seen in Berkeley and Hayward on 19 and 21 April. Because of its scarceness it was questioned whether or not they were the same pair! (AB 30: no. 4). Records accumulated rapidly in the early 1980s and it seems likely that the species was nesting in Central County at least by the middle of that decade.

Breeding and natural history

The Common Raven was noted widely in the county with sightings from 68 blocks and forty-nine confirmations in 26 of them. There were thirty-nine reports of birds "observed" and an additional forty-nine "possible" records—although it appears that atlasers weren't consistent in their use of the codes. There were forty-two reports of pairs beginning as early as 11 March. Adults carrying nest material or building nests were tallied twelve times from 7 March–18 June. Sixteen occupied nests (contents unknown) were reported 26 March–2 June. Nests with young were recorded five times 27 April–11 June. An adult feeding young was found 4 July. The lone record of a fledgling was 13 June. Although second broods are unknown for Common Ravens, some of the later dates are suggestive of re-nesting (Boarman and Heinrich 1999).

Conservation

As of 2009 it would seem more appropriate to say that a number of our breeding birds need conserving from the Common Raven. Its recent population explosion, if sustainable, suggests a successful future for the raven.

COMMON RAVEN

HORNED LARK • *Eremophila alpestris*

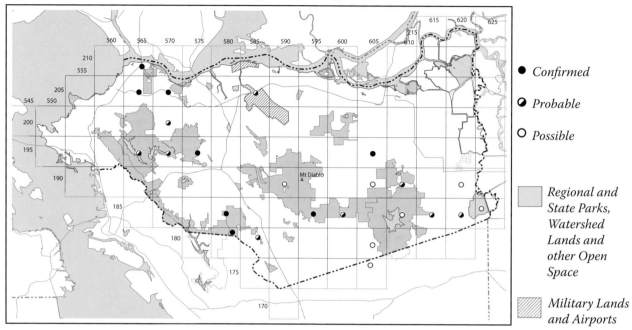

Confirmed ●

Probable ◕

Possible ○

Regional and State Parks, Watershed Lands and other Open Space

Military Lands and Airports

The Horned Lark isn't the most colorful bird in the county, nor does it sing the most beautiful song, but as William Leon Dawson proclaimed in 1923: "… such are the circumstances attending its delivery that it is set down by everyone as "pleasing," while for the initiated it possesses a charm which is quite unique." Dawson was of course referring to the wondrous skylarking performed above open grasslands in early spring.

Current status and distribution

One of the most disappointing results of the atlas project was that of the Horned Lark, both because it was less widespread than had been hoped and because it must have been missed in some areas. The Horned Lark was confirmed breeding in a total of 8 blocks and was "probable" in numerous others. Most known breeding stations are in the Berkeley Hills and in the grasslands of the southeast portion of the county. Because of poor access it is unclear as to whether gaps in much of the northern portion of the county are real. A complete lack of birds in the northeast portion of the county does, unfortunately, appear to be legitimate and is surprising as there are still seemingly suitable patches of habitat present.

Breeding Horned Larks were detected in open, short-cropped grassy habitats of relative dryness. Such habitats are found almost exclusively in the county in the open, rolling hills of the Berkeley Hills and the Diablo Range, although even there they were absent from many suitable locations. The only flatland sites from which the species was detected were around Byron in the extreme southeast corner of the county. A lack of access to some of this area likely led to our missing this species from other blocks.

Historical occurrence

Belding (1890) considered the Horned Lark to be a common resident in the East Bay. The first confirmed nesting for the county is thought to be two eggs collected at Antioch 7 May 1915 (WFVZ #102704). Although Grinnell and Wythe (1927) do not mention Contra Costa County specifically, they considered the species a fairly common resident of dry plains and rolling hills, a common situation in Contra Costa County at that time.

Breeding and natural history

The atlas project turned up a modest amount of data for the Horned Lark, due in part to the fact that atlasers spent much less time in species-poor grasslands and in part to the fact that the species is a rather scarce and local breeder in the county. Although winter populations are bolstered greatly by birds of several different northern races, the local race *actia* is thought to be sedentary. This is confused by the fact that local birds begin to nest early enough that wintering birds may still be present. Despite this complication, it is believed that sightings reflected in the atlas map refer to true breeders. Singing males were noted as early as 27 February, pairs as early as 15 March. The lone report of an adult carrying nest material was 22 March. Adults were seen carrying food 20 June and 4 July and feeding young 13 March and 18 June. Fledglings were noted 12 and 23 May. The Horned Lark is known to double and even triple brood (Beason 1995) and the latter dates generated by the atlas project demonstrate this.

Conservation

The Horned Lark has certainly suffered from significant habitat losses, due both to urban development and the forestation of hills in the central part of the county, particularly around Lafayette, Orinda and Moraga.

HORNED LARK

TREE SWALLOW • *Tachycineta bicolor*

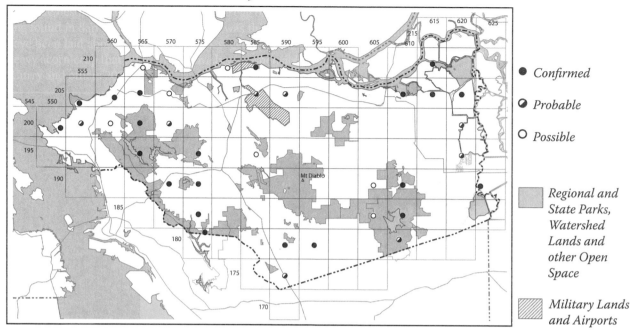

The attractive Tree Swallow, though far less famous than the lauded Barn Swallow, is the only swallow normally present throughout the year. Because the species is an obligate cavity nester, its success is intimately tied to the presence of dead trees with suitable nest holes.

Current status and distribution

The Tree Swallow is a local breeder throughout most of Contra Costa County. Because of a fondness for nesting and foraging around water, the species is infinitely more common around the watershed reservoirs in the Berkeley Hills and around the sloughs of the eastern portion of the county than elsewhere. The choice of nest sites is further restricted by a need for dead or dying trees in open areas. The only nesting confirmation from the Diablo Range came from Marsh Creek Res. west of Brentwood; the species is completely absent from developed areas in West and Central County.

Historical occurrence

Grinnell and Wythe (1927) considered the Tree Swallow to be a common resident of the Bay region but did not specifically cite Contra Costa County. They do mention Oakland, Alameda County. Grinnell and Miller (1944) delineated the species breeding range as "nearly the entire length of the state west of the deserts", including many Central Valley locations, so it can be assumed that the species was at least breeding in East County.

Breeding and natural history

Nesting Tree Swallows were confirmed forty-two times during the atlas project, in a total of 21 blocks. One of the county's earliest returning migrants (discount-ing small numbers of birds that winter primarily in the northern and eastern portion of the county), the earliest returnee was recorded 5 February. Pairs were noted as early as 19 February and were commonly noted throughout March. Occupied nests were noted on twenty-two occasions between 4 April and 21 June. The contents of such nests were unknown but nests with young sticking their heads out of the cavity were discovered three times from 21 April–29 May. The removal of fecal sacs was noted 16 May and 11 June. Fledglings were found four times with a date span of 17 April–6 July.

The Tree Swallow may occasionally nest in tree cavities but it primarily relies upon old woodpecker holes in dead trees for suitable nest sites and, indeed, competition with other Tree Swallows and other cavity nesters can be quite fierce. So much so that Robertson and others (1992) considered nest-site competition to be a "driving force" behind the breeding ecology and behavior of the Tree Swallow, including its early arrival in spring, intense defense of territory, and even sexually selected infanticide.

Conservation

The size of Contra Costa County's Tree Swallow population appears to be limited by the availability of suitable nest sites. The species has eagerly adapted to the placement of bluebird nest boxes in recent years, likely increasing population size, but the removal of dead trees, particularly from sites immediately adjacent to water, remains a concern and should be discouraged whenever possible.

VIOLET-GREEN SWALLOW

149

Violet-green Swallow • *Tachycineta thalassina*

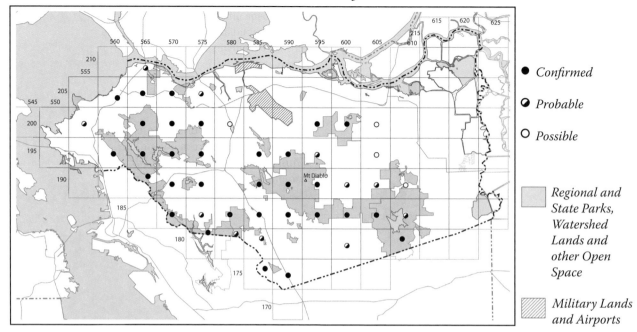

Confirmed

Probable

Possible

Regional and State Parks, Watershed Lands and other Open Space

Military Lands and Airports

While often under-appreciated, a Violet-green Swallow, seen under lighting conditions that bring out its stunning green and purple iridescence, is undoubtedly one of Contra Costa County's most beautiful breeding birds.

Current status and distribution

Less widespread than the similar Tree Swallow, the breeding Violet-green Swallow is completely limited to the open woodlands of the Coast Range; the species is not known to breed in West or East County or in suburban settings. In fact, the range map for the Violet-green Swallow is an exact outline of the wooded portions of the Coast Range.

The Violet-green Swallow is fond of mature, open forests featuring dead or dying trees that have been excavated by woodpeckers and is most common in blue oak and valley oak savannah habitats. Unlike the Tree Swallow, the species is not tied to water and thus its Coast Range distribution is less localized. The species is noted throughout its range to nest in crevices on cliff faces but atlasers made no specific mention of this during the atlas project.

Historical occurrence

The Violet-green Swallow was known by Grinnell and Wythe (1927) as only occurring in the spring in Contra Costa County. There are, however, reported nests from various sources by the early 1950s and it seems likely that nesting was occurring in the interior all along but simply not noted. The earliest known nest record, which is really quite recent, is 8 June 1952 (Gull 34: 30).

Breeding and natural history

Like the Tree Swallow, the Violet-green Swallow arrives early from southern wintering grounds. The first recorded bird during the atlas project was 19 February with the bulk of the population arriving in March. Pairs are widespread by the third week of March. Adults either carrying nest material or building the actual nest were recorded between 24 April and 30 May. But this small set of data is clearly not representative of the true timing of nest building as the first occupied nest (contents unknown) was noted 22 April. An additional twenty-seven occupied nests ranged from 24 April–28 June. Adults feeding dependent young were found on six occasions 16 May–10 July. Fledglings were recorded three times between 23 May and 7 July.

The Violet-green Swallow normally produces a single brood per season but second broods have been reported in Montana, Nevada and Oregon (Brown and others 1992); some of the late dates cited above indicate that this may occur locally as well.

Conservation

It is fortunate that most of the suitable habitat for the Violet-green Swallow in Contra Costa County is within regional and state parklands or protected watersheds. But within such sites the species is vulnerable to the removal of the dead and dying trees which it relies upon for nest sites.

NORTHERN ROUGH-WINGED SWALLOW •
Stelgidopteryx serripennis

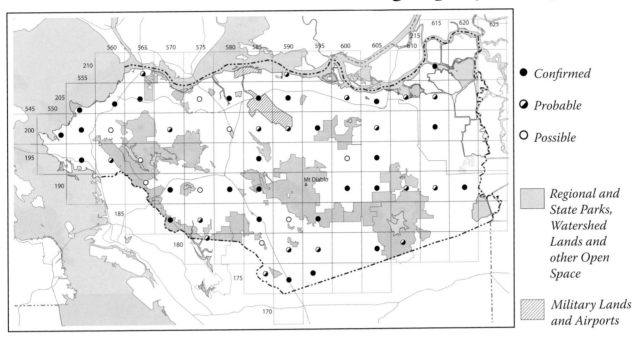

Its plumage is a dull brown, its vocalizations a weak, unmusical "brrrittt" and yet the Northern Rough-winged Swallow is just uncommon enough not to be taken for granted during an average day in the field.

Current status and distribution

Although a glance at the atlas map for the Northern Rough-winged Swallow might suggest a common bird, in actuality it is found only locally. Birds nesting in natural substrates—in this case dirt banks—have become increasingly uncommon, while at the same time the species has responded well to the opportunity provided by drain holes beneath freeways. Nesting birds are still found nesting in dirt banks but such situations are relatively common only in parts of the Diablo Range (especially east of Mt. Diablo) and the Central Valley portion of the county where it nests along sloughs and culverts. Elsewhere in the county, its range matches well with that of the major interstates. Along the Interstate 680 corridor one pair or more nest annually at most locations where the freeway passes over a surface street. The species appears less common when a surface street passes over a busy freeway, possibly because a corresponding increase of fast-moving cars present a greater danger to adults entering and leaving nest holes.

Historical occurrence

Grinnell and Wythe (1927) considered this swallow to be an uncommon summer visitant present at only a few Bay Area localities, including at Lafayette, Contra Costa County. It seems likely that the species was at least slightly more common deeper into the interior, much as it is today.

Breeding and natural history

Like our other local swallows, the Northern Rough-winged Swallow arrives early. The first recorded arrival during the atlas project was 12 March but it has been recorded in Contra Costa County as early as 23 February. Nearly all breeding confirmations during the atlas project were based upon adults repeatedly entering presumed nest sites with dates spanning 29 March–15 July. Although the contents of these nests were rarely visible, it is assumed that this date span encompasses nest building through the fledging of young.

Conservation

Nest sites in natural substrates are imperiled by habitat destruction, particularly cement channelization of streams, but the species adaptation to freeway drain holes may be its saving grace in the long run.

CLIFF SWALLOW • *Petrochelidon pyrrhonota*

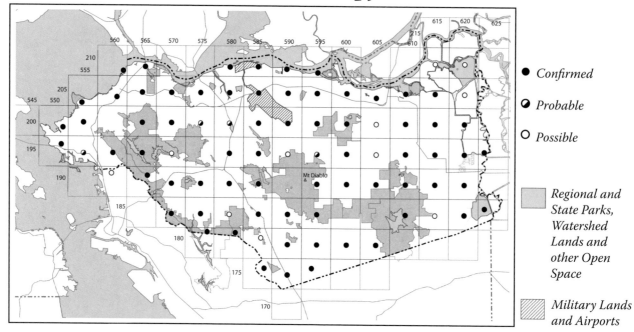

● *Confirmed*

◐ *Probable*

○ *Possible*

▨ *Regional and State Parks, Watershed Lands and other Open Space*

▨ *Military Lands and Airports*

The Cliff Swallow is one of Contra Costa County's most conspicuous breeding birds, gathering in tight-knit colonies that may number in the hundreds. Unfortunately, the Cliff Swallow is oblivious to the concept of private property. When its fondness for placing nests on the smooth walls of houses or businesses clashes with the fondness of a property owner for a sanitary living-space, a battle often ensues which the diminutive swallow can't hope to win.

Current status and distribution

The Cliff Swallow is currently a widespread breeder in Contra Costa County. The map may be somewhat misleading however, as many of the atlas blocks contained only a single colony. Colonies may be located on either a cliff face or, far more commonly, on the side of a building or bridge, nearly always close to water for foraging and gathering mud for nests. The species is most common in the eastern portion of the county where it utilizes many of the bridges over sloughs and irrigation ditches. In much of California it builds nests under freeway overpasses but this seems to be an unusual phenomenon here. Colonies in many areas were noted to move short distances from year to year or even with the breeding season, probably in response to disruption or destruction of its nests.

Historical occurrence

Belding (1890) considered the Cliff Swallow to be an abundant summer resident in Alameda County. Grinnell and Wythe (1927) likewise knew the species as common summer residents of rural districts.

Breeding and natural history

Local Cliff Swallows were recorded as early as 28 February with the bulk of birds present by the end of March. Gathering of mud and/or nest building was recorded on thirty-six occasions between 15 March and 10 June. The bulk of our confirmations were based upon occupied nests (contents unknown), with dates spanning 28 March–30 June. Three egg sets at the MVZ were taken between 3 and 27 May. Nests with young were recorded four times between 12 May and 4 July. Such a low number of such sightings are likely due to the fact that Cliff Swallows are so easy to confirm so early in the season and atlasers turn their attention to other species.

Although some of the late dates of occupied nests and nests with young could conceivably indicate double brooding, this is quite rare in the Cliff Swallow (Brown and Brown 1995) and these sightings more likely pertain to re-nesting, either by single pairs or entire colonies that have been forced to find an alternative nest site.

Conservation

Cliff Swallow populations seem limited only by suitable nest sites that are left in peace for the duration of the breeding season. The species suffers greatly from the destruction of nests when it inconveniences home and business owners. The removal of nesting colonies was the likely cause of new colonies appearing overnight at previously unoccupied sites. Overall, however, it appears that the Cliff Swallow has benefited tremendously from the construction of buildings and bridges and is likely far more common than in pre-settlement times.

BARN SWALLOW • *Hirundo rustica*

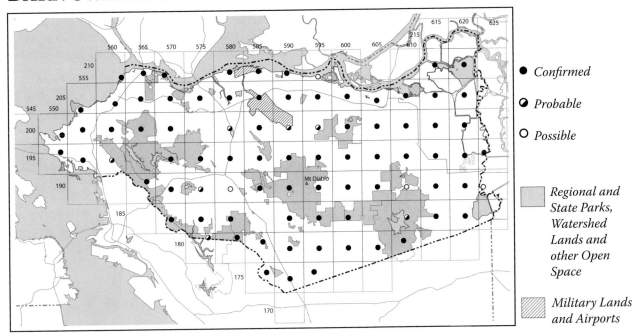

Confirmed

Probable

Possible

Regional and State Parks, Watershed Lands and other Open Space

Military Lands and Airports

One hardly knows what quality to admire most in this boyhood's and life-long friend, the Barn Swallow. All the dear associations of life at the old farm come thronging up at sight of him. You think of him somehow as part of the sacred past; yet here he is today as young and as fresh as ever, bubbling over with springtime laughter, ready for a frolic over the bee-haunted meadows, or willing to settle down on the nearest fence-wire and recount to you with sparkling eyes and eloquent gesture the adventures of that glorious trip up from Mexico.

William Leon Dawson (1923)

Current status and distribution

This bird of open country is as widespread as any of Contra Costa County's breeding birds, likely present and breeding in even the couple of blank spots on the map. This should not necessarily be taken as good news, however, as none of the nests detected during the atlas project were built on natural substrates, indicating that there are no blocks in the entire county without human structures. It appears that the presence of water is a limiting factor for this species but again, man has likely come to the species aid with the widespread creation of stock ponds for cattle.

Historical occurrence

The Barn Swallow was categorized as "tolerably common" by Belding (1890) and as a "common summer resident ... abundant by early April" by Grinnell and Wythe (1927). Continued construction throughout much of the region has clearly made them even more widespread in the ensuing 75+ years. The Barn Swallow originally nest-

ed in caves but a shift in nest sites in North America is thought to have begun before European settlement and was virtually complete by the middle of the 20th century (Brown and Brown 1999). Since caves are rare things in Contra Costa, the Barn Swallow has unquestionably increased tremendously in numbers, as it has throughout western North America (DeSante and George 1994).

Breeding and natural history

Like other nesting swallows, the Barn Swallow arrives earlier in the season than most songbirds with the first arrival during the atlas recorded 8 March. The first pair was noted as early 12 March, as would be expected as pairs are thought to form upon arrival on the breeding grounds or soon thereafter (Brown and Brown 1999). Adults were noted carrying nest material or nest-building 19 March–3 July. Confirmations based upon occupied nests (contents unknown) were achieved on sixty-four occasions between 29 March and 20 June. Nests with young were detected eight times between 17 March and 30 June. Fledglings were seen nine times between 20 May and 21 June and young were watched being fed six times from 14 May–30 July.

Conservation

Because of its wholesale adaptation to manmade substrates, the future of the Barn Swallow in Contra Costa County appears secure.

CHESTNUT-BACKED CHICKADEE • *Poecile rufescens*

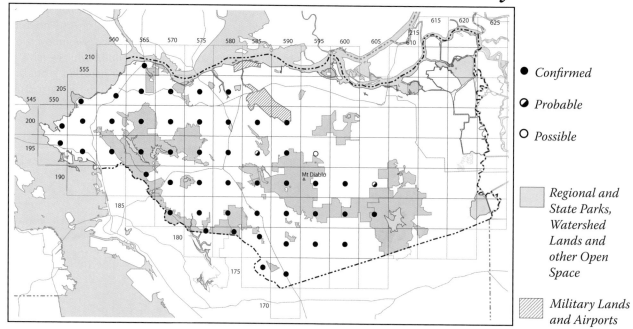

The perky Chestnut-backed Chickadee, now such a welcome presence in natural settings and backyards alike, is a recent émigré to Contra Costa County, having only become established in the last 75 years. In that short amount of time it has come to occupy the suitable habitat in the county.

Current status and distribution

The Chestnut-backed Chickadee is a common and widespread breeder throughout the Berkeley Hills and in moister portions of the Diablo Range. Although less common, the species was also detected in much of the Bay plain around Richmond and throughout the suburban areas of the Interstate 680 corridor. It remains local in some suburban neighborhoods, as around San Ramon, but may well increase as neighborhood vegetation matures. The species was absent from the marshes in the northern portion of the county, urban areas around Pittsburg and Antioch, and from the entirety of East County. Within the Diablo Range it is relegated to moist canyons such as Pine Canyon in Mt. Diablo State Park, Marsh Creek Rd., and along Morgan Territory Rd., appearing to occasionally withdraw from some sites, perhaps in response to drought. The species is completely absent from the grassy foothills south of the mountain.

The Chestnut-backed Chickadee is found throughout woodlands of all types in the Berkeley Hills except for exceptionally dense patches of forest. In the Diablo Range it is found locally in moist coastal oak woodlands of oak, bay, and madrone and along stream courses. It is absent from the open blue oak gray pine woodlands of the Diablo Range, where it may well be outcompeted by the Oak Titmouse. Suburban birds are generally found in association with planted conifers, especially redwoods.

Historical occurrence

As of 1927, the Chestnut-backed Chickadee had been found in the East Bay "once at Berkeley and several times at Hayward (Grinnell and Wythe 1927); the first Contra Costa County record was still well over a decade in the future. Emerson, the discoverer of the initial East Bay record, felt that "they were no doubt common years ago, before the disappearance of the redwoods from the hillsides and canyons" (Emerson 1900). In 1938, Henry W. Carriger discovered a pair of chickadees at a possible nest site near Sunol in southern Alameda County. In 1940, Carriger collected a set of chickadee eggs at Niles, Alameda County, the first nesting confirmation for the East Bay. From there it is believed that the species rather rapidly spread on a northwest course, reaching Redwood Regional Park near Oakland (county unknown) by 1943. Contra Costa County's first breeding record was tallied along Wildcat Creek in Tilden Regional Park in 1945 (Dixon 1954). Expansion into eastern, drier areas was documented at Mt. Diablo State Park 7–8 June 1958, a summery date strongly suggestive of breeding (county notebooks).

The commonly accepted reasoning offered for the explosive range expansion into the East Bay was put forth by Dixon (1954) who asserted that "vegetational discontinuities" in the Santa Clara Valley prior to the arrival of European settlers may have presented an impervious barrier for a mainly sedentary species. He was convinced that it was the widespread planting of fruit and shade trees which allowed the species to make its way across the valley into more hospitable habitats such as the moist forests of the Sunol area.

154

Although the question of whether or not the Chestnut-backed Chickadee formerly roamed the East Bay before the invasion in the late 1930s will likely never be answered, it would appear obvious that it moved seamlessly into an ecological niche intermediate between that of the Bushtit (*Psaltriparus minimus*) and the Oak Titmouse (*Baelophus inornatus*). Root (1964) believed that since each of these three parids already occurred sympatrically elsewhere in the Coast Range of central California, the avifauna "had already evolved the competitive adjustments necessary to accommodate a species of chickadee before rufescens invaded the East Bay area." Hertz and others (1976) further concluded that there was a "fine level of ecological separation even though the three species appear to depend primarily on the same kind of food to rear their young" and that chickadees "show an intermediate niche breadth along almost all components of a foraging site niche axis."

At any rate, when the vanguard of the Chestnut-backed Chickadee invasion reached the East Bay in the late 1930s it met with a flora ideally suited to their needs. As of 2007, it seems likely that the species has come to occupy virtually all suitable habitat in the county as unoccupied eastern areas are likely too arid.

Breeding and natural history

The Chestnut-backed Chickadee was noted carrying nest material or nest building on twelve occasions 15 February–17 April with an additional late report from 14 June. A long-term study at Tilden Park disclosed a mean date for first egg laying of 25 March (Dahlsten and others 2002). Occupied nests (contents unknown) were found five times between 5 April and 17 May; nests with young on another four occasions 5–17 May. Twenty-four records of adults were seen carrying food with dates spanning 12 April through 26 June. Most of these, however, were in April and May; just three were in June. Fledglings were noted on an additional thirty-one occasions 13 April–3 July.

The Chestnut-backed Chickadee renests only rarely if the first nest is successful. At Tilden Park only eight second broods were recorded over a 22-year period (Dahlsten and others 2002). The presence of fledglings in July in Contra Costa County, as well as in Monterey County (Roberson and Tenney 1993), suggests that double brooding may be more common than has been suggested.

Conservation

The Chestnut-backed Chickadee, with its successful colonization of both native woodlands and suburban neighborhoods, would seem to have a secure future.

CHESTNUT-BACKED CHICKADEE

OAK TITMOUSE • *Baeolophus inornatus*

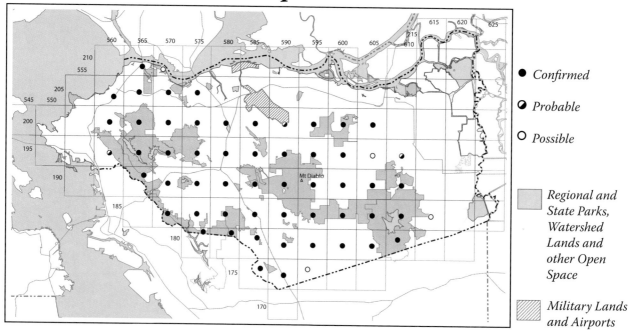

● *Confirmed*

◑ *Probable*

○ *Possible*

▨ *Regional and State Parks, Watershed Lands and other Open Space*

▨ *Military Lands and Airports*

The feisty Oak Titmouse provides the most prominent and tireless voice of the oak woodlands of Contra Costa County. Its vocal repertoire is immense, as commented upon by Dawson (1923): "it's dollars to doughnuts that this very plain bird will give you momentary visions of rare exotics—Troupials and golden Tanagers, and what not—before you acquire the habit of attributing all strange noises to *B. inornatus*."

Current status and distribution

The Oak Titmouse is present throughout the Coast Range though it is decidedly more common in the eastern Berkeley Hills and especially in the Diablo Range where it is one of the most numerous breeding passerines. In the wetter, western portion of the Berkeley Hills, as in Tilden and Redwood Regional Parks, the species tends to be relegated to occasional clumps of sunny woodlands. It is regular, for example, at Jewel Lake in Tilden Park. Just to the east, around San Pablo Res., the habitat opens up dramatically and the titmouse suddenly becomes more common. Elsewhere the species is found in open coastal oak woodlands, blue oak woodlands and Valley oak woodlands throughout the county, including the area around Crockett and Port Costa. In the Diablo Range the Oak Titmouse is quite common in all woodland situations, there being very few situations where the habitat is too shady and dense. Streamside habitats are particularly prized. South of Mt. Diablo it is present in sparse oak savannah and along the few significant streamside thickets. The species remains common to the edge of the Central Valley but is quite scarce on the floor of the valley and is relegated to a few drainages along the western edge

where large valley oaks have been allowed to survive. Smaller numbers occur in residential settings, occasionally even when oaks are lacking.

Historical occurrence

There appear to have been no significant changes in the status of the Oak Titmouse in the past century, though losses due to urbanization have certainly occurred. Such losses have probably been at least partially compensated for by forest fragmentation and they remain quite common.

Breeding and natural history

Oak Titmice form life-long pair bonds (Cicero 2000) and thus the "probable" code was recorded as early in the season as atlasers began fieldwork. The carrying of nest material and actual nest building was recorded on 18 occasions 20 March–30 April with an additional later observation of 23 May. Such late nest building was recorded twice during the Monterey County Atlas Project (1 and 17 June), indicating to the authors either nest replacement or even a second clutch (Roberson and Tenney 1993). Occupied nests (contents unknown) were found seven times between 3 April and 6 June; nest with young were found an additional four times 20 April–22 June. The 22 June record is again suggestive of either nest replacement or a second brood. Adults were recorded carrying food and/or feeding young on 52 occasions between 31 March and 3 July, with the bulk of such activity landing throughout April and the first half of May. Fledglings were tallied 42 times between 2 May and 3 July with an additional early report of 19 April; most were found between early May and the second week of June.

Conservation

Data produced by Breeding Bird Surveys indicate that both the Oak Titmouse and the closely related Juniper Titmouse declined 1.9% per year between 1980 and 1996, leading Audubon's Watchlist 2002 to designate it as a Yellow List Species. The primary culprit is presumed to be the destruction of oak woodland habitats.

PYGMY NUTHATCH

BUSHTIT • *Psaltriparus minimus*

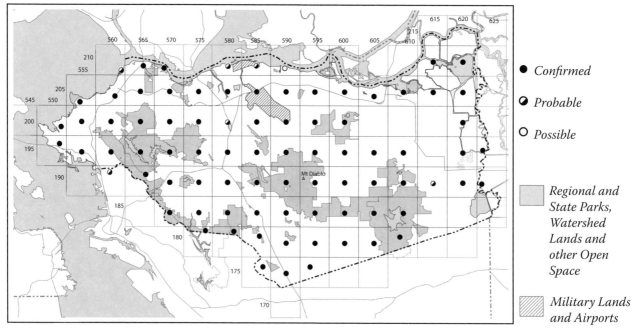

Confirmed

Probable

Possible

Regional and State Parks, Watershed Lands and other Open Space

Military Lands and Airports

The diminutive bushtit is one of the county's most familiar nesting birds and one of the few birds that is almost as common in residential areas as it is in "wilder" settings. What the Bushtit might be perceived to lack in terms of plumage or vocal talents, more than makes up for with the dogged determination required of a bird so small. Anyone who has watched a pair of Bushtits defend their nest against an invading Western Scrub-Jay couldn't have helped but come away impressed.

Current status and distribution

In Contra Costa County the Bushtit occupies virtually every type of habitat other than dense forests, marshlands and open grasslands, resulting in confirmations in a hefty 79 blocks. The only gaps in the atlas map are in East County blocks. The two unoccupied blocks in the southeastern corner of the county are almost solely composed of grassland with small homesteads or windbreaks, their vegetation seemingly insufficient for supporting much other than European Starlings. The situation is much the same in several blocks around Brentwood and east Antioch although it seems inevitable that the newly established neighborhoods in that area will eventually support Bushtits and other development-tolerant species and may well have been overlooked there.

Historical occurrence

The status and distribution of the Bushtit in Contra Costa County has likely changed little, but it has probably increased slightly in both numbers and range with widespread plantings on formerly open grasslands.

Breeding and natural history

Bushtit pairs are said to form in January and early February in Arizona (Sloane 2001). The first pairs noted during the atlas project were 22 February but so little atlasing is done that early in the season that we must have overlooked earlier pairings, particularly when the dates obtained for carrying nest material are considered. Adults noted carrying nest material or nest building were found fifty-two times between 1 February and 30 May. The February date is notably early, as was another report from 10 February. Several late May dates were likely the beginning of a second brood. Occupied nests (contents unknown) were detected on seventeen occasions 10 March-9 May, with additional reports likely pertaining to second broods on 4 and 11 June. Nests with young were found five times between 25 March and 15 July. Adults were noted carrying food twenty-five times between 3 April and 3 July. Fledglings were tallied fifty-six times from 13 April–30 June, although based on obtained dates for adults carrying food dependent young were certainly present significantly later.

Conservation

The future of few passerines in Contra Costa County seems more assured than that of the adaptable Bushtit.

RED-BREASTED NUTHATCH • *Sitta canadensis*

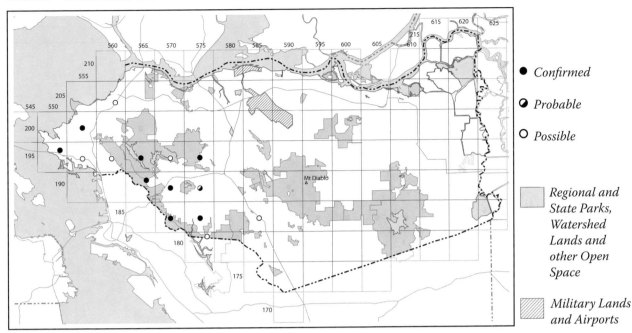

● *Confirmed*

◑ *Probable*

○ *Possible*

▨ *Regional and State Parks, Watershed Lands and other Open Space*

▨ *Military Lands and Airports*

The distinctive nasal "tinhorn" yank of the Red-breasted Nuthatch is a characteristic voice of the coniferous woodlands of the fog-belt, most notably in the introduced stands of Monterey pines that adorn hilltops in the Berkeley Hills.

Current status and distribution

The Red-breasted Nuthatch was confirmed in 7 blocks and may have bred in several more, all in the Berkeley Hills except for two confirmations from the Bay plain around Richmond. A post-atlas pair excavating a nest hole in western San Ramon on 26 Mar 2004 was at an unusually open and arid location. The birds were not noted again at that site (Quail 49: no. 9). The species is not thought to breed east of the Interstate 680 corridor although a report of a pair on Mt. Diablo 21 May was intriguing—and has a precedent (see below)—but breeding was not confirmed.

All known breeding of the Red-breasted Nuthatch in Contra Costa County has been confirmed within the fog-belt of the Berkeley Hills and the Bay plain. Breeding birds nearly always forage and nest in stands of redwoods and introduced Monterey pines.

Historical occurrence

Grinnell and Wythe (1927) were aware of summer records of the "Canada Nuthatch" only from Cazadero, Sonoma County; what was presumably a very late migrant was collected from Pine Canyon, Mt. Diablo 26 May 1925 (MVZ #146313). Grinnell and Miller (1944) cite nesting from Alameda County at Berkeley and Claremont Canyon near Oakland. The latter, considered

the first for the Bay Area, was 15 May 1932 (McCain 1932). The first hint of Contra Costa County nesting was a report of summering at Lafayette in 1967 (AFN 21: no. 5) but it is unclear when the first nesting confirmation occurred.

Breeding and natural history

It is unclear if local Red-breasted Nuthatches are paired for life but atlasers documented pairs as early as fieldwork began. Northern breeding Red-breasted Nuthatches reach the county each fall and winter (although the extent of these "invasions" varies widely from year to year) so single birds present in early spring were considered wintering birds and removed from the map. The atlas database contains only nine confirmations: nest building was recorded three times between 5 April and 5 May; occupied nests (contents unknown) were found 19 April and 8 June; an adult removing a fecal sac from the nest was detected 3 May; adults feeding young were seen 8 and 13 June; and finally a fledgling was recorded 18 June.

Conservation

The long-term future of the Red-breasted Nuthatch as a breeding bird in Contra Costa County is largely dependent upon the health of the county's stands of introduced Monterey pines.

WHITE-BREASTED NUTHATCH • *Sitta carolinensis*

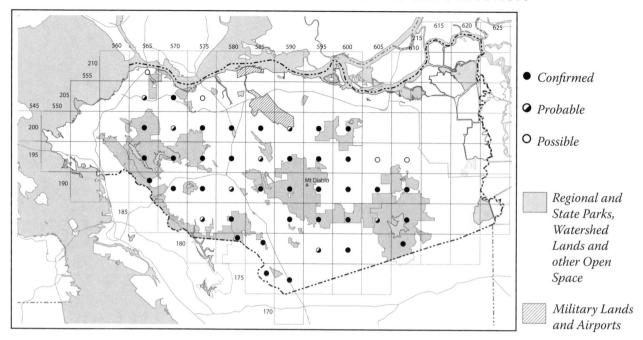

Confirmed
Probable
Possible

Regional and State Parks, Watershed Lands and other Open Space

Military Lands and Airports

The acrobatic White-breasted Nuthatch is one of the quintessential birds of the oak woodlands that dominate the less-developed portions of Contra Costa County. Of our three nesting nuthatches it is the only one that can be called common or widespread.

Current status and distribution

The distribution of the White-breasted Nuthatch only slightly overlaps that of the Red-breasted and Pygmy Nuthatches as it strongly prefers the drier, more open woodlands that only begin to occur around the eastern edge of Tilden and Redwood Regional Parks and become most highly developed in the Diablo Range. Although the species is fairly common most everywhere in the Diablo Range that isn't covered with chaparral, it appears to be most frequent in the valley oak and blue oak woodlands between Mt. Diablo itself and the western edge of the Central Valley. There remains a tiny population on the western edge of the valley floor at Brentwood where large oaks have been allowed to remain, most notably along Marsh Creek, but are otherwise absent from the Central Valley portion of the county. The species is present only in the oldest neighborhoods where oaks have been spared.

Historical occurrence

The sparse data published in the local literature suggests that the status and distribution of the White-breasted Nuthatch has changed very little, if at all, since 29 Apr 1899 when the first known nesting confirmation for the county occurred (MVZ #6414).

Breeding and natural history

The White-breasted Nuthatch seems to mate for life and maintains permanent territories (Grubb and Pravosudov 2008) and thus, pairs were noted as early as atlasers initiated fieldwork. Adults carrying nest material were detected on five occasions between 19 March and 24 April. Five records of occupied nests (contents unknown) ranged from 9 March–9 May and a single nest with young was recorded 15 June. Sixteen records of adults carrying food were observed between 11 April and 12 June. Fledglings, some being fed by adults, were tallied twenty-two times between 20 April and 11 July.

Conservation

Despite some possible local losses due to habitat destruction, most recently in the oak savannah south of Antioch, parks or watersheds protect the bulk of suitable nuthatch habitat in the county so the future of the White-breasted Nuthatch appears secure.

PYGMY NUTHATCH • *Sitta pygmaea*

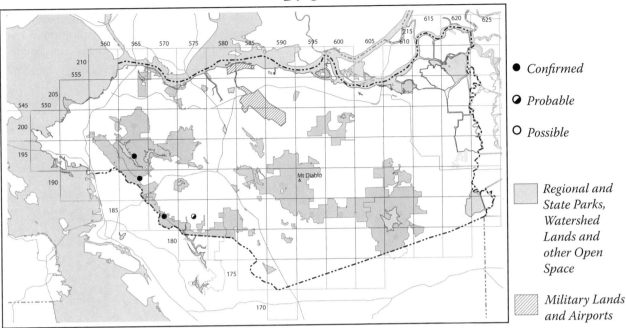

Confirmed

Probable

Possible

Regional and State Parks, Watershed Lands and other Open Space

Military Lands and Airports

The insistent pipping calls of the Pygmy Nuthatch have only recently been heard in Contra Costa County. Although this nuthatch is primarily sedentary, it has, on very rare occasions, been detected at unusual locations slightly out-of-range and it must have been vagrants such as these that first colonized the East Bay.

Current status and distribution

Few of Contra Costa County's breeding birds have a more restricted breeding range than that of the Pygmy Nuthatch and none have more exacting habitat requirements. The species entire range in the county consists of a narrow, vertical strip extending from Tilden Park in the north to Redwood Regional Park in the south, a distance of probably less than 10 miles. Several spots along these western ridges host open stands of introduced Monterey pine and it is in these trees, and apparently nowhere else, that the species builds its nests.

Historical occurrence

Grinnell and Wythe (1927) knew the Pygmy Nuthatch only from Marin and Sonoma counties but the first East Bay record was at Berkeley, Alameda County about 1900. The first Contra Costa record was just north of Berkeley 6 Aug–8 Sept 1935. Not surprisingly, the birds were in Monterey pines (Grinnell and Miller 1944). In 1957 three to four individuals were noted at St. Mary's College near Moraga, still the easternmost record for the county (county notebooks). The first county nest record finally came in 1986 at Redwood Regional Park (AB 40: no. 3).

Breeding and natural history

The Pygmy Nuthatch was found in only four blocks with confirmed breeding in three of them. Adults excavating nests were recorded 21 April and 1 May. The Monterey County atlas team found an occupied nest on 12 March (Roberson and Tenney 1993); in nearby San Mateo County, nest excavation was detected as early as 21 March (Sequoia Audubon Society 2001). An occupied nest was found 24 May and a nest with young was detected 15 May. An adult carrying food was found 13 June. Although the Pygmy Nuthatch is known to double-brood the atlas obtained no evidence of this.

Conservation

The future of the Pygmy Nuthatch in Contra Costa County is anything but secure as the species is bound to a single type of introduced tree within a limited range.

BROWN CREEPER • *Certhia americana*

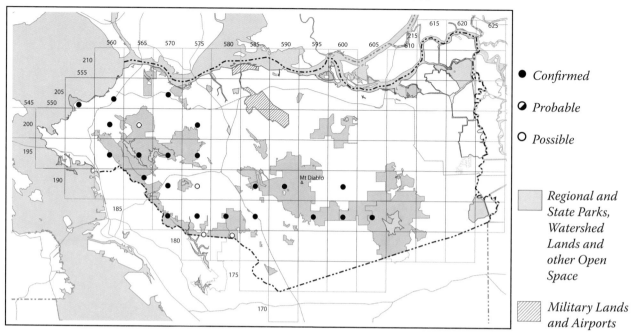

Confirmed

Probable

Possible

Regional and State Parks, Watershed Lands and other Open Space

Military Lands and Airports

The Brown Creeper is a fairly common permanent resident of shady woodlands throughout much of the county, but its bark-mimicking plumage and high-pitched vocalizations often cause it to be overlooked, particularly by those who have lost the upper range of their hearing.

Current status and distribution

The Brown Creeper was confirmed nesting in 21 atlas blocks and was "possible" in four others, providing a fine outline of the range of moist, shaded forests and woodlands in Contra Costa County. Because of the species' sedentary nature it probably bred in all 25 blocks. It is most commonly encountered in the fog-belt of the Berkeley Hills but is notably scarce in the wooded hills around Crockett and Port Costa. In the Diablo Range, suitable habitat is relegated to shady coastal oak woodlands in canyons on the western and southern flank of Mt. Diablo and eastward to Morgan Territory and Marsh Creek roads. The only known breeding station along the Bay plain was in the eucalyptus forest at Pt. Pinole Regional Shoreline. Many areas on Mt. Diablo's eastern flank, as well as the area encompassing Black Diamond Mines, lack suitable habitat. The Brown Creeper was completely absent from the suburban center of the county and from the Central Valley portion of the county.

The Brown Creeper nests and forages in forests and groves of redwood and Monterey pines, shady riparian stands and coastal oak woodlands, particularly when California bay is present. Eucalyptus stands are also used locally. Sunny, open woodlands are inevitably shunned.

Historical occurrence

The Brown Creeper was first noted in the East Bay in 1890 by W. O. Emerson (Emerson 1900). The species was first noted nesting at U. C. Berkeley (near the Greek Theater) in 1918, and thought not to have nested there "until the habitat was altered by man" (Storer 1926). It is unclear when the first Contra Costa breeding record was obtained.

Breeding and natural history

Grinnell and Linsdale (1936) reported that pairs in coastal Monterey County seemed to be formed even during winter. Probably because atlas data is meager early in the season, our first recorded pair was not until 3 March. Adults were noted carrying nest material or nest building eight times between 17 March and 13 June. Second broods are undocumented (Hejl and others 2002) so later dates likely indicate a renesting. Similar late breeding evidence was detected in Monterey County (Roberson and Tenney 1993). An occupied nest with unknown contents was detected 18 April; two nests known to contain young were found 23 April and 2 June. An additional record of an adult exiting a nest with a fecal sac was obtained 6 May. Twelve confirmations based upon adults carrying food were obtained between 8 May and 17 June. Fledglings, some noted being fed by adults, were found on eleven occasions between 5 May and 28 July, the latter dates again suggestive of renesting.

Conservation

There doesn't appear to be any significant threats to Brown Creeper populations in Contra Costa County.

ROCK WREN • *Salpinctes obsoletus*

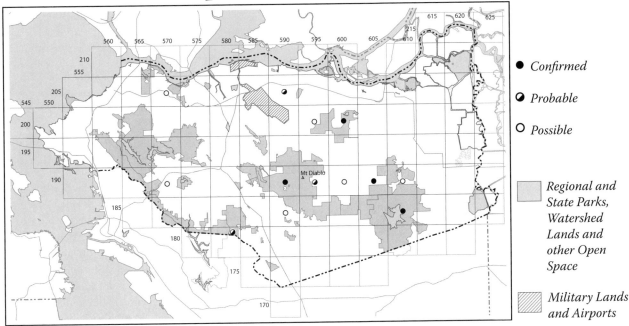

● *Confirmed*

◑ *Probable*

○ *Possible*

▨ *Regional and State Parks, Watershed Lands and other Open Space*

▨ *Military Lands and Airports*

Like the other four wrens found in Contra Costa County, the Rock Wren is cloaked in muted brown tones. Its preference for the most unadorned of habitats and a decided lack of musical ability make it unique amongst local wrens. This solitary permanent resident is found locally in the Coast Range but only as a rare migrant or wintering bird in West and East County.

Current status and distribution

The Rock Wren is uncommon and localized in the wetter Berkeley Hills where most of the hilltops are wooded but manages to occur sparingly in places such as Sibley Regional Preserve and Briones Regional Park. East of Interstate 680 in the Diablo Range it remains somewhat local, but as open rocky habitats increase so does the number of wrens. The species appears to be particularly common in the eastern extremes of the Diablo Range where treeless hillsides are the rule rather than the exception.

The Rock Wren is present on sunny, grassy hillsides and ridges with a complement of broken rocks, wherever such situations occur in the Coast Range. These rocks, as well as any convenient holes in the ground, provide both nooks and crannies that the species is able to exploit with its probing bill, and in which to nest. On occasion, such as around the "Wind Caves" at Las Trampas Regional Park, the Rock Wren is found on large rocky monoliths but such habitats are rare in the county. The Rock Wren almost inevitably shuns shady canyon bottoms, no matter how rocky they might be.

Historical occurrence

Grinnell and Wythe (1927) considered the Rock Wren to be a sparse resident of the Bay Area but do not cite Contra Costa County specifically. However, Palmer (1921) describes the species as frequent on the hillsides east of the Greek Theater (Berkeley, Alameda County) from 1883–1889. This would either have been in Contra Costa or within a stone's throw. It appears safe to assume that the species was long present, at least in the Diablo Range.

Breeding and natural history

The lone instance of nest building recorded during the atlas was 2 April. An adult was noted carrying food 21 June. An adult feeding a fledgling 20 July is strongly suggestive of double brooding. Fledglings were noted three times between 27 May–7 June. The explanation for this low number of breeding confirmations probably lies in the Rock Wrens choice of typically inaccessible nest sites.

Conservation

It is truly fortunate that Rock Wrens are so partial to the sunny, rocky ridgelines of the county, as it is the lower slopes that tend to suffer the most from human development. Much of these habitats are protected within watersheds and parklands, suggesting the species may have a long-term future here.

CANYON WREN • *Catherpes mexicanus*

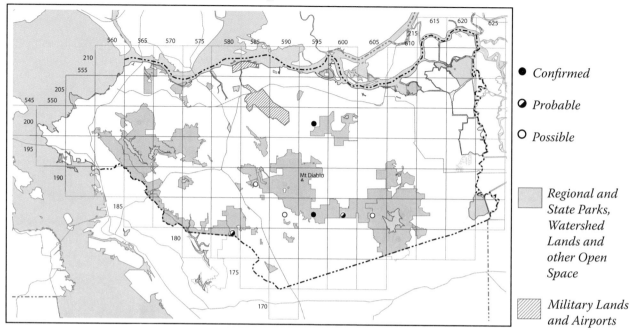

Confirmed

Probable

Possible

Regional and State Parks, Watershed Lands and other Open Space

Military Lands and Airports

The Canyon Wren is a spectacular bird. With a demure, yet dapper, plumage and a voice that is the avian equivalent of Caruso, the Canyon Wren inhabits the wildest, most inaccessible habitats of the Diablo Range. Although the atlas turned up birds from previously unknown locations, its habitat needs dictate that it will remain one of the county's rarest breeding songbirds.

Current status and distribution

The Canyon Wren prefers cliff faces and boulder-strewn river bottoms, a scarce situation in Contra Costa County. Although it will occasionally forage in chaparral and at the base of trees, this is coincidental; their ironclad tie to boulders and cliff faces is noteworthy for it is one of our few breeding species not associated with any plant community. These strict habitat needs dictate the species to be completely absent from West and East Counties and the entire northern shoreline area. In the Berkeley Hills it was only recorded from the "Wind Caves" area at Las Trampas Regional Park west of Danville, and even that bird was felt to be unmated. All other records are from the Diablo Range, but even there the species is extremely local. At Morgan Territory Regional Preserve, just southeast of Mt. Diablo, there may be but a single pair on a steep cliff face visible from Morgan Territory Rd. Several pairs (at most) were present during the atlas project at Black Diamond Mines Regional Park, just northeast of Mt. Diablo, particularly around the Nortonville portion of the park. Most of the county's breeding pairs reside on Mt. Diablo itself, usually in shady, rocky gullies and canyon bottoms. Representative localities include Castle Rock, the mouth of Riggs Canyon and Sycamore Canyon.

Historical occurrence

Belding (1890) states that W. E. Bryant had seen a pair at Mt. Diablo but doesn't cite a date. The species was apparently not seen again in the county until a spate of sightings from Mt. Diablo between 1950 and 1952 (Gull). Another gap ensued and the Canyon Wren wasn't detected again on the mountain until Kevin Hintsa found one in Pine Canyon 14–27 Sept 1988 (AB 42: no. 1). Nesting was finally confirmed there 26 June 1991 when three fledglings were seen (AB 45: no. 5).

Breeding and natural history

The Canyon Wren was detected in 6 blocks but confirmed in just 2: an adult was seen carrying food in the Nortonville side of Black Diamond Mines Regional Park 15 June 2002 and a fledgling was noted near Knobcone Pt., Mt Diablo State Park 2002. The other twelve records accumulated during the atlas were all singing males. Because of its strongly sedentary nature, it might be assumed that this wren bred in at least most of the blocks in which it was recorded (but see the Las Trampas record listed above).

Bent (1948) cites 68 egg sets from California, with dates spanning 28 March to 11 July; San Diego County data is in general agreement (Unitt 2004). Monterey County atlasers found a nest with young as early as 20 May (Roberson and Tenney 1993).

The Canyon Wren is usually considered to be extremely sedentary, but wintering birds are occasionally found out of range, as at Tilden Park 30 Dec 1963 (AFN 17: no. 3) and 3 Jan 1971 (Gull 53:12).

Conservation

The Canyon Wren, because of strict habitat needs, is an extremely rare breeder in Contra Costa County and it is doubtful that there are more than twenty to twenty-five breeding pairs in the entire county. It is fortunate, however, that all known breeding stations exist in protected parklands.

CANYON WREN

BEWICK'S WREN • *Thryomanes bewickii*

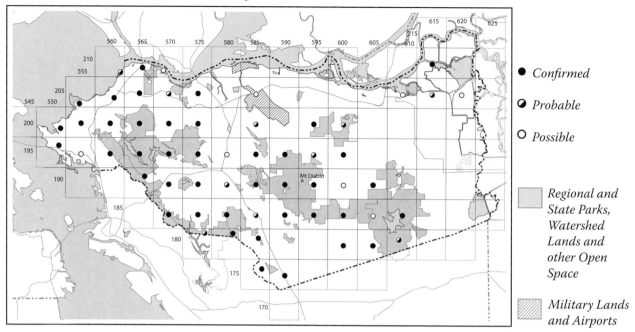

No bird more deserves the protection of man than Bewick's Wren. He does not need man's encouragement, for he comes of his own accord and installs himself as a member of the community, wherever it suits his taste. He is found about the cowshed and barn along with the Pewee and Barn Swallow; he investigates the pig-sty; then explores the garden fence, and finally mounts to the roof and pours forth one of the sweetest songs that ever was heard.   ❧ *Ridgeway*

Current status and distribution

The Bewick's Wren is a common, noisy resident of woodlands and chaparral throughout much of the county, particularly in the Coast Range where it is present in every block. The species was confirmed in 41 blocks and, due to its sedentary nature, more than likely bred in each block in which it was detected. Throughout the Berkeley Hills and the Diablo Range it is found in virtually every type of woodland featuring a shrubby understory, stands of chamise and mixed chaparral, on hillsides of coastal scrub, particularly in coyote brush, and in riparian settings. This acceptance of disturbed stands of coyote brush has allowed it to maintain a presence around Richmond. The Bewick's Wren is most common in the extensive mixed chaparral stands of the Diablo Range where it often seems to be the most abundant breeding species. The Bewick's Wren went undetected in some suburban blocks around Concord, San Ramon, Antioch and Pittsburg (although it may have been present somewhere in those blocks), as well as in most of the Central Valley portion of the county.

Historical Occurrence

Such a common bird as the Bewick's Wren rarely rates mention in local sightings columns but it appears likely that little about the status and distribution of the Bewick's Wren has changed in the past century. The avifauna of East County, however, received almost no attention from early fieldworkers, and it is possible that the species was more widespread there than at present.

Breeding and natural history

California's non-migratory populations regularly form pair bonds in March (Miller 1941) and this seems to be the case locally. Adults carrying nest material or building nests—insufficient for breeding confirmation for this species—were recorded eight times between 10 March and 28 June, suggesting double broods. Occupied nests (contents unknown) were noted four times 28 April–21 June; nests with young were discovered 23 May and 5 July. Adults carrying food or feeding young were tallied on thirty-one occasions 20 April–22 July. Fledglings were recorded twenty times between 9 May and 11 July. A nest with eggs was collected at Kensington, Alameda County on the late date of 15 July (MVZ #13120), hinting that the atlas may have missed late summer breeding evidence by ending the season too early.

Conservation

The clearing of shrubby understory, particularly in urban settings, has likely caused some modest declines but otherwise there appear to be no serious threats to the local population.

HOUSE WREN • *Troglodytes aedon*

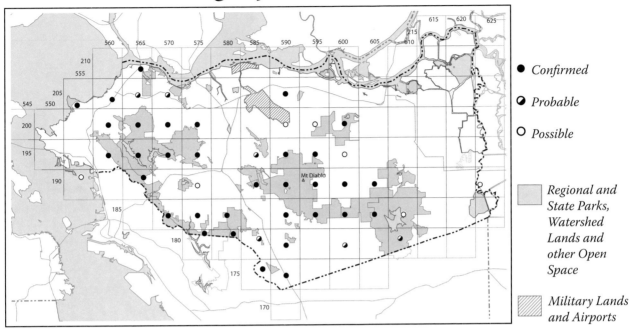

Similar in appearance to the resident Bewick's Wren, the House Wren differs in several notable aspects: Its vocal repertoire is far less diverse, its habitat needs far more specific, and, since the species is a neotropical migrant, its time with us is mostly limited to the spring and summer months.

Current status and distribution

The House Wren is a common, conspicuous summer resident of the Coast Range, particularly in the more arid interior. The species was confirmed in 33 blocks and probably bred in most of the other blocks in which it was recorded. It was absent from the marshlands of the northern portions of the county as well as from the suburban areas along the Interstate 680 corridor. In the Central Valley, where it winters routinely in significant numbers, it was detected in several blocks as late as mid-May but all had seemingly departed by June and all reports are now assumed to pertain to migrants. The species did formerly breed at Piper Slough on Bethel Island but the latest it was recorded there during the atlas project was 22 May.

Despite a slight amount of overlap, the habitat needs of House and Bewick's wrens differ markedly. The House Wren is a bird of open areas and thus shuns dense forests and chaparral stands. The species is most often found in Contra Costa County in riparian thickets or open oak woodlands, sometimes with a shrubby but sparse ground cover but often with virtually no understory whatsoever. The species is a cavity nester, usually opting for cavities in trees—sycamores seem particularly prized—but will utilize nest boxes when provided. Although its name

suggests an affinity for human settlements, and they are indeed often found around homesteads in the east, local House Wrens strongly prefer native habitats.

Historical occurrence

Nothing in the literature suggests that the status and distribution of the House Wren has changed significantly in historical times although there surely was some loss of habitat when the Interstate 680 corridor was converted to suburbs.

Breeding and Natural History

Breeding House Wrens arrive early in Northern California and were detected during the atlas project as early as 11 March. The earliest pair was noted 1 April, although they doubtless occurred earlier. Male House Wrens are famed for building "dummy" nests and thus this was not considered a confirmation of breeding. The carrying of nest material or actual nest building was detected a surprisingly low seven times between 28 April and 29 May. These dates are obviously not representative of House Wren breeding as an already occupied nest was found 10 April. Six other occupied nests were located as late as 12 June. Seven nests with young were tallied 14 May–3 July. Adults carrying food were found on twenty-eight occasions between 9 May and 4 July. Fledglings were recorded nine times 23 May–2 July. The July sightings are strongly suggestive of double broods.

Conservation

Local losses of habitat have certainly occurred, particularly in riparian settings, but local House Wren populations appear quite healthy.

167

WINTER WREN • *Troglodytes troglodytes*

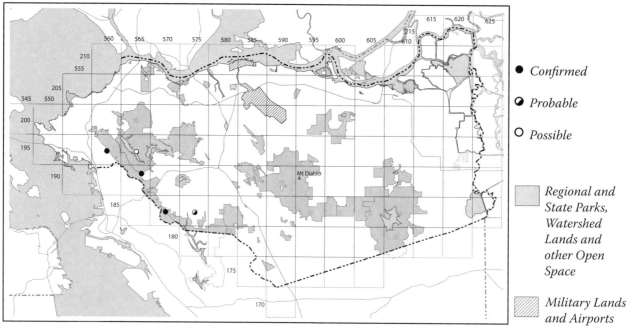

Confirmed
Probable
Possible

Regional and State Parks, Watershed Lands and other Open Space

Military Lands and Airports

The bubbly little Winter Wren and its song that never seems to end is a scarce commodity in Contra Costa County, having invaded only recently and with little chance of becoming more common.

Current status and distribution

The Winter Wren, like the redwood, is a member of the humid, coastal forest and, like the redwood, is present only locally in Contra Costa County. Each of the county's known breeding Winter Wrens are present in the western Berkeley hills, from Tilden Park south to Redwood Regional Park and including Pinehurst Rd. to the east, a total of only five blocks. In truth, suitable habitat exists nowhere else in the county.

Preferred haunts include shady, moist montane riparian woodlands and the floor of redwood forests featuring sparse shrubbery, ferns and fallen logs. Occasionally, such as around Jewel Lake and Inspiration Point at Tilden Park, the species inhabits the floor of densely forested hillsides with a dense, riotous undergrowth of blackberry, thimbleberry and poison oak.

Historical occurrence

Grinnell and Wythe (1927) were unaware of any Winter Wrens breeding in the Bay Area away from the immediate coast and there appears to be no suggestion of East Bay nesting until the 1990s other than the categorization of the species as assumed nesting (Erickson 1989). The first Contra Costa County nesting confirmation was from the Stream Trail in Redwood Regional Park 24 June 1992 (pers. obs.). Although it is tempting to think that little Troglodytes was present and breeding all along, the Berkeley hills have been well explored, even during the first half of the 20th century, by naturalists unlikely to overlook the species and its distinctive vocalizations.

Breeding and natural history

Our three breeding confirmations consist of an adult carrying food 6 May, a fledgling on 18 May and an adult carrying a fecal sac from the nest on 2 June. In San Mateo County, nest-building was detected as early as 11 April and a nest with eggs was found 23 April. Fledgling detections there ranged from 21 May–21 July (Sequoia Audubon Society 2001). Food carrying by adults was confirmed in Humboldt County, northwestern California, between 12 May and 20 July (Hunter and others 2005).

Small numbers of Winter Wrens assumed to derive from northern populations are detected in Contra Costa County during migration and in winter but our tiny breeding population is presumed to be sedentary.

Conservation

It is fortunate indeed that the entirety of Contra Costa County's small population of Winter Wrens reside in acreage protected by either the East Bay Regional Parks District or the East Bay Municipal Utility District.

MARSH WREN • *Cistothorus palustris*

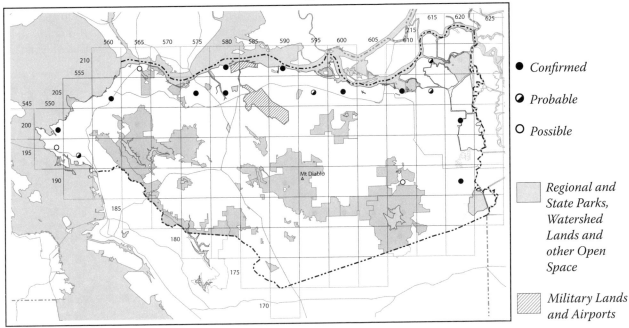

Confirmed

Probable

Possible

Regional and State Parks, Watershed Lands and other Open Space

Military Lands and Airports

Next after the frogs, the Tule Wrens are the noisiest choristers of all sunlit February swamps. One hesitates to call the medley of clicking, buzzing, and sputtering which welters in the reeds, music; but if one succeeds in catching sight of a Tule Wren, holding on for dear life to a cat-tail stem, and vibrating like a drill-chuck with the effort of his impassioned utterance, he feels sure that music is at least intended. 🐦 *William Leon Dawson (1923)*

Current status and distribution

Breeding Marsh Wrens are present patchily, although locally quite commonly, around the western, northern and eastern fringe of the county and are most common in the extensive marshes along the northern fringe of the county from Martinez eastward. The species is completely absent from the interior of the county during the summer months, although breeding has been suspected at Marsh Creek Res. in the past.

The Marsh Wren seems to require standing water and tall, dense marsh vegetation for nesting. In Marin County, nesting Marsh Wrens apparently prefer stands of cattails and tules, usually avoiding bulrush (Shuford 1993).

Historical occurrence

The overall distribution of the Marsh Wren has likely changed little, although significant losses of suitable habitat have occurred throughout the past century and a half. The first confirmed nesting in the county wasn't reported until a nest was collected from Giant, near Pinole, 26 Feb 1938 (MVZ #3348).

Breeding and natural history

Male Marsh Wrens build "dummy" nests to attract females, thus relegating the "carrying nest material" and nest building codes to probable status. Perhaps atlasers were made too aware of this fact, as there are no records of either in the atlas database. Occupied nests (contents unknown) were recorded 4 and 10 June; nests with young were found three times between 13 May and 11 August, indicating double brooding. An adult carrying food was noted 12 May. Fledglings were found six times between 2 June and 4 July. There is a nest at the MVZ taken near Pinole 26 Feb 1938 (#3348). Data from the San Mateo atlas (Sequoia Audubon Society 2001) suggests a more prolonged breeding season. There a nest with young was found as early as 26 April and an adult feeding young was detected as late as 26 August.

Conservation

Marsh Wren populations have undoubtedly suffered greatly from severe habitat destruction, both in bayside and inland freshwater marshes. Healthy populations in the future depend upon the protection of the remaining marshes and tolerance of emergent growth around sewage and other ponds.

BLUE-GRAY GNATCATCHER • *Polioptila caerulea*

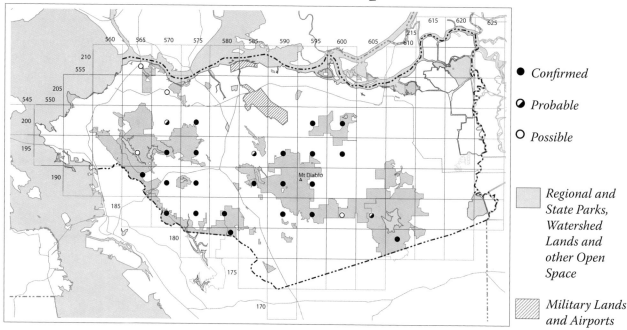

Confirmed

Probable

Possible

Regional and State Parks, Watershed Lands and other Open Space

Military Lands and Airports

The fussy, feisty Blue-gray Gnatcatcher seems to be in perpetual motion, flitting through the oaks and scrub as if there isn't enough time in the day to snatch insects, feed young and protect the nest from the goliath scrub-jay.

Current status and distribution

The Blue-gray Gnatcatcher is exclusively found in the Coast Range, particularly in the arid Diablo Range. The species is typically at the edge of fairly dense woodlands adjacent to chaparral or forest openings with a brushy component. In true chaparral stands it generally shuns pure stands of low-growing vegetation, instead occupying areas of mixed chaparral interspersed with taller shrubs or trees such as manzanita or oak. It is quite abundant on the arid, eastern slope of Mt. Diablo where oak stands are shady but never extensive and where there is a conspicuous amount of low growing shrubs.

Historical occurrence

The status of the Blue-gray Gnatcatcher in Contra Costa County seems little changed since 1927 when the *Directory to the Bird-life of the San Francisco Bay Area* was published, although the first actual confirmation of breeding in the county wasn't until 27 Apr 1940, when eggs were collected from a nest on Mt. Diablo (WFVZ #69045). The only significant published note since that time gives the impression that its population in the East Bay's "hard" chaparral exploded in the five years between 1980–85 (AB 39: no. 3).

Breeding and natural history

The Blue-gray Gnatcatcher arrives early in spring in Contra Costa County, with records of non-wintering birds as early as 4 March. The earliest date recorded during the atlas project was 23 March but earlier birds were likely missed because most atlasing didn't commence until April. The 23 March record was of a pair, not surprising since the species often pairs within 24 hours of reaching the breeding grounds (Ellison 1992). Adults were observed carrying nest material or nest building on seven occasions between 20 April and 19 June. Adults toting food and feeding young were recorded thirteen times between 11 May and 5 August. Fledglings were found six times from 11 June–29 July. Second-broods have been recorded in central California (Root 1969) and, based upon records of fledglings into August, must have occurred here.

Conservation

With the vast majority of gnatcatcher habitat on rugged hillsides and within protected parklands or watersheds, there appears to be little need for concern for its future in the county.

WESTERN BLUEBIRD • *Sialia mexicana*

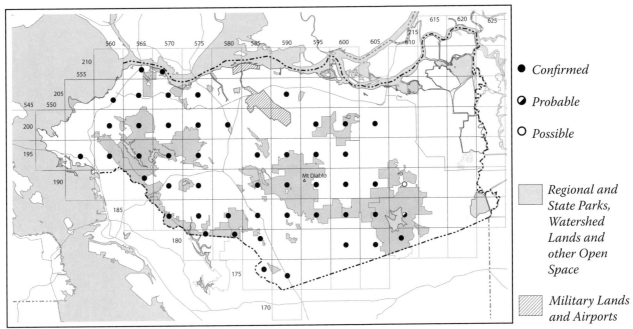

Confirmed

Probable

Possible

Regional and State Parks, Watershed Lands and other Open Space

Military Lands and Airports

Despite the conspicuous absence of anything resembling a true song, the Western Bluebird has long been a favorite of local birdwatchers. In recent years, fervent supporters have planted numerous nest boxes throughout the Coast Range in hopes of boosting the bluebird population.

Current status and distribution

The Western Bluebird is a conspicuous component of open blue oak and valley oak woodlands throughout the Coast Range, and also inhabits grasslands near the openings of forests and coastal oak woodlands. Because the forests of the Berkeley Hills tend to be more uniformly continuous, the bluebird tends to be less common in the western, moister areas, but quickly becomes common just to the east, as around Briones Regional Park. The species is more common still in the Diablo Range where oak savannah woodlands occur frequently and extensively. The bluebirds shun the Bay plain around Richmond, the river plain at Pittsburg and Antioch, the entirety of East County, and the treeless prairies of the Altamont Pass area. The Western Bluebird can be found locally around "ranchette" housing, particularly in the Orinda/Lafayette area but is absent from true urban and suburban areas, hence the gaps in the map along the Interstate 680 corridor.

Historical Occurrence

The historical status of the Western Bluebird is muddled but it seems likely that little has changed in the past century with the exception of local declines due to habitat loss. Grinnell and Wythe (1927) state that bluebirds nested in the oak belt around Walnut Creek and, exceptionally, at Berkeley and Hayward, Alameda County. A set of eggs taken at Moraga Valley 25 May 1925 is at the MVZ (#13404). Nesting in a pasture in the lowlands of Berkeley as recently as 1924 (Clabaugh 1924) suggests the possibility that nesting could have once occurred on the Bay plain at Richmond but we will likely never know for sure.

Breeding and natural history

Adult Western Bluebirds visiting probable nest sites were detected as early as 17 February during the atlas project. Adults carrying nest material or nest building were recorded on eleven occasions between 31 March and 13 May. Occupied nests (contents unknown) were found fourteen times from 27 March–22 June. Nests with young were tallied on ten occasions 2 May–12 August. Adults carrying food were recorded twenty-four times between 16 April and 8 June. Fifty reports of fledglings, half of them involving birds being fed by adults, were found 29 April–1 August.

Conservation

Local declines have been noted within the range of the Western Bluebird, the suspected culprits being the removal of dead and dying trees, changing agricultural practices, and competition from European Starlings and even House Sparrows. In Contra Costa County, however, populations appear stable. Losses incurred have likely been compensated for by the opening of suitable habitats through forest fragmentation and by the widespread placement of artificial nest boxes.

Swainson's Thrush • *Catharus ustulatus*

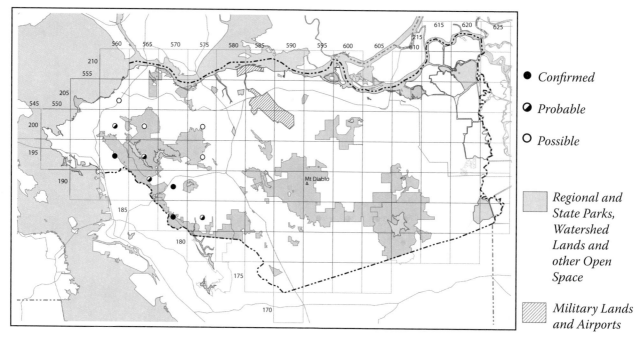

Confirmed

Probable

Possible

Regional and State Parks, Watershed Lands and other Open Space

Military Lands and Airports

The almost other worldly, flute-like song of the Swainson's Thrush is a haunting summer presence in the tangled stream bottoms of the Berkeley Hills.

Current status and distribution

The true status of the Swainson's Thrush in Contra Costa County is muddied by its close similarity to the Hermit Thrush and its tendency to migrate through the county as late as the first week of June. Although true breeding birds usually arrive in late April to early May, northbound migrants continue to course through for several more weeks, the result being many records of "possibles" in areas where the species isn't known to nest. Many such sightings have been culled from the atlas database, leaving behind what is thought to be an accurate representation of the current nesting range of the Swainson's Thrush. This range, like that of other species such as Red-breasted Nuthatch and Winter Wren, is confined to the moistest forests of the western Berkeley Hills.

The haunts of the Swainson's Thrush inevitably include dense tangles of vegetation in shady forests and woodlands, nearly always along streams but also up hillsides if suitable ground-cover exists. Such situations are inevitably in fog-prone areas, where dense undergrowth is promoted. Grinnell and Miller (1944) state that the species nested in lowland orchards but this has never been proven to be the case locally and, in any event, there are very few, if any, orchards remaining within its current range in the county.

Historical occurrence

Grinnell and Wythe (1927) didn't specifically site nesting in Contra Costa County, but they did state that the species was abundant wherever suitable habitat existed in the Bay Area, including Berkeley, and thus breeding throughout the 20th century is assumed. Nesting had been confirmed prior to 1927, however. Eggs were collected from Moraga Valley 1 June 1889 (MFVZ #131314).

Breeding and natural history

Most of the Swainson's Thrush database consists of possible breeding based upon the presence of singing males (the earliest being 24 April) and probable breeding based upon males singing from the same location at least seven days apart. The lone confirmations obtained during the atlas project involved an adult carrying food on 22 June and an adult feeding young on 3 July. Published atlases from other northern California counties confirm the difficulty of finding confirming evidence of Swainson's Thrush breeding—nests, in fact, have proven almost impossible to find. The Monterey County atlas detected adults carrying nest material between 3 and 16 May, and fledglings 23 June through 3 August, suggesting that the local breeding season extends later than our meager data might suggest (Roberson and Tenney 1993).

A report of an adult carrying food on Mt. Diablo on 10 May 1999 has been discounted because there have never been any other indications of nesting in the Contra Costa County portion of the Diablo Range and because the date would be extremely early for food carrying.

Conservation

Swainson's Thrush populations are apparently declining throughout its range, including an ominous disappearance from Yosemite Valley (Beedy and Granholm 1985). Of published northern California atlas projects, only Napa (Napa-Solano Audubon Society 2003) noted serious population declines. Pacific populations have likely suffered from the destruction of riparian habitats and grazing (Evans and Yong 2000).

WESTERN BLUEBIRD

HERMIT THRUSH • *Catharus guttatus*

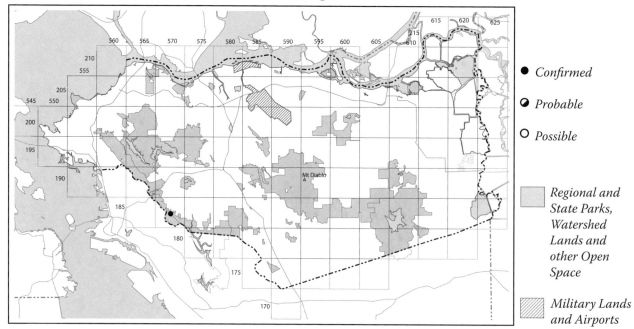

- ● *Confirmed*
- ◗ *Probable*
- ○ *Possible*

▢ *Regional and State Parks, Watershed Lands and other Open Space*

▨ *Military Lands and Airports*

The song of the Hermit Thrush is a thing apart. It is sacred music, not secular. Having nothing of the dash and abandon of Wren or Ouzel, least of all the sportive mockery of the Western Chat, it is the pure offering of a shriven soul holding acceptable converse with high heaven.

> ❧ *William Leon Dawson (1923)*

Current status and distribution

None of Contra Costa County's breeding passerines has a more restricted range than does the Hermit Thrush. Found in just a single block, and not even suspected to occur in any others, the total population can hardly be more than a handful of pairs. All known pairs reside on the moist, shaded eastern slopes of Redwood Peak in Redwood Regional Park, with additional pairs breeding in Alameda County just to the south.

The habitat where these few birds breed consists primarily of redwoods which form a dense canopy, and a sparse, widely spaced undergrowth primarily composed of huckleberry—dense understories are unsuitable for nesting Hermits. This population's breeding sites are directly adjacent to numerous Swainson's Thrush territories that are along Redwood Creek.

Historical occurrence

Grinnell and Wythe (1927) were unaware of any East Bay nesting of the "Monterey" Hermit Thrush. The first summer records of the Hermit Thrush in the East Bay were in July of 1937 when Leroy Jensen discovered singing birds at the exact site at which nesting currently occurs. Attempts at confirming nesting were unsuccessful in the ensuing few years but finally, on 1 June

1941, Milton Seibert found a nest with three young in a California huckleberry, just inside Contra Costa County (Seibert 1942). The next summer records for the area didn't follow until 4 July 1956 when three singing males were detected in the same area (AFN 10: no. 5). It would be another 41 years before this area was rechecked with the specific hope of finding this species. On 12 July 1997 an adult was seen feeding a fledgling in Alameda County, just south of the county line with an additional 15+ singing males detected, a few of which were in Contra Costa County (pers. obs.).

Breeding and natural history

Because the atlas database includes just a single record of Hermit Thrush, it is impossible to state much about its local breeding chronology. The atlas record was an adult nest building on 12 May 1998. The 1941 nest record pertained to three young in the nest on 1 June. On 12 July 1997 an adult was seen feeding a fledgling in Alameda County, just south of the nest found during the atlas (pers. notes). In San Mateo County, adults carrying nest material were found 6–13 May. Adults carrying food were detected 27 May–16 July. The earliest fledgling was 21 June (Sequoia Audubon Society 2001).

Conservation

The entirety of Contra Costa County's known breeding population of Hermit Thrushes is protected within the confines of Redwood Regional Park and seems to be at little risk.

HERMIT THRUSH

AMERICAN ROBIN • *Turdus migratorius*

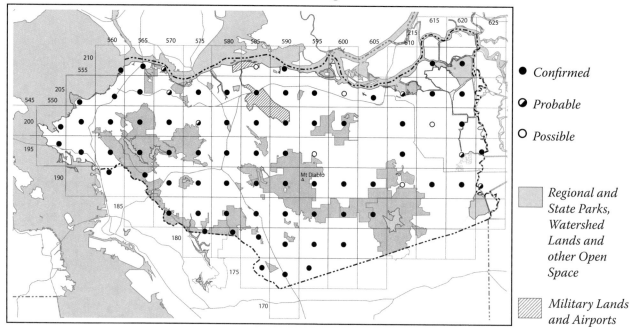

* Confirmed

◐ Probable

○ Possible

▨ Regional and State Parks, Watershed Lands and other Open Space

▨ Military Lands and Airports

Robin has cast in his lot with ours, for better or worse. Our lawns are his lawns, our shade trees were set on purpose to hold his homely mud-cup, and he has undertaken with hearty good will the musical instruction of our children. ❧ *William Leon Dawson (1923)*

Current status and distribution

Breeding American Robins are present throughout much of Contra Costa County. The species is perhaps most common in the Berkeley Hills and in wooded residential neighborhoods around Richmond and along the Interstate 680 corridor. In the Diablo Range, it is less common but still found wherever shady canyons occur. It is absent from the Coast Range only around Black Diamond Mines Regional Park, where it is just too arid, and from the extensive grasslands in the southeastern portion of the county. The extent of its presence in the Central Valley portion of the county came as a surprise. Although still somewhat local, the American Robin was found nesting in surprisingly small parcels of habit, often around homesteads with exotic plantings.

In "wild" situations, the American Robin typically inhabits forest and woodland edges rather than dense forest and is present in such situations nearly wherever they occur. In urban and suburban habitats, the robin may be found on lawns, playing fields, and in orchards, and breed even when a bare minimum of trees are present.

Historical occurrence

Grinnell and Wythe (1927) did not believe that the American Robin nested south or east of Marin County before 1915 when its range apparently began to expand.

The first recorded East Bay nesting was at north Oakland on 15 May 1917 (Allen 1917). The first known nest record for Contra Costa County was likely a set of eggs taken from Pine Canyon, Mt. Diablo State Park, on 29 May 1925 (MVZ 13391). In the Central Valley, robins may have bred as early as 1911 in Sacramento (Storer 1926), raising the possibility that the species may have nested in eastern Contra Costa County earlier than 1925.

Breeding and natural history

Atlasers amassed 115 breeding confirmations of the American Robin. A pair involved in courtship display was detected 10 February but because few atlasers were in the field that early, most pairs were first noted in March. Adults carrying nest material or nest building were recorded on forty-eight occasions between 14 March and 29 June. Ten occupied nests (contents unknown) were found 18 April–28 June; nests proven to contain eggs were found three times from 3 April–17 June and nests with young were detected five times from 25 May–15 July. Adults were seen carrying food or feeding young on forty occasions between 19 April and 11 August. Fledglings were found an additional nine times from 23 May through 30 August. This data suggests that the bulk of robin nest activity occurs between mid-March and early August, with at least two broods involved.

Conservation

There are no apparent threats to the long-term future of the American Robin.

AMERICAN ROBIN

WRENTIT • *Chamaea fasciata*

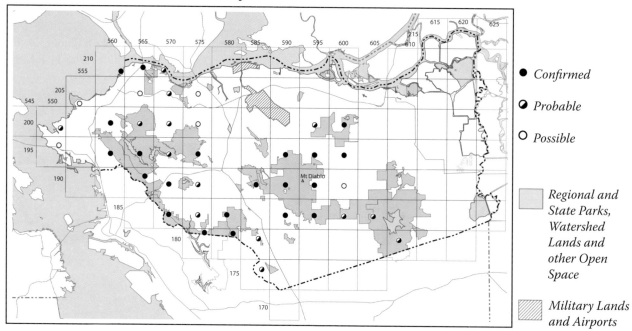

● *Confirmed*

◑ *Probable*

○ *Possible*

▨ *Regional and State Parks, Watershed Lands and other Open Space*

▨ *Military Lands and Airports*

The familiar marble-dropping song of the Wrentit as it rings out from a tangled maelstrom of chamise, sage and manzanita, is the characteristic voice of Contra Costa County's chaparral underworld. This fascinating little bird has been described as the most sedentary species in North America—the young, on average, disperse only 400 meters (Geupel and Ballard 2002)—and apparently a mere road can present a formidable obstacle to movement.

Current status and distribution

The Wrentit is a common nester in the Coast Range, reaching maximum population densities in the extensive chaparral stands on or near Mt. Diablo. The species is uncommon and local on the Bay plain around Richmond where it inhabits extensive stands of coyote brush. In the Berkeley Hills it is also found in coyote brush as well as "hard" chaparral wherever it occurs. In addition, it is also found in more limited numbers on shady hillsides with significant ground cover. East of the Interstate 680 corridor the Wrentit is abundant in extensive stands of chaparral dominated by chamise and other shrubs and is locally found in streamside situations with extensive dense understories, often including blackberry and poison oak. The species is completely absent from urban areas along the Interstate 680 corridor and in the Pittsburg/Antioch area. Although formerly recorded at a handful of sites in the Central Valley portion of the county well into the 1990s (pers. notes), it is now thought that the species has been extirpated there.

Historical occurrence

The status of the Wrentit seems little changed in historical times. The sad exception to this is its disappearance from the eastern portion of the county sometime in the mid to late 1990s. Prior to this, the Wrentit was found at Piper Slough on Bethel Island and at Eucalyptus Island near Clifton Court Forebay. Whether it was ever more common or widespread in these areas will likely never be known.

Breeding and natural history

The Wrentit forms a lifelong pair bond and defends its territory throughout the year (Geupel and Ballard 2002) and thus pairs were detected as early as fieldwork began. Because of the secretive nature of the Wrentit and its preference for impenetrable nest sites, most confirmations obtained during the atlas were based upon adults carrying food or the presence of fledglings. Adults carrying nest material or nest building were found on six occasions 16 April–18 June. Nest building at Palomarin, Marin County begins as early as 10 March and can continue as late as 10 July (Geupel and Ballard 2002). This suggests that we missed this activity early and late in the season. A nest with young was detected 23 July. Adults carrying food were noted eight times between 3 May–24 July. Fledglings were noted nine times between 27 May and 26 August. The later dates cited above suggest double brooding but in a four-year study at Berkeley, Erickson (1938) never detected double brooding. However, at Palomarin, the Wrentit has been found to double brood about 20% of the time (Geupel and Ballard 2002). A set of eggs taken in Contra Costa County 3 June resides at the MVZ (#3310).

Conservation

Because nearly all suitable habitat in Contra Costa County is found in areas that are either protected or unsuitable for development, the local situation appears bright. Elsewhere within its limited range, however, the species has suffered local declines, mostly due to habitat destruction but possibly also partly due to overgrazing, feral cats, and fire. The concern caused by such declines has led to its designation as a Yellow List Species on Audubon's Watchlist 2002.

WRENTIT

NORTHERN MOCKINGBIRD • *Mimus polyglottos*

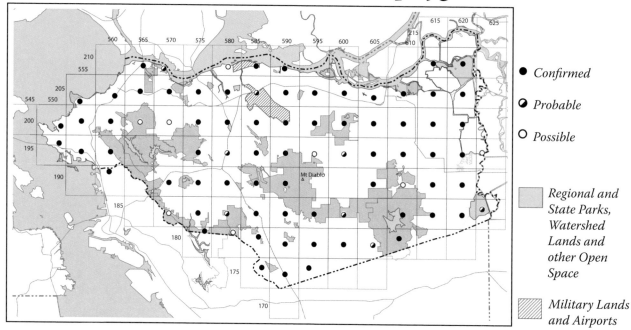

● *Confirmed*

◑ *Probable*

○ *Possible*

Regional and State Parks, Watershed Lands and other Open Space

Military Lands and Airports

Song is the Mocker's raison d'etre. It is his own true love, his passion, his obsession, no less than his trade. Not content with his own inspirations, masterly, varied, and abundant as these are, the singer lays under tribute everything else that sings, or yodels, or squawks withal.

William Leon Dawson (1923)

Vivacious and brazen, the Northern Mockingbird maintains a conspicuous and tireless vigil over the suburbs of Contra Costa County that is the bane of interloping birds and light-sleepers alike. So constant is its presence that one might wonder how neighborhoods could have been considered complete before its relatively recent colonization.

Current status and distribution

In Contra Costa County, the Northern Mockingbird is truly a bird of the suburbs. The vast majority of the county's breeding birds literally nest in our own backyards and are rarely found in "wild" situations. Because "natural" areas are not extensive in the county, the atlas map shows an almost solid distribution across the county with the exception of a handful of blocks around San Pablo Res. and Mt. Diablo. True centers of abundance are at Richmond, the urban Interstate 680 corridor, the Pittsburg/Antioch region, and the entirety of East County.

The Northern Mockingbird inhabits gardens and city parks featuring plantings of shade and fruiting trees. In East County the species is readily found in open country where even a few trees have been planted around a homestead.

Historical occurrence

The conquering of Contra Costa County, as well as most of lowland California, has been well documented, particularly by Grinnell (1911) and Arnold (1935, 1980). Belding (1890) reports nesting at Marysville, Yuba County; and the Sutter Buttes, Sutter County, both in the Sacramento Valley. Grinnell (1911) found no evidence of contemporary nesting that far north and concluded that the mockingbird had not found conditions there "sufficiently congenial" to allow its permanent establishment. He instead records them as a "constant and common resident" as far north as Merced, Merced County, with additional winter and summer records from Stockton, San Joaquin County. Further, Grinnell was unaware of any coastal nesting north of Santa Barbara County. Twenty-three years later, Arnold (1935) documents range extensions in the Central Valley to as far north as north-central San Joaquin County and coastally to as far north as Walnut Creek, where it had begun nesting in 1929, and Richmond, where it became established in 1931. Arnold (1980) cites nesting as far north as central Mendocino County and, in the Central Valley, as far north as Redding, Shasta County. Arnold's map shows a lack of mockingbirds from southeastern Contra Costa County. While this may have been true in 1980 it is hardly the case any longer, as evidenced by the atlas map.

Arnold (1935) hypothesized several factors for the spread of the Northern Mockingbird. Chief among these was widespread arboreal plantings, particularly fruiting ornamental shrubbery such as pyracantha, which provided food and nesting sites.

Breeding and natural history

Adult Mockingbirds carrying nest material or nest building were found on seventeen occasions 10 March–17 June. Three nests with young were detected 12–27 June. The bulk of our confirmations were based upon adults carrying food (thirty-one records spanning 3 April–21 July) or the presence of fledglings (forty records from 13 April to 11 August).

Conservation

Almost as if urban planners have mockingbirds in mind, Mimus polyglottos is supremely fit for taking advantage of the open setting and smorgasbord of exotic fruiting trees offered by suburban neighborhoods.

NORTHERN MOCKINGBIRD

CALIFORNIA THRASHER • *Toxostoma redivivum*

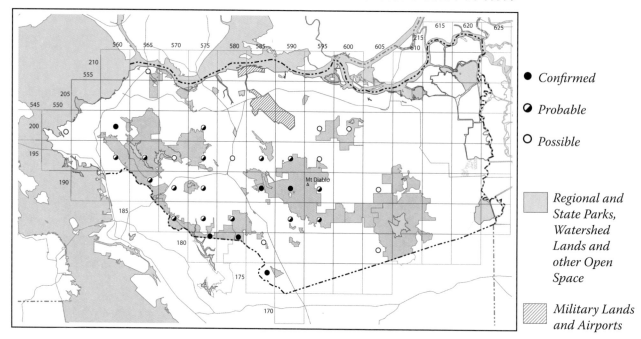

Confirmed

Probable

Possible

Regional and State Parks, Watershed Lands and other Open Space

Military Lands and Airports

Dawson's (1923) "poet of the common weed", the sickle-billed California Thrasher spends most of its life foraging in loose dirt within the confines of an almost impenetrable chaparral jungle, avoiding detection by even the keenest observer. His cover is blown, however, when he hoists himself upon a convenient perch and begins to let loose a loud, mimicking song that sounds like a raspy-throated Northern Mockingbird.

Current status and distribution

Because the California Thrasher tends to be extremely sedentary, it is assumed that it bred in each of the 31 blocks in which it was detected. Except for a singing bird on 12 May 1998 near Pt. San Pablo, the species was found exclusively in the Coast Range, particularly in the more arid Diablo Range. It seems likely that it was present but went undetected in a few blocks east of Mt. Diablo where access was restricted to roadsides. The species was believed to be completely absent from suburban neighborhoods and it is unclear if it ever inhabited such areas.

The California Thrasher prefers chaparral habitats, including coastal scrub in the Berkeley Hills and particularly stands of chamise and mixed chaparral in the Diablo Range. The species is also quite sparingly found in forested habitats featuring a very dense understory.

Historical occurrence

Perhaps because the California Thrasher is so readily found in appropriate habitats, only a handful of sightings from Contra Costa County have ever been published. It is probably safe to assume that its status and distribution is little changed in the past century.

Breeding and natural history

Because of its affinity for dense, inaccessible habitats, the atlas project managed just seven breeding confirmations of California Thrasher. An adult carrying nest material was detected on 7 April. Adults were noted carrying food on five occasions 20 April–26 June. An adult feeding young was found 6 June. In Monterey County, adults carrying food and/or fledglings were found between early May and late July (Roberson and Tenney 1993). Recently fledged young were detected as late as 15 August in Sonoma County (Burridge 1995). Confirmations in July and August likely pertain to second or even third nest attempts.

Conservation

The majority of thrasher habitat in Contra Costa County lies on steep, inaccessible hillsides, most of it lying within protected parklands or watersheds, suggesting a secure future. Declines have been noted within its limited range (which is mostly within California), and it was designated a Yellow List Species on Audubon's Watchlist 2002.

EUROPEAN STARLING • *Sturnus vulgaris*

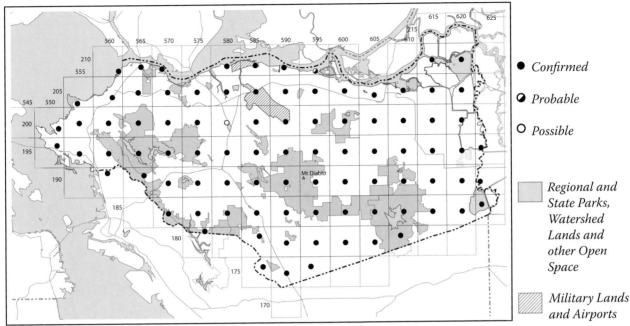

- ● Confirmed
- ◑ Probable
- ○ Possible

▢ Regional and State Parks, Watershed Lands and other Open Space

▨ Military Lands and Airports

What could be called one of the most successful (and unfortunate) introductions of an alien species in the history of North America has come at the expense of Contra Costa County's native cavity-nesting birds. Since the first known county record in 1950 the European Starling has likely become the most numerous breeding bird in the county.

Current status and distribution

The European Starling is present nearly everywhere in the county, reaching maximum abundance around human settlements. It is most common in urban settings, agricultural areas, riparian woodlands and open woodlands. The species is absent as a nesting species only from dense forests, open grasslands and marshlands, though the latter two may be utilized for foraging.

Historical occurrence

In an oft-told tale, a total of about 100 birds were set free in Central Park, New York City in 1890–1891. The modern North American population, estimated at more than 200 million individuals, is all descended from this small group (Cabe 1993). The first starlings found in California were detected in the northeast corner of the state at Tule Lake in 1942 (Jewett 1942). The first report from Contra Costa County was eight to ten birds at Pt. Isabel near Richmond 26 Jan 1950 (Kessel 1953). It is unclear when the first nesting occurred although one might be tempted to guess that it followed soon thereafter. The first Alameda County nesting to be confirmed was at Bay Farm Island in April of 1963 (AFN 17: no. 5).

Breeding and natural history

Atlas data indicate that pairs had begun to form as early as late February but more commonly in early March. Adults carrying nest material or nest building were recorded forty-three times between 3 March and 30 May. Occupied nests (contents unknown) were detected on twenty-eight occasions 27 March–8 June; nests with young were found seventeen times between 26 April and 21 June. Adults carrying food were particularly easy to find, resulting in fifty-four records spanning 14 March–25 June. Fledglings were noted twenty-six times 16 April–24 June. European Starlings are well known for producing second broods (Cabe 1993). Based on the large number of late confirmations it seems clear that this is the case in Contra Costa County.

Conservation

Though the European Starling cannot be implicated in the extirpation, even locally, of any of our breeding species, there can be no doubt that it has out-competed several local cavity-nesters such as woodpeckers, Tree and Violet-green swallows and Western Bluebirds. It seems doubtful that any conceivable level of effort, even if the will existed, could eradicate the European Starling.

CEDAR WAXWING • *Bombycilla cedrorum*

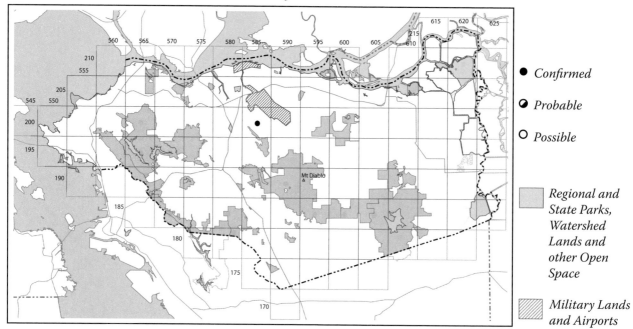

A conspicuous and often common migrant and wintering bird, the delightful Cedar Waxwing is generally confined to the forests of northwestern California and points north during the breeding season. That it chose to breed on one occasion during the atlas was an unanticipated but warmly welcomed development.

Current status and distribution

The Cedar Waxwing is best considered an accidental breeder in Contra Costa County. The lone record during the atlas that did not pertain to a migrant was of an adult accompanying a fledgling at Markham Park in suburban Concord.

Historical occurrence

The Cedar Waxwing was unknown by Grinnell and Wythe (1927) or Grinnell and Miller (1944) to nest anywhere in the Bay Area. In fact, Grinnell and Miller knew of no California nesting except around Eureka in the northwest corner of the state. The earliest indications of nesting in the East Bay came in 1960 when it was noted at El Cerrito on 24 July (AFN 14: no. 5). An adult feeding a Brown-headed Cowbird at Berkeley, Alameda County 18 July 1971 is apparently the first breeding confirmation for the East Bay (AB 25: no. 5). In 1972 a pair was noted in Tilden Park, Contra Costa County on 3 July and two groups of five to eight birds were noted there on 4 July (AB 26: no. 5), strongly suggesting that nesting took place that year. Small groups of twenty-five to thirty birds were also noted over Lafayette on 1 July 1979 (AB 33: no. 6) and twelve birds on 6 July 1985 (AB 39: no. 5).

The Cedar Waxwing has occasionally been recorded nesting well out of range in California, including a partic-ularly stunning nest record from Doheny Beach in coastal Orange County in 1965 (Gallagher 1997). This species has also nested once each in Napa and Santa Clara counties, and twice in San Mateo County (Bousman 2007).

Breeding and natural history

The sole breeding confirmation during the atlas project involved an adult feeding a begging fledgling on 4 June.

A probable breeding record from Monterey County involved two adults feeding a fledgling on 11 June 1987 (Roberson and Tenney 1993). Roberson and Tenney believed the record to be valid but without accompanying notes or photos they couldn't rule out the possibility that the record pertained to an adult feeding another adult, rather than a fledgling.

In Humboldt County in northwest California the Cedar Waxwing is an uncommon but regular breeder. The Humboldt County atlas (Hunter and others 2005) compiled the following confirmations. The earliest breeding record was of adults carrying nest material 27 May but nesting surely commenced earlier, as the earliest fledgling was detected 10 June. A nest with young was found 26 June, with the young fledging on 6 July. Adults feeding young were reported as late as 29 August.

Conservation

The lone confirmation during the atlas project is very similar to the probable record from Monterey County (see above). Although the observer was convinced that the bird being fed was a fledgling rather than an adult taking part in courtship, no photographs were obtained, leaving the record open to question. In addition, the presence of a fledgling in early June is unusual, though not unprecedented. The Cedar Waxwing is considered one of the latest-nesting birds in North America, with egg-laying typically commencing in early June and continuing through early August (Witmer and others 1997).

WINTER WREN

PHAINOPEPLA • *Phainopepla nitens*

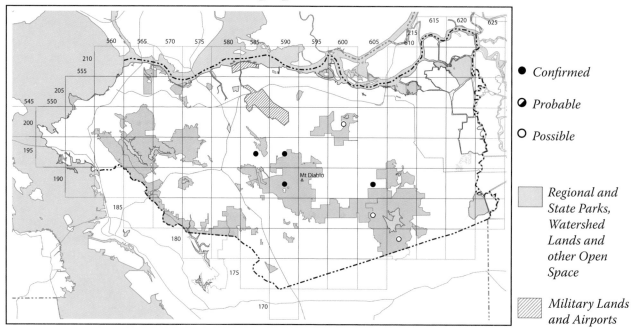

● *Confirmed*

◑ *Probable*

○ *Possible*

▢ *Regional and State Parks, Watershed Lands and other Open Space*

▨ *Military Lands and Airports*

Certain baffling contradictions, and many elusive qualities besides, mark this wayward son of the desert. Handsome he is, indeed; and they have given him a high-sounding Grecian title in appreciation of his magnificence. Yet he is ever the soul of modesty, and the sudden consciousness of a spying eye will scatter all his show of finery, and send him dashing into the bush with "peps" of disgust. ➤ *William Leon Dawson (1923)*

The Phainopepla is present erratically and only locally in Contra Costa County with significant patches of arid woodlands and attendant mistletoe clumps left unoccupied most years. This paucity only adds to its allure amongst local birders.

Current status and distribution

The true status and distribution of the enigmatic Phainopepla is vexing to say the least. It is commonly thought that the Phainopepla nests in the desert southwest during the spring before flying north to re-nest again during the summer (Chu and Walsberg 1999). Yet the Contra Costa County Christmas Bird Count, despite relatively light coverage in prime areas, detects this species nearly annually. Most such records are either from the mountain itself or, just as often, from neighborhoods and city parks west of the mountain, usually near the base but sometimes as far west as Lafayette. Additional March records that probably represented wintering birds were also procured during the atlas project.

In any event, breeding Phainopeplas are clearly confined to the Diablo Range, particularly in and around Mt. Diablo. Nesting was confirmed in two blocks on the mountain itself and in a canyon just north of Clayton.

The other nest was at Round Valley Regional Park west of Brentwood. The three "possibles" on the map may well pertain to wintering birds as all three were recorded in March.

The preferred haunts of the Phainopepla are blue oak foothill pine woodlands featuring abundant mistletoe clumps, though mistletoe is of less importance when young are being fed and at that time adults may wander more widely. It is unclear why vast amounts of suitable habitat remain unoccupied.

Historical occurrence

Grinnell and Wythe (1927) considered the Phainopepla to be a rare resident in the Bay Area and cite only a winter record from Contra Costa County. Anecdotal evidence from local Audubon newsletters strongly suggests that the species was certainly nesting by the early 1960s in the arid interior, particularly at Mt. Diablo State Park. The first certain nest record for the county was obtained in Pine Canyon, Mt. Diablo State Park on 16 June 1989 (AB 43: no. 5).

Breeding and natural history

The five breeding records obtained during the atlas project are far too few to be of great use in laying out a nesting chronology. An occupied nest was detected 21 May, adults were noted carrying food on three occasions between 14 April and 26 July and an adult was found feeding young 7 July. The Monterey County atlas (the only published northern California atlas for a county with a sizeable population of Phainopeplas) produced the following nesting chronology: nest-building as early as 9 April; active nests between mid-April and early July with the latter considered to be a second brood; and recently fledged young late May–late June (Roberson and Tenney 1993).

Conservation

The primary conservation concern for the Phainopepla appears to be the protection and restoration of wintering and breeding grounds, particularly in its Sonoran Desert stronghold. Locally, an abundance of apparently suitable habitat—much of it unoccupied—is already in existence and protected in parks and watersheds.

PHAINOPEPLA

ORANGE-CROWNED WARBLER • *Vermivora celata*

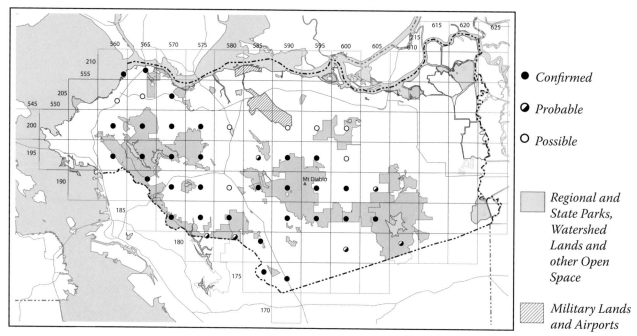

The Orange-crowned Warbler has non-distinctive plumage compared with most other warblers and yet it as always a welcome sight in our still drab early spring chaparral and woodlands. Its song, a melodious trill reminiscent of a horse whinny, adds a bright note, and this earliest arriving of our neotropical migrants indeed seems to announce the coming of spring in the East Bay hills.

Current status and distribution

The Orange-crowned Warbler breeds widely and commonly throughout wooded situations in the Coast Range. However, the species was completely absent from the non-hilly regions of West and East County, as well as from residential neighborhoods along the Interstate 680 corridor.

The Orange-crowned Warbler is commonly encountered in open upland woodlands, near openings and edges of denser forests, in riparian woodlands, and in chaparral featuring taller shrubs such as coyote brush, ceanothus or manzanita. Extensive, dense forests are avoided. In all situations the species requires a shrubby understory for nesting. Of twenty-eight nests found in Contra Costa County (Tilden Park Nature Area), twenty-three were directly on the ground, four were in dead sword ferns, and one was just above the ground in poison oak (Sogge and others 1994).

Historical occurrence

Grinnell and Wythe (1927) considered the Orange-crowned Warbler to be an uncommon summer resident in "hilly" portions of the Bay Area, a situation that appears unchanged.

Breeding and natural history

Newly-arrived Orange-crowned Warblers have been heard singing as early as 20 February in Contra Costa County, although most males arrive on territory after 1 March (Sogge and others 1994). Adults carrying nest material were detected on four occasions from 1–20 April. The mean start date for twenty-five nests in central California was 4 April (Sogge and others 1994). Occupied nests (contents unknown) were found 17 and 20 April; a nest with eggs was recorded 15 April. Nests with young were found 25 April and 17 June. Adults carrying food or feeding young were tallied on twenty-six occasions between 22 April and 23 July. Double brooding is thought to be rare but many pairs attempt re-nesting if the first nest is destroyed (Sogge and others 1994). Our later nest records more than likely pertain to such re-nesting.

Conservation

The obligatory issue of habitat on the wintering grounds that seems to face all neotropical migrants is a concern for the Orange-crowned Warbler, as well. The situation on its breeding grounds in Contra Costa County, fortunately, appears bright, with few pressing threats.

LAWRENCE'S GOLDFINCH

YELLOW WARBLER • *Dendroica petechia*

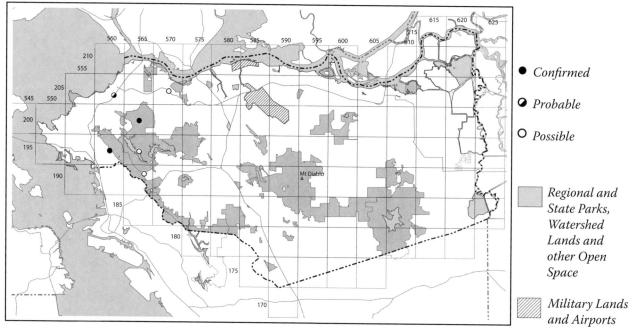

- ● *Confirmed*
- ◕ *Probable*
- ○ *Possible*

▨ *Regional and State Parks, Watershed Lands and other Open Space*

▨ *Military Lands and Airports*

Once considered a fairly common breeding bird in Contra Costa County, the aptly named Yellow Warbler is one of our rarest breeding birds with a mere handful of pairs known to currently breed. The rediscovery of two pairs of breeding birds after a decades-long absence was perhaps one of the most satisfying finds of the atlas project.

Current status and distribution

The only nesting Yellow Warblers detected during the atlas project were at Jewel Lake in Tilden Regional Park and on East Bay Municipal Utility District property near Briones Valley north of Orinda. After the atlas project, on 13 June 2004, two males were found counter-singing in appropriate willow habitat at San Pablo Res. (R. DiGuadio, pers. comm.). Breeding Yellow Warblers are an indication of relatively healthy riparian habitats, a scarce commodity in Contra Costa County. The species prefers young thickets of willow and alder and, not coincidentally, each atlas confirmation came from stands of willows.

Historical occurrence

In the early 20th century the Yellow Warbler was considered to be a fairly common summer resident in the Bay Area (Grinnell and Wythe 1927). Grinnell and Miller (1944) made no mention of declines in its California range yet a thorough check of the local literature turns up no nest records for Contra Costa County between 1931 (at St. Mary's College near Moraga) and the beginning of the atlas.

Breeding and natural history

Because northern populations of the Yellow Warbler commonly migrate through the county well into June, the atlas turned up many "possible" reports that almost certainly pertained to late migrants rather than potential breeders. In light of this, the atlas database has been purged of all records from East County, most of which involved single birds in May. Several of the "possibles" on the map may also pertain to late migrants but we were more lenient since other pairs bred nearby.

The sole breeding confirmations were an adult carrying food 9 June and an adult feeding young 16 June. In Napa County, nest-building was recorded between 30 April and 25 May (Napa-Solano Audubon Society 2003). The Monterey atlas (Roberson and Tenney 1993) records fledglings as early as mid-May, indicating that eggs could be laid in early April. Such an early date would likely be the exception, however, as the bulk of the data from published Bay Area atlases suggests fledglings are typically present from late May through early July.

Conservation

Yellow Warbler populations declined throughout much of California during the 20th century, most conspicuously in southern California and in the Central Valley. Losses have apparently not been as wholesale in the greater Bay Area, although the species is believed to have declined significantly in Marin (Shuford 1993) and Napa (Napa-Solano Audubon Society 2003) counties. Roberson and Tenney (1993) believed that its overall range in Monterey County had remained stable but that it was found to have become patchier within that range. There, as elsewhere, the blame falls upon loss of riparian habitats, degradation of riparian habitats primarily due to grazing, and an increase in the Brown-headed Cowbird. For these reasons, it has been assigned the rank of Second Priority California Bird Species of Special Concern (Shuford and Gardali 2008).

YELLOW WARBLER

BLACK-THROATED GRAY WARBLER • *Dendroica nigrescens*

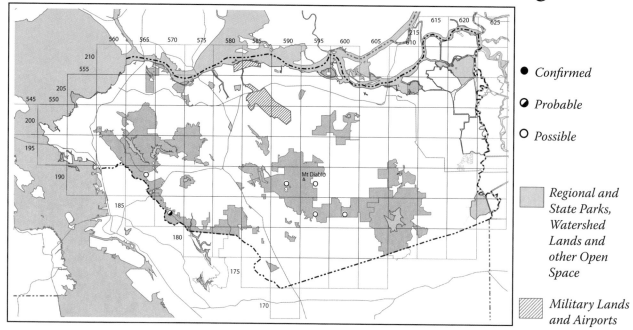

Confirmed

Probable

Possible

Regional and State Parks, Watershed Lands and other Open Space

Military Lands and Airports

The wonderfully understated Black-throated Gray Warbler, with its patchy distribution and erratic presence, is a prized find in Contra Costa County during the breeding season.

Current status and distribution

The Black-throated Gray Warbler is currently considered to be an extremely local and erratic breeder in the woodlands of the Coast Range. The only breeding confirmation for the county was in Pine Canyon at Mt. Diablo State Park, where birds nested in shady coastal oak woodland. In nearby Marin County, breeding birds inhabit "reasonably dry, open mixed evergreen forests usually dominated by Douglas fir (not present in Contra Costa County) but generously mixed with coast live, canyon live, or tanbark oaks or other broad-leaved evergreen trees, saplings, or shrubs. The species also breeds here sparingly in relatively moist but open mixed woodlands of black oak, madrone, and live oaks" (Shuford 1993). In Monterey County, breeding birds seem to prefer a mixture of oaks and dense chaparral (Roberson and Tenney 1993).

Historical occurrence

Grinnell and Wythe (1927) cite suspected nesting only from Ft. Ross, Sonoma County. The first nesting confirmation for the county wasn't until 1990, when adults feeding young were found in Pine Canyon, Mt. Diablo State Park 28 June 1990, this after a couple of years of suspected breeding that couldn't be proved (AB 42: no. 5). Interestingly, four birds were found at this same location on 8 June 1952 (AFN 6: no. 5). It is entirely possible that tiny numbers of this erratic bird bred early in the 20th century and were simply missed due to poor coverage.

Breeding and natural history

There are only six records of the Black-throated Gray Warbler in the atlas database, none of them confirmations. A couple of records of singing males from mid-May have been left on the map, but may pertain to late migrants. Likely breeding birds included a singing male at Upper San Leandro Res. on 18 June (J. Robinson, pers. comm.), Riggs Canyon, Mt. Diablo State Park on 19 June, and at Redwood Regional Park through at least 27 May.

In San Mateo County, adults carrying nest material were noted on four occasions between 20 April and 28 May. Adults carrying food were tallied nine times with dates spanning 9 May–13 July. Adults feeding young were found as early as 3 June and as late as 15 July. Fledglings appeared as early as 9 June through 10 August (Sequoia Audubon Society 2001). This wide disparity in dates, also noted in Monterey County, suggest to Roberson and Tenney (1993) that double-brooding might well be occurring.

Conservation

None of the published Northern California atlases discuss declines in local populations, although the species is relatively uncommon as a breeding bird in much of the Bay region and it appears to have been poorly studied. Guzy and Lowther (1997) felt that the species tends to occur in habitats which are unprofitable to convert to other uses and therefore the species' overall range has likely been little affected by human activity.

MacGillivray's Warbler • *Oporornis tolmiei*

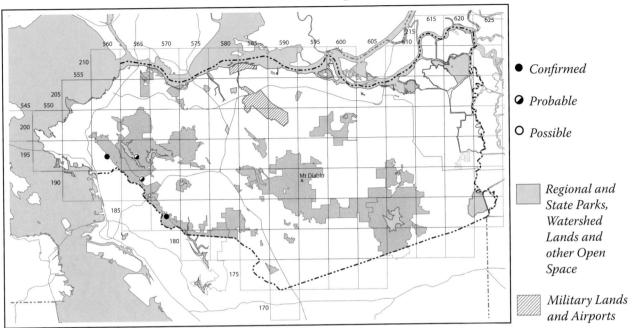

Legend:
- ● Confirmed
- ◐ Probable
- ○ Possible
- ▓ Regional and State Parks, Watershed Lands and other Open Space
- ▨ Military Lands and Airports

The distinctive little MacGillivray's Warbler graces us with its presence at just a handful of Berkeley Hills nest sites and yet even there this little *Oporornis* is a master at remaining hidden from view as it weaves through its tangled underworld domain.

Current status and distribution

The MacGillivray's Warbler was confirmed breeding in just two atlas blocks although it more than likely nested in the two "probable" blocks as well. All of these birds were in the wetter, more fog-prone western edge of the Berkeley Hills with no suggestion of breeding even as far to the east as San Pablo Reservoir.

In Marin County, the MacGillivray's Warbler inhabits "moist, dense shrubbery of riparian thickets, especially where they adjoin the moist phase of coastal scrub" (Shuford 1993). Our few local breeders seem to dwell in similar circumstances. For example, birds at Inspiration Point, in Tilden Park are found in extensive stands of shrubbery, particularly blackberry, beneath a canopy of introduced Monterey pines. Shuford (1993) suspects that the moistness of occupied habitats was important, as the species doesn't inhabit drier chaparral habitats in either Marin or Contra Costa counties.

Historical occurrence

"Macs" were known by Grinnell and Wythe (1927) to nest in Alameda County as close as Redwood Canyon, the northern portion of which is in Contra Costa County. An older record of eggs taken at "Danville" 12 May 1897 (MVZ 3326) should be considered questionable based on the unlikely location. These eggs were almost certainly collected further west, making the county appellation questionable. Sightings from a variety of sources indicate that the species nested in Contra Costa County with certainty by the mid-1950s but it seems likely that this was taking place all along and it simply wasn't detected.

Breeding and natural history

Because of the scarcity of breeding MacGillivray's Warblers, the atlas database contains just a handful of records which aren't sufficient for establishing a sturdy breeding chronology. The earliest date of arrival during the atlas was 17 April but local breeding birds are known to arrive by late March. An adult was found feeding young 30 May and a fledgling was detected 23 August. The lone egg set at the MVZ attributed to Contra Costa County was collected 12 May. The San Mateo County Breeding Bird Atlas (Sequoia Audubon Society 2001) documents the following chronology: nest with eggs 14 May; adult carrying nest material 17 May; adults carrying food 21 May–1 July; and fledglings (some being fed by adults) 6 June–21 July.

Conservation

The MacGillivray's Warbler appears on no "watchlists" but its uncommon presence south of Mendocino County leaves the species vulnerable to habitat destruction. Its status in Marin County is stable (Shuford 1993) but some obvious declines have been noted in Sonoma County (Burridge 1995). The very small East Bay population would appear particularly vulnerable but it is fortunate that local breeding grounds fall entirely within lands protected by regional parks and watersheds.

COMMON YELLOWTHROAT • *Geothlypis trichas*

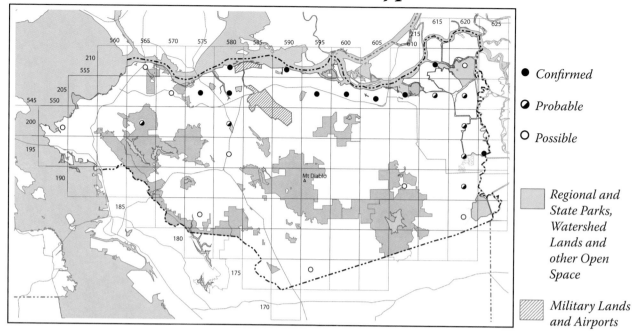

It is a shame that such a startling bird as the Common Yellowthroat is obligated to spend so much time weaving its way through tules and cattails rather than out in the open where it would be more easily enjoyed. As it is, we must be content much of the time with verifying its presence based upon its distinctive "tisking" chip note and rhythmic "*witchity, witchity, witchity*" song.

Current status and distribution

Most of Contra Costa County's breeding Common Yellowthroat population is found in the saline emergent and fresh emergent marshes of the northern portion of the county and in the Central Valley. Although a few pairs are thought to breed in a handful of freshwater ponds in the Coast Range, as at Marsh Creek Reservoir, some atlas records likely represented wintering birds.

Common Yellowthroat taxonomy is controversial. The small, dark subspecies *sinuosa* (the San Francisco or Saltmarsh Common Yellowthroat) would presumably be the subspecies present at Richmond if birds bred there, but this was not confirmed during the atlas. Birds taken in August of 1960 at Martinez (where Yellowthroats are known to breed) were *sinuosa* (Marshall and Dedrick 1993). It is unclear, however, where *sinuosa* leaves off and the paler *arizela*, which breeds from southeast Alaska to central California (Guzy and Ritchison 1999) picks up. Marshall and Dedrick (1993) cite specimens of *arizela* from as close as San Joaquin County. This suggests that birds in the Central Valley portion of Contra Costa County may refer to *arizela*. Which subspecies might be represented in the Coast Ranges is similarly muddled.

Historical occurrence

Although Grinnell and Wythe (1927) cite Common Yellowthroats as a common breeder in the marshes of San Francisco Bay and at Suisun Marsh, Solano County, they make no mention of breeding either along the southern shore of Suisun Bay or in far eastern Contra Costa County. Grinnell and Miller include the eastern two-thirds of the county within the range of the yellowthroat but this was based upon likely range rather than actual records.

Breeding and natural history

The first pair of Common Yellowthroats was noted 7 March but this is likely an artifact of light coverage in February. Because of its preference for dense marshes for breeding, the atlas database contains no records of adults carrying nest material or building nests. One nest with eggs was found 2 June. Five records of adults carrying food were recorded 22 April–27 June. Fledglings were tallied on eight occasions between 13 May and 2 August.

Conservation

The taxonomy of the Common Yellowthroat is more than an obscure exercise in taxonomy of interest to just a few specialists. *Sinuosa*, because it is closely tied to the salt marshes of the San Francisco Bay system, has suffered immensely from the destruction of wetlands and has been designated a California Bird Species of Special Concern with a Third Priority rank (Shuford and Gardali 2008).

194

WILSON'S WARBLER • *Wilsonia pusilla*

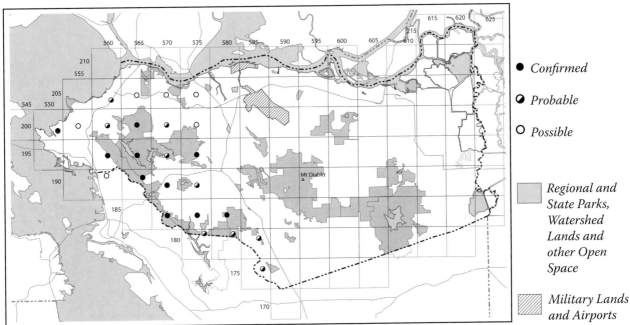

● *Confirmed*

◑ *Probable*

○ *Possible*

▨ *Regional and State Parks, Watershed Lands and other Open Space*

▨ *Military Lands and Airports*

Once known as the Golden Pileolated Warbler, what we now call the Wilson's Warbler is a characteristic bird of riparian corridors and wet forests of the Berkeley Hills. This active, bright yellow little warbler arrives in late March, its presence being announced by the males' emphatic "chatter" song. The species is actually quite common in Contra Costa County's remaining suitable breeding habitat and, partly because the young are so conspicuous, a favorite of atlasers.

Current status and distribution

Breeding Wilson's Warblers were found almost exclusively in the Berkeley Hills during the atlas project, the only exception being a confirmation in block 550-200 near Pt. San Pablo. There were many reports submitted from the Diablo Range, but it is thought that all of them represented spring migrants, which is not surprising since the species is often detected into early June in Contra Costa County. It was recorded as probable, based on the presence of singing males over the span of at least seven days, in two blocks at Las Trampas Regional Park, but it is unclear if birds actually remain to breed there.

The Wilson's Warbler is a bird of the moist understory of forests, with streamside willow groves being particularly prized. At some locations, as around Briones Valley, breeding birds are present along narrow riparian corridors that shelter dense clumps of blackberry vines. Elsewhere, nesting Wilson's Warblers are known to nest in coastal chaparral, suggesting that the thick undergrowth is more crucial than the surrounding forest (Shuford 1993).

Historical occurrence

Belding (1890) considered the Wilson's Warbler to be a "rare summer resident" in Oakland and its vicinity. Grinnell and Wythe (1927), however, categorize the species as a common summer resident, just as it is now. The latter is presumably closer to the truth. The first known nest record for the county is a nest with eggs collected from Moraga Valley 27 May 1925 (MVZ #13427).

Breeding and natural history

The earliest record of the Wilson's Warbler during the atlas project was 20 March, just slightly later than the first birds typically appear in Contra Costa County. Territories in Tilden Park, Contra Costa County, were all established between 17 March–14 April in 1997 and 14 March–10 April in 1998. Males at Tilden seem to ease up on their persistent singing by mid-April, suggesting that most pairs have formed by that date (Ammon and Gilbert 1999). The first carrying of nest material or nest building was recorded by the Atlas project on 15 April. The earliest date recorded for nest construction at Tilden was 8 April, with a mean construction date of 17 April (Ammon and Gilbert 1999). An adult carrying nest material 27 May might have been attempting to renest. Atlasers never reported finding an actual nest during the project, but the early date for first eggs at Tilden is 12 April with an average date for first egg of 22 April (Ammon and Gilbert 1999). Adults carrying food were recorded on seven occasions between 3 May and 27 June. Fledglings were noted 12 May–8 July. The early record for a fledgling from an initial nest at Tilden Park is 7 May (Ammon and Gilbert 1999).

Nests of the subspecies found on the west coast, *W. p. chryseola*, are almost always located in low shrubs, usually within a meter of the ground. At Tilden they are usually in blackberry vines or sword ferns. Re-nesting, following nest destruction by predators, can occur multiple times over the extended breeding season, which can last into August. Second nestings, following successful initial attempts, are frequent (Ammon and Gilbert 1999).

Conservation

Published breeding bird atlases from the Bay Area don't suggest that there have been any drastic reductions in the status and distribution of the Wilson's Warbler, although several state that there have likely been some local reductions. The likely cause is apparently the degradation or outright destruction of riparian woodlands, usually due to construction but at least occasionally due to grazing. The zealous protection of the county's remaining riparian forests is crucial to its long-term survival in Contra Costa County.

WILSON'S WARBLER

YELLOW-BREASTED CHAT • *Icteria virens*

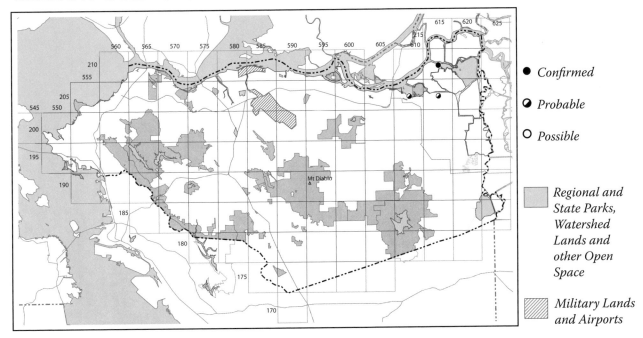

● *Confirmed*

◐ *Probable*

○ *Possible*

▨ *Regional and State Parks, Watershed Lands and other Open Space*

▨ *Military Lands and Airports*

It would be hard to imagine a songbird that is heard more often and yet is seen so rarely and yet the Yellow-breasted Chat manages to sing a raucous mockingbird-like song day and night from so deep within soggy willow and blackberry clumps that, except when engaging in flight song, it is rarely seen for more than a brief instant.

Current status and distribution

Sadly, the Yellow-breasted Chat has managed to eke out only a marginal existence in Contra Costa County, with but a handful of pairs present each summer in the northeast portion of the county. Throughout much of the chat's range it appears to prefer extensive riparian forests and yet in Contra Costa County it is found in soggy willow clumps with an extensive component of blackberry brambles. Known nest sites in the county feature willows of only occasionally large size and while these willow clumps may be lengthy they are rarely more than five to ten yards in depth. Cottonwoods, a common component of chat habitat throughout much of the west, are nearly absent from East County except as planted windbreaks.

The modern local stronghold for the Yellow-breasted Chats is at Piper Slough at the north end of Bethel Island, where an average of four to five pairs have nested annually for more than a decade. An additional two to three pairs were noted during the atlas project from the southern shore of "Big Break" near Oakley. Although it is certainly possible and even likely that a few additional pairs breed at unknown sites on private property—the north end of Holland Tract springs to mind—it is clear that its toehold here is tenuous at best.

Historical occurrence

Historically, The Yellow-breasted Chat was more widespread in the county, ranging west into the center of the county. The Golden Gate Audubon Society took annual field trips via train to Lafayette as early as 1919, the star attraction being the chat. Chats continued there at least through the early 1930s. An egg set taken at Walnut Creek 20 May 1894 (MVZ #11137) is the first known nesting confirmation for the county. Additional egg sets exist at the MVZ and the MFVZ which were taken from Danville and "Mt. Diablo."

Breeding and natural history

The small local population of the Yellow-breasted Chat arrives sometime around mid-April, though the earliest atlas record was 27 April. The lone breeding confirmation involved a nest with young at Piper Slough 25–26 June 2001. This fits well with four egg records from 12 May through 1 June and with published data from other Northern California atlases.

Conservation

With a breeding population that is surely less than 20 pairs (and possibly closer to 10), the Yellow-breasted Chat is extremely vulnerable to habitat destruction. Its stronghold at Piper Slough is unprotected from development. Fortunately the explosion of development in the eastern portion of the county hasn't yet extended as far as Bethel Island. Elsewhere, chat populations have declined due to habitat destruction and cowbird parasitism, as in Monterey County (Roberson and Tenney 1993) and Napa County (Napa-Solano Audubon Society 2003).

The Yellow-breasted Chat is currently designated as a Third Priority California Bird Species of Special Concern (Shuford and Gardali 2007) and should be diligently watched locally, as well.

YELLOW-BREASTED CHAT

WESTERN TANAGER • *Piranga ludoviciana*

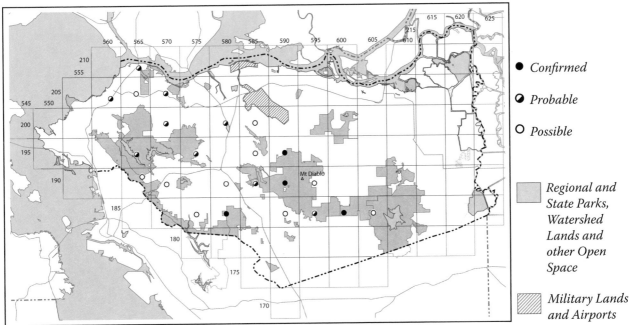

Confirmed

Probable

Possible

Regional and State Parks, Watershed Lands and other Open Space

Military Lands and Airports

With a plumage that Dawson (1923) likened to "a costume for a king," the Western Tanager provides Contra Costa County with a tantalizing glimpse of both the Sierra forests and the tropical rainforests of Central and South America.

Current status and distribution

The Western Tanager in Contra Costa County is locally and irregularly distributed in the forests of the Coast Range, common nowhere and often absent from apparently suitable habitat. Of five confirmations, two came from the Berkeley Hills and three from the Diablo Range, as far to the east as Morgan Territory Rd.

When nesting the Western Tanager prefers forests that are neither too densely forested, such as the stands of redwoods in the Berkeley Hills, nor too open, as much of the oak woodlands of the Diablo Range tend to be. Oak woodlands with a component of pines seem to be occupied most commonly.

Historical occurrence

Grinnell and Wythe (1927) were unaware of any tanagers nesting in the Bay Area except in Sonoma County, but a male present at U. C. Berkeley, Alameda County 24 July 1924 and three males, a female and two juveniles present at the same site on 9 August is suggestive of breeding (Kellogg 1924). The first nesting confirmation was a pair with two young near Moraga, Contra Costa County on 29 June 1930 (Gull 12: no. 9). It seems entirely possible, based on its current scarcity, that the Western Tanager has long bred in the county but was never detected by the handful of active birders early in the 20th century.

Breeding and natural history

Evidence of breeding was difficult to obtain for this very uncommon species. The earliest pair was recorded 30 April though it is likely that the species was overlooked on slightly earlier dates. The lone confirmations were nest building on 25 May, adults feeding young on 31 May and 22 June, and a fledgling on 14 July. A report of a fledgling on 16 May seems far too early for this species and does not appear on the atlas map. In Monterey County, records of dependent fledglings or adults carrying food spanned 31 May–2 July (Roberson and Tenney 1993).

Conservation

There appears to be no serious threats to the Western Tanager in Contra Costa County as virtually all breeding pairs reside within the confines of parks and watersheds. Further, there appears to be little concern for it throughout its breeding range.

SPOTTED TOWHEE • *Pipilo maculatus*

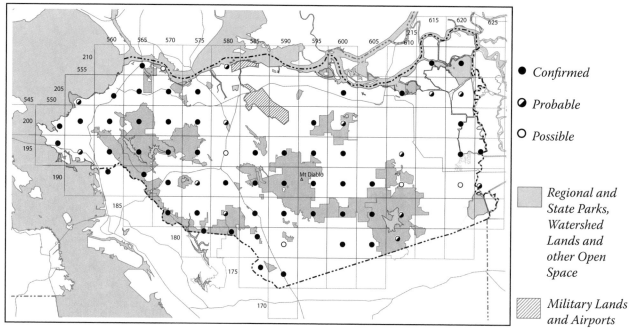

Confirmed

Probable

Possible

Regional and State Parks, Watershed Lands and other Open Space

Military Lands and Airports

The Spotted Towhee bulks large in the economy of the underworld. He is, in fact, its acknowledged prince; not, of course, in the Mephistophelian sense, but as the undoubted aristocrat amongst those humble folk who skulk under dark ferns, thread marvelous mazes of interlacing sticks and stalks, sort over the leafy wastage of the careless trees, and understand the foundation of things generally

ꙮ *William Leon Dawson (1923)*

Current status and distribution

The Spotted Towhee is a ubiquitous permanent resident throughout most of Contra Costa County. The species is most common and occasionally abundant throughout the Coast Range, likely reaching maximum abundance in chamise and mixed chaparral stands and scrubby blue oak gray pine woodlands in the Diablo Range. In the western portion of the county it is readily found in coastal scrub. Well-wooded neighborhoods in the residential central portion of the county are lightly populated. In the Central Valley it is nearly as common as in the Diablo Range, however, suitable habitats there are patchier and thus the species is more localized. There the species is typically found in narrow riparian strips and particularly in clumps of blackberry and willow. The Spotted Towhee was absent only from extensive grasslands around Concord and east of San Ramon, as well as from the farmlands of East County.

Historical occurrence

There seems little reason to believe that the status and distribution of the Spotted Towhee has changed in historical times.

Breeding and natural history

Adults were noted carrying nest material on six occasions 19 April–15 May and actually seen nest building on 27 April. Nests with eggs were found four times between 29 April and 10 June. There is an additional egg record in the possession of the MVZ collected 11 April, suggesting that some early breeding activity went undetected during the atlas project. Adults carrying food were recorded twenty-four times 29 April–20 July while adults seen feeding young were noted an additional fourteen times 21 May–22 July. Fledglings were observed twenty-five times from 9 May–16 August, the vast majority falling between very late May and the end of June.

Conservation

The Spotted Towhee appears on none of the "watchlists" and doesn't appear to be in any jeopardy at the county level. Spotted Towhees seem to respond well to modest development when enough shrubby groundcover is retained. Just like other ground-hugging birds, especially those in residential settings or even those in parklands adjacent to residential neighborhoods, feral cats pose a special problem and one that is likely growing.

CALIFORNIA TOWHEE • *Pipilo crissalis*

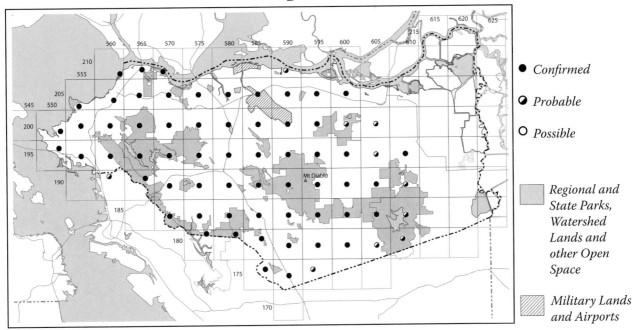

The California Towhee is a large, outgoing sparrow that appears as comfortable in garden settings as it does in chaparral. Though its plumage is startlingly dull ("every-day duds" according to Dawson), its charming devotion to a life-long mate and constant presence in local gardens makes it a sentimental favorite for many.

Current status and distribution

The California Towhee is a common, conspicuous permanent resident of open areas and woodland edges throughout most of the county. Throughout the western 75% of the county, the species is found nearly everywhere with suitable undergrowth including coastal scrub, stands of chamise and mixed chaparral, riparian corridors, scrubby oak woodlands, and residential gardens. It is absent only from pure grasslands and marshes. The species' historical status in East County is unknown, but it has been completely absent since the area began to be seriously birded in the 1980s.

Historical occurrence

With the possible exception of some local declines due to development, there is nothing in the historical record to suggest any significant changes in the status and distribution of the California Towhee.

Breeding and natural history

Adults were noted carrying nest material on twenty-two occasions between 22 March and 27 June, the later dates presumably representing second or even third broods. Adults carrying food were detected twenty-three times 2 May–14 July. Eight nests with young were found 1 April–5 July. Eighteen instances of adults feeding young were tallied 13 April–16 August. Fledglings were noted twenty-eight times between 4 May and 13 July.

Conservation

In general, it appears that few habitat disturbances other than outright destruction are enough to seriously faze the flexible California Towhee. The primary concern for urban and suburban populations is feral cats. Brood parasitism by Brown-headed Cowbirds has also been noted in Contra Costa County but Purcell and Verner (1998) felt that nest predation by Western Scrub-Jays was a more significant cause of reproductive failure in California.

RUFOUS-CROWNED SPARROW • *Aimophila ruficeps*

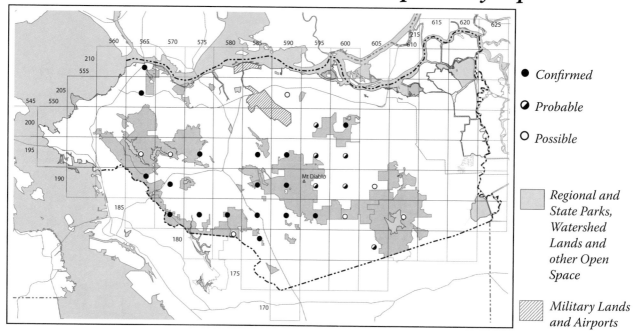

Few lives are so devoted to the humbler levels. Even the Savanna Sparrow will go rocketing off through the air when disturbed. But the Rufous-crown steps about through the grass-stems or tufted cover of a rocky hillside without ostentation or appearance of effort; and even when hard-pressed seems to regard flight as unprofessional, a pitiful and degrading last resort.

ᴥ *William Leon Dawson (1923)*

The Rufous-crowned Sparrow is often overlooked by beginning birders unfamiliar with its subtle "*deer-deer-deer*" calls and less than booming song but it is a reliably found permanent resident if the proper habitats are scoured. In fact, during the breeding season it is the only sparrow likely to be found in its preferred habitats.

Current status and distribution

The Rufous-crowned Sparrow has specific habitat needs but it is almost inevitably present whenever those needs are met. Ideal habitats feature open, sparse coastal scrub habitat, especially California sagebrush, on rocky, south-facing hillsides. Other plants, such as poison oak, may take the place of sagebrush and, on occasion, nearly pure grasslands may be utilized as long as a sunny hillside is present. Unlike our other chaparral sparrows, the Rufous-crowned Sparrow is virtually never found in dense, extensive stands of chamise and manzanita such as those that cloak vast acreages of Mt. Diablo, although it may be found on peripheral areas where vegetation thins dramatically. Appropriate habitats are found primarily in the Diablo Range but are present in reduced numbers in the eastern Berkeley Hills, particularly around

Las Trampas Regional Park but also at Sibley Volcanic Preserve. Although it could conceivably occur in coastal scrub in far West County, the species is not known to have done so. The species is completely absent from East County.

Historical occurrence

There is nothing in the historical literature that would suggest any significant changes in either the status or the distribution of the Rufous-crowned Sparrow in Contra Costa County.

Breeding and natural history

Adult Rufous-crowned Sparrows were found carrying nest material or nest building on four occasions between 25 March and 15 June. Two occupied nests (contents unknown) were recorded 9 and 30 May. Adults carrying food were tallied six times from 2 May–14 July. Fledglings (some being fed by adults) were found on eleven occasions between 16 April and 27 August.

Conservation

Although the bulk of Contra Costa County's local population is protected within parklands and watersheds, local losses have likely occurred, and will continue to occur, as new housing developments move higher up hillsides.

CHIPPING SPARROW • *Spizella passerina*

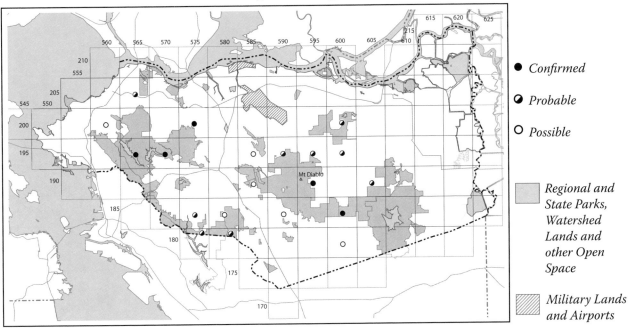

Confirmed

Probable

Possible

Regional and State Parks, Watershed Lands and other Open Space

Military Lands and Airports

The Chipping Sparrow is a subdued summer member of the local avifauna, with a drawn out, buzzy song reminiscent of a Dark-eyed Junco and a drab plumage interrupted only by a bright chestnut cap.

Current status and distribution

The Chipping Sparrow has an enigmatic distribution in Contra Costa County with vast amounts of seemingly suitable habitat left unoccupied. The species is found in blue oak and valley oak woodlands and in grasslands where they connect with forest edges. In certain very local situations in the eastern Diablo Range the species inhabits the grassy floor of sparse but shady oak woodlands.

The Chipping Sparrow is found exclusively in the Coast Range. It is absent from the wetter western portion of the Berkeley Hills but is present locally further east, such as at Briones Regional Park, where habitats open up. The Chipping Sparrow is much more common in the Diablo Range, with its more extensive savannah habitats, and yet even there significant stands of habitat are left unoccupied.

Historical occurrence

Grinnell and Wythe (1927) considered the Chipping Sparrow to be a locally common summer resident, although less common than previously. They did neglect citing Contra Costa specifically, but two sets of eggs were taken at Danville in 1898 (MVZ #3339 and #3340).

Breeding and natural history

The Chipping Sparrow was first recorded during the atlas project on 27 March, a typical arrival date for the county. Pairs were noted as early as 8 April. The small amount of data collected for this species makes a concise chronology impossible but confirmations included: an adult carrying nest material on 17 May; a nest with young on 22 June; adults carrying food 24 May and 27 June; and fledglings on three occasions 19–25 June. The egg sets mentioned above were collected 6 May and 22 June. The Sonoma County atlas project found a nest with eggs as early as 20 April (Burridge 1995). Adults feeding young were detected as late as 10 August in San Mateo County (Sequoia Audubon Society 2001), suggesting the local breeding season is more prolonged than our data suggest.

Conservation

Although the Chipping Sparrow in Contra Costa County is generally found on property that is already protected within park or watershed lands, recent development along the western and eastern edges of the Diablo Range must have come at the expense of some Chipping Sparrows.

BLACK-CHINNED SPARROW • *Spizella atrogularis*

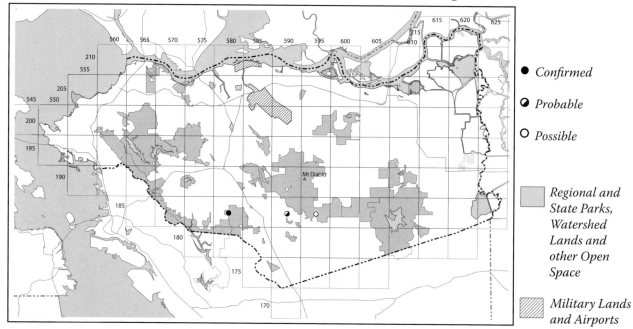

● *Confirmed*

◑ *Probable*

○ *Possible*

▨ *Regional and State Parks, Watershed Lands and other Open Space*

▨ *Military Lands and Airports*

The Black-chinned Sparrow has long been one of Contra Costa County's most sought after species by bird seekers from around the Bay Area. Even though present each summer on Mt. Diablo, its scarceness and unpredictable choice of breeding sites from year to year usually makes it a challenge to find, particularly for those unfamiliar with its distinctive song.

Current status and distribution

As the atlas map indicates, the Black-chinned Sparrow was detected in only two blocks and confirmed in only one. The confirmation came from near Las Trampas Peak in Las Trampas Regional Park west of Danville. The species was detected several times along South Gate Rd. in Mt. Diablo State Park, traditionally the most reliable spot in the county.

In years prior to the atlas, the species has been found higher up the western slope of the mountain, most notably around Muir Picnic Area, and also in White Canyon, a spur from Mitchell Canyon on the mountain's northern flank. Historical records exist from Black Diamond Mines Regional Park near Antioch, just northeast of Mt. Diablo, but the habitat there during the atlas project appeared to be too dense and in desperate need of a fire.

The Black-chinned Sparrow exclusively inhabits extensive stands of chamise and mixed chaparral on sunny interior hillsides. Such hillsides are generally south facing and cloaked with dense but not overgrown stands primarily composed of chamise, often mixed with black sage and various species of manzanita and ceanothus. Overgrown stands in need of fire are usually spurned (Shuford 1993). However, the lapse between a fire and occupation by

these sparrows varies greatly. Chamise dominated stands in Glenn County, California were found to be occupied in 7–10 years; breeding was confirmed in Sonoma County just 18–24 months after a fire (Burridge 1995).

On rare occasions the species has been found in coastal chaparral, including breeding birds found in coyote brush and California sagebrush by Alden H. Miller in 1924 in Strawberry Canyon, Alameda County (Miller 1929). Singing males were detected in similar habitat in Tilden Park, Contra Costa County in at least five seasons between 1968 and 1984, but not since.

Historical occurrence

Grinnell and Wythe (1927) knew the Black-chinned Sparrow only from southeast Alameda County. But just two years later Alden H. Miller himself collected two males from Las Trampas Peak in what is now Las Trampas Regional Park (MVZ #53948 and #69961). These two specimens represent the type of the race *caurina* (Miller 1929). Birds on Mt. Diablo are first mentioned in literature in 1960 when an adult was found feeding a full-sized fledgling on 15 July 1960 (AFN 14: no. 5).

Breeding and natural history

The Black-chinned Sparrow was found on just four occasions in two blocks during the atlas project, although it seems likely that this is partially due to modest coverage within its very limited range. Singing males were noted 10 May and 15 June and a pair was watched visiting a probable nest site on 11 June, all along South Gate Rd. in Mt. Diablo State Park. The lone confirmation for the atlas was achieved near Las Trampas Peak in Las

Trampas Regional Park when fledglings were observed on 29 June.

Published breeding records from elsewhere in Northern California are few but allow at least a rough breeding chronology. In Monterey County, adults carrying nest material were noted 24 May and carrying food 20 June (Roberson and Tenney 1993). In Marin County, nest building was confirmed 12 June, a nest with young was monitored from 4–10 June, and a fledgling was seen 23 July (Shuford 1993). In Sonoma County an occupied nest was found 18 May and a fledgling was detected 13 July (Burridge 1995).

Conservation

Although the vast majority of suitable Black-chinned Sparrow habitat is protected within the confines of regional and state parks, declines have been noted throughout its range, particularly in Southern California, the species stronghold. The culprit there has been habitat loss and degradation, primarily from development, but mining and off-road vehicles have also been implicated. Fire suppression, now necessary due to encroaching housing developments, may also have severe long-term repercussions. The Black-chinned Sparrow has been placed on Audubon's Watchlist 2002 as a Yellow List Species.

DARK-EYED JUNCO

LARK SPARROW • *Chondestes grammacus*

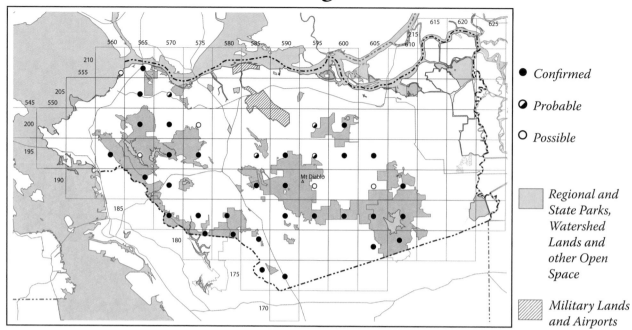

● *Confirmed*

◑ *Probable*

○ *Possible*

▢ *Regional and State Parks, Watershed Lands and other Open Space*

▨ *Military Lands and Airports*

The Lark Sparrow, possessor of one of the most outstanding head patterns of any North American bird and a song that Dawson called one of "nature's sacraments," is a fairly common but enigmatic member of the local avifauna, common in some situations yet rare or absent in seemingly similar circumstances.

Current status and distribution

As a breeding bird, the Lark Sparrow is truly a bird of the Coast Range, particularly the drier Diablo Range. The species favors valley oak and blue oak savannah habitats but is also found at the juxtaposition of woodlands and grasslands. Extensive grasslands lacking in trees or shrubs for perching and nest concealment are shunned. The species is completely absent as a breeding bird from west and east counties, suburban areas and the extensive marshes of North County.

Historical occurrence

No changes in the status and distribution of the Lark Sparrow have been noted in historical times. The earliest known nest record for the county involved a set of eggs collected at Danville 20 June 1897 (MVZ #3336).

Breeding and natural history

Adults noted carrying nest material or in the process of nest building were detected on nine occasions 5 April–15 June, with later dates suggesting a second brood since young were noted out of the nest in May. Adults carrying food were detected eleven times 30 April–16 August and adults feeding young another eight times 6 June–21 July. Fledglings were tallied nine times 5 May–14 July.

Conservation

Although its status in the county is likely secure, the population has undoubtedly suffered due to the destruction of oak savannah habitats and will continue to do so, particularly in the hills south of Antioch.

SAGE SPARROW • *Amphispiza belli*

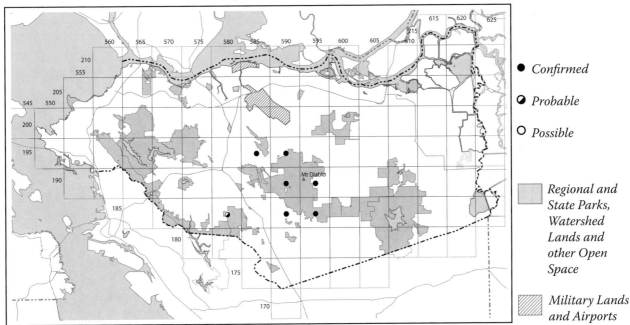

● *Confirmed*

◑ *Probable*

○ *Possible*

▨ *Regional and State Parks, Watershed Lands and other Open Space*

▨ *Military Lands and Airports*

The Sage Sparrow is an under-appreciated permanent resident of interior chaparral, its thunder stolen by the highly coveted Black-chinned Sparrow, alongside of which it dwells. The local Sage Sparrow, of the coastal race "*belli*," is a permanent resident in Contra Costa County, although it becomes far more difficult to find in the winter when it stops singing.

Current status and distribution

The Sage Sparrow in Contra Costa County has very specific habitat needs: extensive stands of chamise and mixed chaparral that are neither too sparse (young), nor too dense (old and in need of fire). The primary component of this chaparral is chamise, which may be interspersed with black sage, ceanothus and manzanita. Such habitat is found in extensive amounts only on Mt. Diablo, where it thrives on hot, sunny south-facing hillsides with poorly drained rocky soils. A small Sage Sparrow population is present around Las Trampas Ridge west of Danville and it has been reported sporadically from Black Diamond Mines, although not during the atlas project; the habitat there appears too dense and in need of fire.

Historical occurrence

Early references document the nesting of the Sage Sparrow in areas further west than it is currently found, including Leona Heights near Oakland and Claremont Canyon near Berkeley, both in Alameda County (Grinnell and Wythe 1927). A nest with young in Reliez Valley near Lafayette in 1932 was also from an area where this species is no longer thought to occur (Gull 14: no. 6).

Breeding and natural history

The Sage Sparrow was confirmed only six times during the atlas project, not surprising considering the low number of blocks with suitable habitat and the density of that habitat. Adults were noted carrying nest material 29 April and 21 May. An adult was seen carrying food 9 June. Fledglings were detected on three occasions: 15 and 18 June and 28 August. In Marin County, nest-building was observed 19 April and 25 May (Shuford 1993). During the Monterey atlas, the earliest record of an adult carrying food was 9 May; the early date for fledglings was 17 May (Roberson and Tenney 1993). In Sonoma County, an occupied nest was found 28 April and an adult was seen attending young 12 July (Burridge 1995). The Napa County atlas achieved three confirmations: an adult carrying food on 8 June, and recently fledged young 29 June and 27 July (Napa-Solano Audubon Society 2003).

Conservation

The vast majority of suitable habitat for this species is steep and remote and generally protected within parklands. The primary threat in Contra Costa County appears to be from fire suppression, which causes chaparral stands to become too dense for this species.

SAVANNAH SPARROW • *Passerculus sandwichensis*

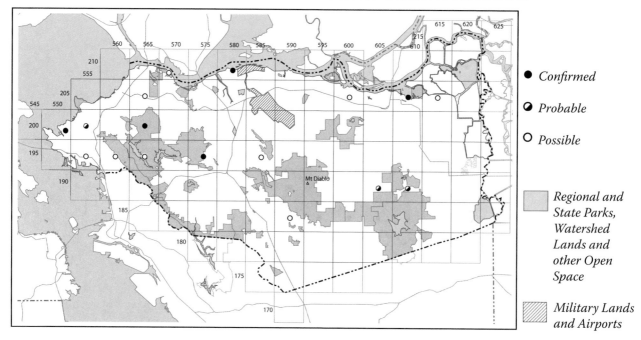

Confirmed

Probable

Possible

Regional and State Parks, Watershed Lands and other Open Space

Military Lands and Airports

Few of the county's breeding birds are less assuming in appearance or vocalization than the drab Savannah Sparrow and its weak insect-like "song." It is almost as if it revels in being low-key as it goes about its sparrow business within the confines of grasslands and marshes.

Current status and distribution

The Savannah Sparrow is currently believed to be a very scarce and local breeder at widely scattered sites and in radically different habitats. Breeding birds are present in both open, moist grasslands and extensive saline emergent marshes. During the atlas there were two confirmations from marshlands, one in a salt marsh near the mouth of San Pablo Creek in Richmond and one from the brackish marshes near the Concord Naval Weapons Station. Grassland nesting was proven on EBMUD property near Briones Valley, at Briones Regional Park, and on Iron House Sanitary District property at Oakley, the only nesting suspected in the Central Valley portion of the county.

In Marin County, breeders in salt marshes nest in older, higher portions of the marsh where low-growing pickleweed grades into wet, upland grasslands. Grassland nesters inhabit moist grasslands within the reach of summer fogs. Such sites have a reasonably dense layer of grasses at ground level and an accumulation of litter. A lack of moisture may be tolerated if vegetation requirements are fulfilled (Shuford 1993).

The lone nest site in the eastern portion of the county, at Iron House Sanitary District in Oakley, was in grassland that is periodically flooded with treated sewage and where the grass is interspersed with low growing wetland plants.

Historical occurrence

Grinnell and Wythe (1927) cite nesting in marshes and/or upland slopes at San Pablo and Pt. Richmond, but make no mention of nesting interior birds. Grinnell and Miller's (1944) California range map for breeding Savannah Sparrows shows this sparrow to be completely absent from the Central Valley in summer.

Breeding and natural history

Atlasers often had difficulty separating true breeding birds from a much larger array of wintering birds lingering before their return to northerly breeding grounds. Because of this, many records have been removed from the final map, although it must be said that this was based on sheer judgment.

The only nest observed was detected on 25 April and on that date already contained young. This relatively early date overlaps some of the wintering population and means that pairing and courtship surely begins by at least March, making the task of sorting out true breeders exceptionally difficult. Fledglings were noted on four occasions spanning 4 June–1 August.

Conservation

Breeding birds in central coastal California are of the small, dark race *P. s. alaudinus*, a race which has been designated a Third Priority California Bird Species of Special Concern (Shuford and Gardali 2008). Birds nesting in salt marshes have undoubtedly steeply declined due to extensive habitat destruction. The situation is less clear as it pertains to inland grasslands. Extensive conversion of grasslands in the moist Berkeley Hills to housing and even forests of eucalyptus and Monterey pine has likely been costly.

GRASSHOPPER SPARROW • *Ammodramus savannarum*

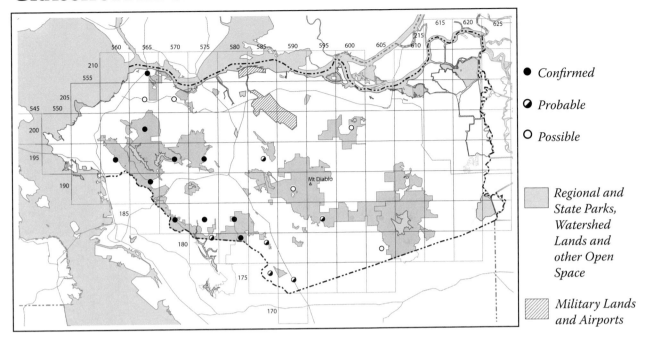

Legend:
- Confirmed
- Probable
- Possible

Regional and State Parks, Watershed Lands and other Open Space

Military Lands and Airports

This unique and mysterious semi-colonial grassland sparrow is seen only occasionally but may be detected in suitable habitat by those familiar with the buzzy songs for which the species is named.

Current status and distribution

The Grasshopper Sparrow is found on purely grassy hillsides of the Coast Range with small colonies present at favored locations year after year, though elsewhere colonies are known to move from site to site in succeeding years. Significant parcels of seemingly suitable habitat curiously lack this sparrow, perhaps because its habitat needs are stricter than we understand. The species' winter status is muddled: occasional wintering birds are found but it remains unclear if a few breeding birds over-winter or if such birds are northerly breeders seeking milder climes.

The majority of breeding birds were detected in the Berkeley Hills, probably because this sparrow prefers moister grasslands than are found in the more arid Diablo Range. A handful of birds were found on Mt. Diablo, at Black Diamond Mines Regional Preserve near Antioch, and in the extensive grasslands south of Mt. Diablo.

In Marin County, breeding Grasshopper Sparrows occupy grasslands of short to medium height with a "fairly thick but low cover of grasses and a variety of taller forbs and usually occur on dry upland sites" (Shuford 1993). Preferred habitats generally feature taller and more diverse grasslands than those occupied by Savannah Sparrows (Shuford 1993).

Historical occurrence

Grinnell and Miller (1927) considered this sparrow to be rare and local in spring and summer, with only spring records for Contra Costa County (Moraga Valley). Grinnell and Miller (1944) listed Moraga Valley and "Bald Peak" as stations of "known or probable residence."

Breeding and natural history

The earliest Grasshopper Sparrow detected during the atlas was on 22 March but there are many county records earlier than that. In fact, because a few of these very secretive birds have been found wintering on local breeding grounds, it is possible that at least some local breeders are actually permanent residents. The first pair noted was on 25 March. The lone report of an adult carrying nest material was on the very late date of 12 July and may possibly have actually represented an adult carrying food. With great diligence, a nest with eggs was found 9 May. An occupied nest was tallied 20 June. Adults carrying food were recorded 20 June and 5 July. Five records of fledglings, usually the easiest way to confirm this species, spanned 26 May–10 July.

Conservation

Here, as elsewhere, Grasshopper Sparrow populations have suffered from the conversion of grasslands to housing. Such losses have led to its designation as a Second Priority California Bird Species of Special Concern (Shuford and Gardali 2008).

SONG SPARROW • *Melospiza melodia*

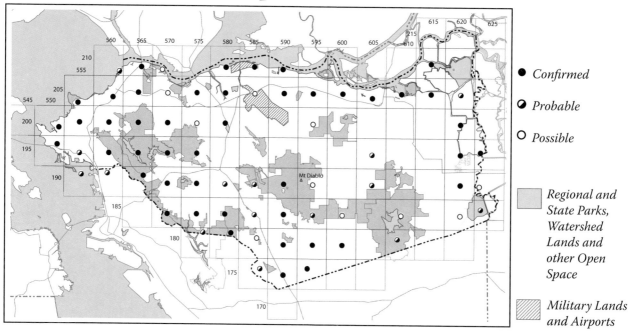

Confirmed

Probable

Possible

Regional and State Parks, Watershed Lands and other Open Space

Military Lands and Airports

For where is the bird-lover whose face does not unconsciously relax, or whose heart does not turn tender at the mere mention of this magic name, Song Sparrow! He is the poet of common day. He is the familiar of childhood; for knowledge of him comes at a time of life when one can poke about without rebuke in little cool dingles, or, perchance, accompany recreant watercourses in their perilous journeys to the sea.

⬥ William Leon Dawson (1923)

The common Song Sparrow, an unassuming resident of wet areas throughout the county, is represented by five breeding subspecies in the tight confines of Contra Costa County, thus making it of great interest to evolutionary biologists, as well as birders.

Current status and distribution

The Song Sparrow is a widespread permanent resident throughout most of the county, thought to be absent only from some densely urbanized blocks in the center portion of the county, a few particularly dry blocks in the Diablo Range, and some heavily agricultural blocks in East County. It is possible that a few birds went undetected in some of those blocks.

Breeding Song Sparrows are present in fresh emergent wetlands, saline emergent wetlands, riparian forests, and wet, weedy fields and ditches. They are very locally found in residential settings in the central portion of the county if sufficient shrubbery is existent near water.

Song Sparrow systematics are deeply complex and far beyond this scope of this book. The following brief summary follows Patten (2001), who identified 24 diagnosable subspecies, 9 of which occur in California.

M. m. gouldii is the common Song Sparrow of central coastal California away from the shores of San Francisco Bay and is commonly found in Contra Costa County in wet areas in the Coast Range. It is hemmed in to the west by *M. m. samuelis*, to the north by *M. m. maxillaris*, and to the northeast and east by *M. m. heermanni*. This includes *M. m. santaecrucis*, described by Grinnell in 1901.

M. m. samuelis, the "Samuel's" or "San Pablo" Song Sparrow, is a permanent resident of salt marshes along the shores of San Pablo Bay, including areas around Richmond and Pinole, probably southeast to Pt. San Pablo. The pre-development population of the Samuel's Song Sparrow has recently been estimated at between 297,000 and 329,000 birds. The current breeding population is thought to number between 81,000 and 90,000 birds (Spautz and Nur 2006).

M. m. maxillaris, the "Suisun" Song Sparrow, permanently inhabits tidal salt and brackish marshes along the shore of Suisun Bay, from Martinez eastward. It is unclear how far to the east this dark, thick-billed sparrow ranges, or if it comes into contact with the more widespread *M. m. heermanni*. Historically, the subspecies ranged from Pt. Costa on the west to as far east as Browns Island north of Antioch. The pre-development population has recently been estimated at between 202,000 and 313,000 birds. The most recent estimate of the current population is about 43,000 to 66,000 birds (Spautz and Nur 2006).

M. m heermanni breeds throughout the Central Valley. Following Patten (2001), this includes *M. m. mailliardi*, first described by Grinnell in 1911. Birds nesting in the eastern portion of the county, particularly in low-lying delta areas, are presumably this subspecies. It is unclear how far west the range of this race extends along the northern shore of the county before it meets (if it indeed does) with *M. m. maxillaris*.

M. m. pusillula, the "Alameda" Song Sparrow, inhabits the salt marshes along the shores of south San Francisco Bay. Marshall (1948), in his seminal works on the Song Sparrows of the San Francisco Bay estuary, identified the Song Sparrows present at Stege, just north of Pt. Isabel Regional Shoreline, as *pusillula*, likely the only location in the county where the subspecies occurs. The historical population of the subspecies has recently been estimated at between 92,000 and 138,000. The current population is estimated at just 13,400-20,000 individuals (Chan and Spautz 2006).

Historical occurrence

The overall status and distribution of the Song Sparrow is likely broadly similar to historical times, although numbers of the marsh-dwelling subspecies have undoubtedly been hit hard by habitat destruction.

Breeding and natural history

Even though there may be significant differences in the timing of breeding among the five local subspecies, it was beyond the scope of this project to detect them, partially due to the difficulty of identification and partially due to time constraints. The following data, unfortunately, average out any differences, leaving the less common subspecies, particularly *pusillula* and *samuelis*, underrepresented.

Nest building and the carrying of nest material was recorded nine times between 14 March and 5 June. Three nests with eggs were discovered 24 April–2 June. Adults carrying food or feeding young were noted on twenty-nine occasions spanning 5 April–11 August. Fledglings were particularly easy to detect, with twenty-seven records from 2 May–7 July, with the majority of records from June.

Conservation

Of the Song Sparrow subspecies known to breed in Contra Costa County, only *M. m. heermanni* and *M. m. gouldii* have large ranges with apparently healthy populations. The Alameda Song Sparrow, which presumably still breeds at Richmond, has been given Second Priority status as a California Bird Species of Special Concern (Shuford and Gardali 2008). Samuel's Song Sparrow and the Suisun Song Sparrow have been designated a Third Priority species (Shuford and Gardali 2008). All three subspecies, particularly the Alameda Song Sparrow, have suffered from wholesale habitat destruction from filling for development or agriculture and from the construction of salt evaporation ponds.

Song Sparrow

WHITE-CROWNED SPARROW

WHITE-CROWNED SPARROW • *Zonotrichia leucophrys*

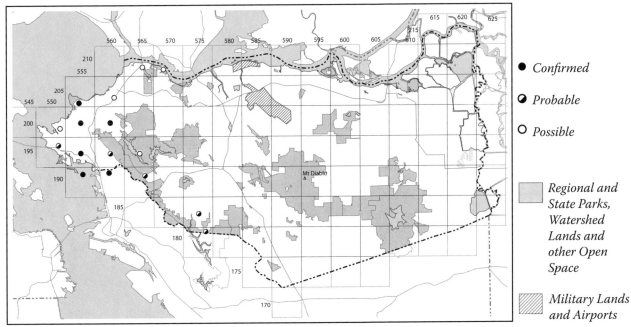

● *Confirmed*

◑ *Probable*

○ *Possible*

▨ *Regional and State Parks, Watershed Lands and other Open Space*

▨ *Military Lands and Airports*

Few of our local breeding birds face a more uphill battle to produce young each year than does the White-crowned Sparrow. Its range and habitat needs expose it to a harrowing array of threats including a growing army of cats—both domestic and feral—as well as the ever-lurking Brown-headed Cowbird.

Current status and distribution

The true status of the "Nuttall's" White-crowned Sparrow is slightly muddled by the winter presence of two other races, each superficially similar to local breeding birds and each much more common. It is thus possible that some sightings of "possibles" and "probables" may actually refer to wintering birds from the north.

True breeding birds are known to occur only along the Richmond Bay plain and in the wet, fog-shrouded western edge of the Berkeley Hills, where the species prefers open, scrubby habitats, including coastal scrub where it occurs, and in suburban neighborhoods. During the atlas, the species was confirmed in six blocks and thought to probably breed in a handful more, all within reach of persistent daily summer fogs.

Historical occurrence

Grinnell and Wythe (1927) state that *nuttalli* was common near the bay in Alameda County opposite the Golden Gate. Grinnell and Miller neglected to mention Contra Costa County but clearly include breeding stations around Richmond. In addition, the MVZ has a plethora of specimens, mostly from the 1930s, taken in the western Berkeley Hills, at Brooks Island, Red Rock,

along the Richmond shoreline, and even almost as far eastward as Lafayette. On 10 May 1941, Milton Seibert and Henry Carriger discovered numerous singing *nuttalli* on Rocky and Las Trampas ridges, now within Las Trampas Regional Park (Seibert 1942). This is well away from, and far more arid than, areas where the species currently breeds.

Breeding and natural history

The "Nuttall's" White-crowned Sparrow is a sedentary resident and thus birds were recorded as early as atlasing began. Adults carrying nest material were found 25 April and 3 May. An adult carrying food was found 13 June. Nests with young were detected 15 May and 18 July. Adults feeding young were tallied 31 May, 18 June, and 11 July. An adult feeding a fledgling at Marina Bay, Richmond on 9 Sept 2003 suggests that the breeding season is far more prolonged than the atlas database indicates (Quail 50: no.4).

Conservation

Although little concern appears to exist for any subspecies of the White-crowned Sparrow, the local population should be the exception. Luis Baptista, who studied song dialects of the White-crowned Sparrow extensively, felt that the East Bay population was reproductively isolated (Shuford 1993). With no gene flow from coastal populations, habitat degradation and fragmentation, and a vulnerability to nest parasitism from the Brown-headed Cowbird that appears to be greater than in other populations, the local population deserves careful monitoring.

213

DARK-EYED JUNCO • *Junco hyemalis*

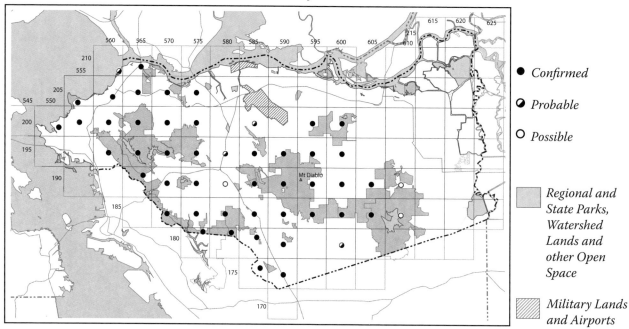

● *Confirmed*

◐ *Probable*

○ *Possible*

�(shaded) *Regional and State Parks, Watershed Lands and other Open Space*

▨ *Military Lands and Airports*

Looking much like a comical little henchman, the affable "Oregon" Dark-eyed Junco has become one of Contra Costa County's more common and certainly conspicuous breeding birds, in recent years even adapting to some residential neighborhoods and urban areas. Once the noisy, streaked young leave the nest, there are few woodland birds easier to confirm breeding.

Current status and distribution

The map for the Dark-eyed Junco is for the most part a mirror of the wooded portions of the Coast Range where the species is generally one of the most common and most conspicuous breeding birds. The species nests in open coastal oak woodlands and near the edges and openings of denser forests. It is more localized in the Diablo Range where much of the habitat is too open, and is generally present only in the shadier canyons. The Junco is absent from the river plain around Pittsburg and Antioch as well as from the entirety of East County. Much of the acreage south of Mt. Diablo is open grassland and completely unsuitable for nesting Juncos. In recent years, the species has begun to nest in certain urban situations, as around Bishop Ranch Business Park in San Ramon. There, planted conifers with even modest amounts of shrubbery seem to be sufficient.

Historical occurrence

Known to Belding (1890) only as a winter visitor, the first known nest record for the East Bay wasn't established until 1917. On that date, partly feathered young were found at the Claremont Country Club, Alameda County (Allen 1917). A pair had been seen on the U. C. Berkeley campus as early as 1912, but without any signs of breeding. It was Joseph Grinnell (1914) himself who speculated, "sooner or later, as planted groves become denser and taller, a colony will establish itself, as at Stanford." It did and has since spread throughout the woodlands of the East Bay, a spread that continues to the present even in select urban areas. The first known nest record for Contra Costa County was provided by an egg set taken "near Clayton" 12 Apr 1936 (WFVZ #34966).

Breeding and natural history

The Dark-eyed Junco is a permanent resident of Contra Costa County so individuals were observed as early as atlasers were out in the field. The earliest pair was recorded 1 February. Adults either carrying nest material or noted in the process of nest building were tallied on twelve occasions between 14 March–9 May. Four nests with young were found 4–26 May. Adults carrying food or feeding young were noted forty-two times from 3 April–8 July. The fledglings were notably conspicuous and found on forty-eight occasions spanning 17 April–18 July. The later dates are presumably of second broods.

Conservation

The ability of the Dark-eyed Junco to nest in a wide range of shady woodland habitats, in combination with its recent colonization of some urban and suburban situations, bodes well for its long term future in Contra Costa County.

BLACK-HEADED GROSBEAK • *Pheucticus melanocephalus*

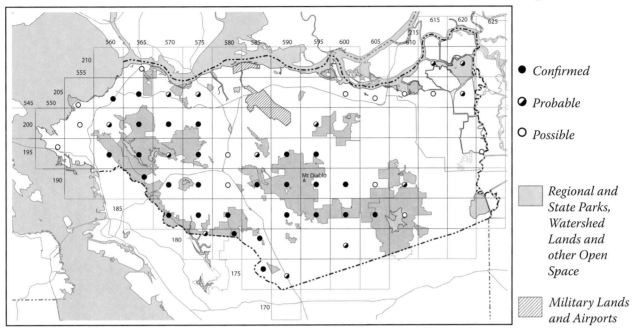

The glory of the Black-headed Grosbeak is his song —not often a brilliant or wonderful song, but always a jovial, rolling, or eumoirous song. Sometimes it is a little argumentative, as though the singer, having taken a brief for optimism, had encountered a skeptic. Sometimes the singer's heart is so full that he carries his song with him while he works.   ❧ *William Leon Dawson (1923)*

Current status and distribution

The Black-headed Grosbeak is a fairly common summer resident of the Coast Range. The species is quite common in the Berkeley Hills but in the Diablo Range it is generally relegated to moist canyon bottoms and riparian strips. Breeding was never confirmed during the atlas from the Bay plain around Richmond or from the Central Valley portion of the county although it is assumed to have occurred. The Black-headed Grosbeak breeds locally in well-wooded residential neighborhoods in the central portion of the county but not in the northern or eastern portion where vegetation appears insufficient.

Preferred habitat is often somewhat open coastal oak woodlands with "edge" habitats. Truly dense forests are unsuitable, although at least some canopy is required. Most of the county's breeding birds inhabit riparian habitats, often featuring willows, alders and cottonwoods. Within the Coast Range, moist coastal oak woodlands usually border such habitat.

Historical occurrence

Grinnell and Wythe (1927) classified the Black-headed Grosbeak as a common summer resident throughout the Bay Area, suggesting that its status remains unchanged in the past century.

Breeding and natural history

The first singing male Black-headed Grosbeak is typically one of our earliest arriving neotropical migrants; the earliest arrival during the atlas project was 22 March. The first pair was noted 28 March. Adults carrying nest material or nest building were found six times between 14 April and 16 June, the latter of which may represent a re-nesting. Occupied nests were detected, some with visible young, on five occasions spanning 4 May–4 July. Adults carrying food and feeding young were found fifteen times from 22 May–11 July. Fledglings were detected an additional nine times from 19 May–16 August.

Conservation

Black-headed Grosbeak populations are thought to be "large and relatively stable" (Hill 1995). The opening up of forests and the planting of fruiting trees has likely compensated for habitat destruction, at least partially.

215

BLUE GROSBEAK

BLUE GROSBEAK • *Passerina caerulea*

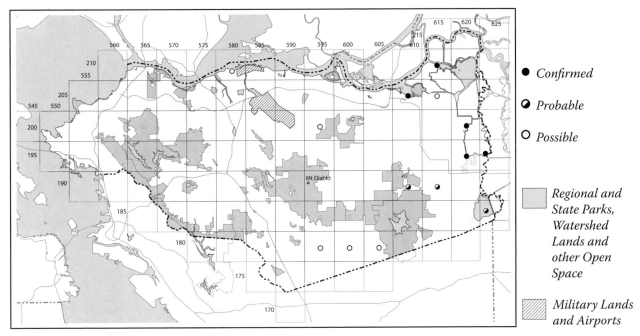

Legend:
- ● Confirmed
- ◑ Probable
- ○ Possible
- ▨ Regional and State Parks, Watershed Lands and other Open Space
- ▨ Military Lands and Airports

The brilliant deep blue plumage and warbling song of the Blue Grosbeak does much to brighten the weedy areas of East County during the hot summer at a time and place where there is often little avian activity. The male often sings endlessly atop brambles and telephone wires while its more subdued mate goes about familial responsibilities below.

Current status and distribution

The Blue Grosbeak is a fairly common summer resident of far East County, where it inhabits willow clumps, drainage ditches and weedy, bramble-choked fields. Riparian habitats featuring anything but willows and blackberry brambles are rare in East County but a few pairs inhabit narrow strips of oaks and walnuts in the Brentwood area. Some favored locations where the species is particularly common include Jersey Island, the north end of Bethel Island, Holland Tract and Orwood Rd.

Prior to the atlas project, the Blue Grosbeak was almost unknown away from traditional breeding areas in the Delta. Quite a few birds however, were detected during the atlas project well out of range and possibly prospecting for potential nest sites. Amongst the locations was the Nortonville side of Black Diamond Mines Regional Park, the Concord Naval Weapons Station, just south of Marsh Creek Res. (a pair), and near the south end of Lawrence Rd. near Blackhawk. Prior to the atlas project, the only county records of true migrants (colonizers?) was one at West Pittsburg 22 May 1979 (AB 33: no. 5) and a young male at Briones Regional Park 16 June 1985 (AB 39: no. 5).

Historical occurrence

Grinnell and Wythe (1927) make no mention of the Blue Grosbeak from the eastern portion of the Bay Area but Grinnell and Miller (1944) did include eastern Contra Costa County on their range map, although this is based upon an assumed range rather than actual sightings or specimens. The first known county record, strongly suggestive of breeding, is now thought to have been three birds at Bethel Island 6 July 1956 (county notebooks). There are a handful of recent breeding records for other Bay Area counties, including Alameda, Santa Clara and Sonoma (Bousman 2007), all possibly related to the same phenomenon which produced the extralimital records from this project.

Breeding and natural history

The Blue Grosbeak begins to arrive in Contra Costa County about 20 April, but the first singing male detected during this atlas project was 27 April. The first pair wasn't recorded until 5 May, although they doubtlessly occurred earlier. The lone instance of an adult carrying nest material was discovered 22 May. Adults were observed carrying food on five occasions spanning the narrow window of 25 June to 6 July. A fledgling was noted 30 June. In years prior to and after the atlas project, assumed family groups have been noted on Bethel Island deep into August (pers. obs.).

Conservation

Blue Grosbeak populations in the eastern and northeastern portion of the county may be reasonably secure since development of such low-lying areas is inherently risky. Central Valley birds on slightly higher ground, however, are highly vulnerable to recent unrestrained development.

LAZULI BUNTING • *Passerina amoena*

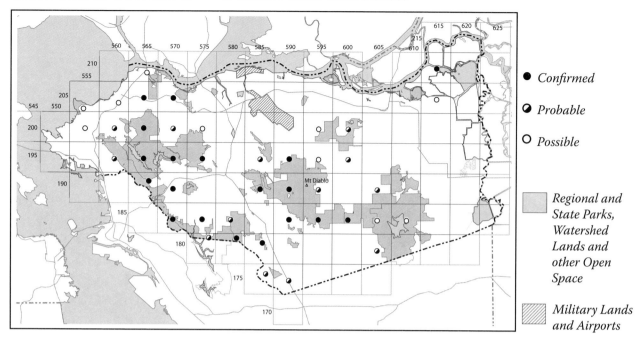

Confirmed
Probable
Possible

Regional and State Parks, Watershed Lands and other Open Space

Military Lands and Airports

The Lazuli Bunting, as its name would suggest, is a superbly plumaged summer resident of open woodlands throughout the interior hills and, locally at least, in East County. The number of Lazuli Buntings present from one year to the next is quite variable, perhaps as much as with any of Contra Costa County's breeding birds.

Current status and distribution

During the breeding season, the Lazuli Bunting is fairly common in the Coast Range, particularly in the more arid Diablo Range. Nesting was not confirmed on the Bay plain at Richmond. Singing males at Richmond on 15 and 31 May might have represented breeders but could also pertain to migrants. The sole confirmation for East County was at Piper Slough on Bethel Island; the species is quite rare elsewhere in the Central Valley portion of the county and even at Piper Slough the number of pairs can differ dramatically from year to year. Breeding birds are completely absent from any of the suburban areas of the county.

Preferred habitats of the Lazuli Bunting are invariably open. It will nest at the edge of moist forests and coastal oak woodlands, along riparian corridors and in chamise and mixed chaparral, as long as such habitats are close to grasslands or weedy, disturbed areas. Open areas with coyote brush, poison oak and hemlock seem particularly prized. Many sites with seemingly suitable habitat in the Berkeley Hills go unoccupied each summer.

Historical occurrence

Considered a "common summer resident, practically throughout the Bay Area" by Grinnell and Wythe (1927),

the status and distribution of the Lazuli Bunting appears to have changed little in the past century. A set of eggs collected in Moraga Valley 14 May 1931 (MVZ #5064) is the first known nest record, but the species had almost certainly been nesting all along.

Breeding and natural history

The earliest Lazuli Bunting detected during the atlas project was 11 April, but this is notably early; most arrive during the latter third of April. The first pair was detected 25 April. Carrying of nest material was noted on only three occasions spanning 4–25 April but note that the peak of nest-building in Monterey County (Roberson and Tenney 1993) is probably during mid-May, as it is in San Mateo (Sequoia Audubon Society 2001). Nests with young were noted on the disparate dates of 26 May and 6 July. Adults either carrying food or actively feeding young were detected on sixteen occasions between 29 May and 16 August, with a decided peak during the latter half of June and the first week of July. The August record, by far the latest during the project, may well refer to a second brood. Fledglings were detected three times from 6–25 July. It appears that all breeding birds have departed the county by late August.

Conservation

Any losses attributable to habitat destruction have likely been compensated for by the opening of forests and by an increase in thistles (Shuford 1993).

218

INDIGO BUNTING • *Passerina cyanea*

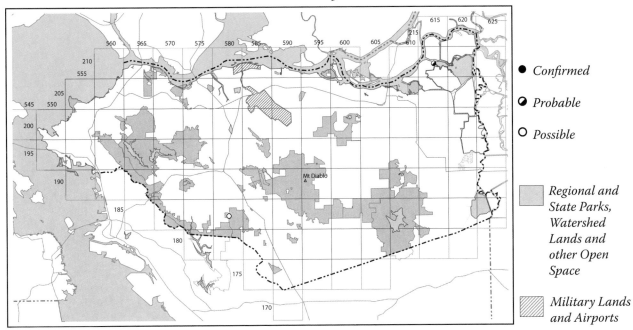

● *Confirmed*

◑ *Probable*

○ *Possible*

▨ *Regional and State Parks, Watershed Lands and other Open Space*

▨ *Military Lands and Airports*

The stunning little Indigo Bunting, once found only east of the continental divide, has rapidly expanded its breeding range in recent decades, particularly in the American Southwest. In recent decades the presence of territorial males in spring and early summer has come to be expected both along the coast and inland Northern California.

Current status and distribution

Singing males were noted on three occasions during the atlas project. One was at Las Trampas Regional Park west of Danville 30 May 1998. Another was at Piper Slough, Bethel Island 30 May–28 July 1998 with possibly the same bird noted there 1 June 2000. On 28 July 1998, the male at Piper Slough was watched singing and flying about a small territory, at the center of which was what appeared to be a female Lazuli Bunting feeding begging young. It is impossible to say with certainty that the male Indigo was the father of the young, but no male Lazuli Buntings were noted in the vicinity during that particular breeding season.

Historical occurrence

The Indigo Bunting has occurred sporadically in the East Bay since at least 1939 (Grinnell and Miller 1944), most often as spring vagrants. The first Bay Area nesting involved a hybrid pair at Olema, Marin County in 1984 (Shuford 1993). Additional hybrid pairs have been confirmed breeding in Santa Clara and Alameda counties (Bousman 2007), as well as in Contra Costa County (see above). An apparently "pure" pair of Indigo Buntings was found feeding young at Pescadero, San Mateo County in 1994 (Bousman 2007).

Breeding and natural history

Very little can be said about the breeding cycle of the Indigo Bunting in Northern California but it is likely very similar to that of the Lazuli Bunting.

Conservation

Other than its popularity as a cage bird, there appears to be little reason for concern for the Indigo Bunting.

RED-WINGED BLACKBIRD • *Agelaius phoeniceus*

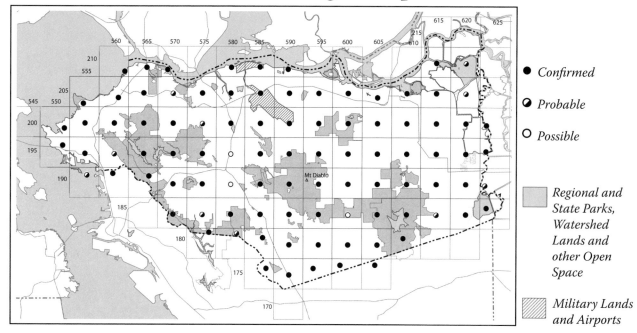

● *Confirmed*

◐ *Probable*

○ *Possible*

▨ *Regional and State Parks, Watershed Lands and other Open Space*

▨ *Military Lands and Airports*

The Red-winged Blackbird, with its flaming red epaulets and curious but eminently familiar song, is one of Contra Costa County's most recognizable breeding birds, even to those who rarely stop even for a moment to look at a mere bird.

Current status and distribution

Few birds are as abundant or widespread as the Red-winged Blackbird. It is one of the few species detected in every block and it likely bred in each of them. The species is most often found nesting in fresh and saline emergent wetlands and in riparian habitats but has also adapted readily to stands of mustard. In all cases, its distribution is limited by nearby foraging opportunities and to some extent, the presence of water.

Historical occurrence

Grinnell and Wythe (1927) considered the Red-winged Blackbird to be an abundant local resident, just as it is today.

Breeding and natural history

The earliest pair of Red-winged Blackbirds detected during the atlas was 13 February, although light coverage early in the season may have missed earlier pairings. Adults carrying nest material or observed nest building were found thirty-seven times between 12 March and 16 May with a great majority of reports coming from April. An additional report from 2 June was notably late. Occupied nests with unknown contents (but likely eggs) were tallied on seven occasions 5 April–17 May. Four of five egg sets collected in the county and now in possession of the MVZ were taken on 31 May, later than any

of our observations. A large number of confirmations were based upon adults carrying food or actually feeding young, with sixty records spanning 26 April–7 July. Fledglings were observed an additional fourteen times from 7 May–25 July.

Conservation

The local Red-winged Blackbird population is in little danger in the foreseeable future. However, protection of the marshes and open fields preferred by this species would benefit a plethora of more vulnerable species.

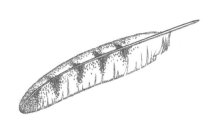

TRICOLORED BLACKBIRD • *Agelaius tricolor*

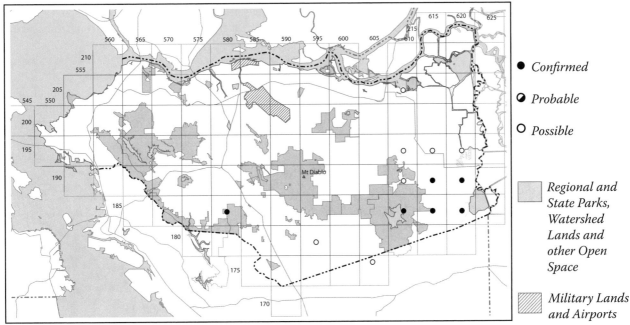

- ● *Confirmed*
- ◑ *Probable*
- ○ *Possible*

▨ *Regional and State Parks, Watershed Lands and other Open Space*

▨ *Military Lands and Airports*

Agelaius tricolor *is intensely gregarious, more so perhaps than any other American bird. Every major act of its life is performed in close association with its fellows. Not only does it roost, or ravage grain fields, or foregather for nesting, in hundreds and thousands, but the very day of its nesting is agreed upon in concert.*

↳ William Leon Dawson (1923)

Current status and distribution

The Tricolored Blackbird, nearly a California endemic, is a fairly common permanent but highly local resident of freshwater marshes and weedy fields, particularly in East County but also locally elsewhere. Most breeding birds were present in the vicinity of the hamlet of Byron in the southeast portion of the county. The largest colony, with perhaps several hundred pairs, was present beyond the eastern end of Camino Diablo in Byron. The only colony west of the Central Valley was present in the Dougherty Valley east of San Ramon.

The Tricolored Blackbird is an itinerant breeder. At least a portion of the population is known to nest in spring in the San Joaquin Valley, later moving north to nest again in the Sacramento Valley and northeastern California. Additionally, nest sites may shift from year to year, possibly as an adaptation to exploit ephemeral habitats which provide suitable nest sites and a sufficient food supply.

Traditionally, this colonial nesting species was dependent upon fresh emergent wetlands with tall emergent vegetation for nesting. In recent years, however, the Tricolored Blackbird has adapted to nesting in upland situations such as blackberry brambles and mustard or thistle fields. Of 252 breeding colonies observed in the Sacramento Valley from 1931–1936, nearly 93% were in freshwater marshes. In the 1970s, just 53% of colonies in the Central Valley occupied freshwater marshes (Beedy and Hamilton 1999).

Although not applicable to Contra Costa County, dairies and feedlots have seemed to increase in importance in recent decades. In 1994, 55% of studied nest colonies were associated with dairies (Beedy and Hamilton 1999).

Historical occurrence

Grinnell and Wythe (1927) make no mention of the occurrence of Tricolored Blackbirds in Contra Costa County even though a female was taken in Moraga Valley on the intriguing date of 21 May 1921 (MVZ specimen 41906). Grinnell and Miller (1944) include the Sacramento and San Joaquin Valleys in their nesting range so breeding likely occurred in East County, as it does now.

Breeding and natural history

Males may begin to sing as early as the end of February. Initial nesting, which may initiate synchronously, may occur as early as late March; by the end of April, most members of the species are associated with breeding colonies. Egg-laying may begin as early as two days after nest initiation, usually in late March or early April. Incubation is estimated to last 11–12 days. The species fledges at 11–14 days. Fledglings often disperse in sizable assemblages to suitable foraging areas and at that time

221

may be mistaken for colonies. All breeding is generally completed by late July–early August, although autumnal breeding has been recorded (Beedy and Hamilton 1999).

Conservation

There has been a clear decline in the total Tricolored Blackbird population during the 20th century. A systematic survey in 1934 estimated more than 700,000 adults in just eight counties. A statewide survey conducted in 1994 estimated the total population at 370,000 (±15%). A similar survey in 1997 estimated just 233,000 adults (±15%), a 37% decline in just three years (Beedy and Hamilton 1999). Additional surveys recorded 104,786 adults in 1999 and 162,508 adults in 2000 (Beedy in press). A 2004 survey which focused only on 184 sites that had supported at least 2000 adults in any previous year found only 33 of them to be active at the time of the survey (Green 2004).

The single most important factor for such declines is habitat alteration and destruction. Much of the Central Valley has been converted from grasslands, marshlands, and riparian woodlands, and replaced by agriculture and urbanization. Harvesting and plowing of silage and weedy fields has resulted in the destruction of nest colonies, as has the aerial spraying of herbicides or mosquito abatement oil.

The Tricolored Blackbird has been named a First Priority California Bird Species of Special Concern (Shuford and Gardali 2007), as well as a Yellow List Species on Audubon's Watchlist 2002.

TRICOLORED BLACKBIRD

WESTERN MEADOWLARK • *Sturnella neglecta*

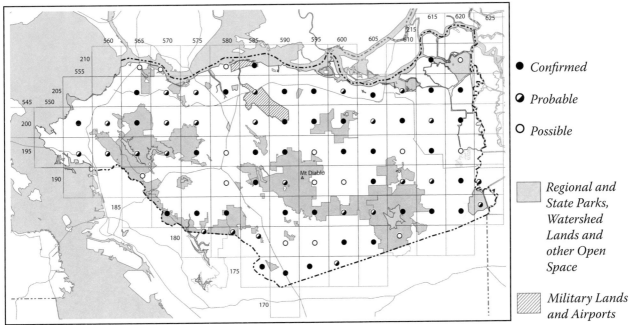

● *Confirmed*

◑ *Probable*

○ *Possible*

▨ *Regional and State Parks, Watershed Lands and other Open Space*

▨ *Military Lands and Airports*

A blackbird of the driest grasslands, the Western Meadowlark sings a wondrous song able to brighten even the most barren backcountry road. In a portion of what must surely be one of the finest paragraphs ever devoted to a bird, Dawson (1923) had this to say: "Born of the soil and lost in its embraces for such time as it pleases him, he yet quits his lowly station ever and again, mounts some fence-post or tree-top, and publishes to the world an unquenchable gladness in things-as-they-are."

Current status and distribution

The Western Meadowlark breeds in open grasslands throughout nearly the entire county with just a handful of blocks unoccupied. The county's grasslands, however, are not distributed as equally as the map might suggest, but instead are rather patchy, particularly in the western half of the county, most of which is forested or has been urbanized. In the center of the county the species is particularly common in the grasslands around Port Costa and Crockett, in the hills around Concord and Pittsburg and again in the rolling hills east of San Ramon. The meadowlark is common on the eastern flank of the Diablo Range, much of which is completely uninterrupted grasslands. Meadowlarks appear to reach maximum abundance in the fields of the eastern portion of the county, yet regrettably, its preferred haunts there are rapidly being usurped by relentless development.

Historical occurrence

The Western Meadowlark has been a common breeding bird in Contra Costa County for as long as anyone has been keeping track.

Breeding and natural history

The local Western Meadowlark population is bolstered significantly in winter by birds from the north but the breeding population is assumed to be sedentary. Singing birds were noted as early as mid-February and pairs by the end of the month. Adults carrying nest material were detected only five times between 31 March and 18 June. The vast majority of confirmations involve adults carrying food with thirty-three records 26 April–9 July. Fledglings were detected on eight occasions between 2 June and 30 July. The late nest building and fledgling dates suggest double brooding.

Conservation

Even though the future of the Western Meadowlark in Contra Costa County appears secure, populations must have taken a severe blow during the 20th century with wholesale development of the Bay plain around Richmond and the Interstate 680 corridor. These losses have continued in the Dougherty Valley east of San Ramon and especially in East County, where development has been nothing less than explosive.

WESTERN MEADOWLARK

BREWER'S BLACKBIRD • *Euphagus cyanocephalus*

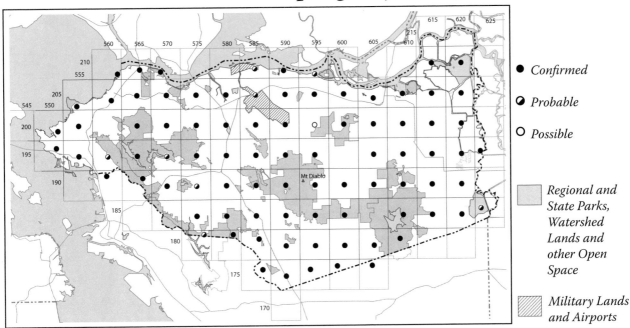

Confirmed

Probable

Possible

Regional and State Parks, Watershed Lands and other Open Space

Military Lands and Airports

To most birders, the Brewer's Blackbird seems to be little more than a "ho-hum" kind of bird because it is so common in places where people congregate. Of course it should be admired for its success even if its groveling for food in public places sometimes appears to suggest a lack of dignity.

Current status and distribution

The Brewer's Blackbird is a common, sometimes abundant permanent resident throughout most of the county and easily one of the most common species in the county. The atlas map for the Brewer's Blackbird, while indicative of a healthy population, is also indicative of something that might be seen, at least to lovers of wild places, as somewhat sinister, for the Brewer's Blackbird is anything but a bird of the wilderness. The species is generally a bird of open, disturbed settings such as cattle pens, orchards, vacant lots, playing fields and shopping center parking lots. The fact that Brewer's Blackbirds were detected in all but three blocks is a telling sign that no significantly large parcels of true wilderness have persisted in the county.

Historical occurrence

Grinnell and Miller (1927) summarized the Brewer's Blackbird as a common resident, an apt description of its current status.

Breeding and natural history

The first pair of Brewer's Blackbirds noted during the atlas was 3 March but atlasing activity generally increases later in the season and earlier pairings were undoubtedly missed. Thirty-six records of adults carrying nest ma-

terial or nest building were detected 14 March–7 June, with the bulk of the records from April. Occupied nests (contents unknown) were tallied nine times from 2–22 May; nests with young were found on three occasions 18–24 June. Adults carrying food were noted on thirty-one occasions 5 May–24 June. Fledglings were recorded thirty times 5 May–25 July.

Brewer's Blackbirds commonly second brood in coastal California (Martin 2002) and this was undoubtedly the case here. Three sets of eggs at the MVZ, all taken in Contra Costa County on 31 July, make it clear that much late nesting activity of this species was missed as little atlasing took place so late in the season.

Conservation

There appears to be no serious threats to the long-term future of the Brewer's Blackbird.

GREAT-TAILED GRACKLE • *Quiscalus mexicanus*

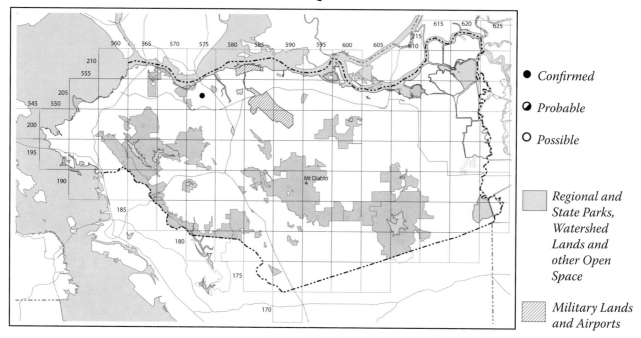

Confirmed

Probable

Possible

Regional and State Parks, Watershed Lands and other Open Space

Military Lands and Airports

The arrival of the Great-tailed Grackle as a breeding species in Contra Costa County was long awaited yet at the same time dreaded. The Great-tailed Grackle was confirmed nesting for the first time in the county during the atlas project and it would not be surprising to see it become far more common in the coming decades.

Current status and distribution

The colonization of Contra Costa County was relatively slow in coming but, in fact, may have just begun. The first record for Contra Costa County was found at Martinez Regional Shoreline 10–11 Jan 1985 (county notebooks). After that records were few and far between, with a handful of records of spring migrants and winter visitants, almost exclusively in the eastern portion of the county. The first nest record, found during the atlas project, was confirmed at McNabney Marsh near Martinez when a female was watched building a nest in tall, emergent vegetation within the marsh. The species has continued to nest through 2009 and is reliably found throughout the year.

Though nesting has yet to be confirmed away from McNabney Marsh, winter records are accumulating rapidly from the southeastern portion of the county. Favored settings appear to be tule-lined artificial ponds, most often thus far around artificial ponds as at Discovery Bay near Byron.

Historical occurrence

Since the first California record of Great-tailed Grackle at Imperial Dam, Imperial County 6 June 1964 (McCaskie and others 1966), the species has expanded rapidly but unevenly throughout settled areas of the state's lowlands, first reaching Contra Costa County in 1985 (AB 39; no. 2). By 2008, the species had been recorded in each of California's 58 counties (Sterling 2008), and Bay Area breeding records have been obtained from Alameda, San Francisco, Santa Clara, Sonoma and Solano counties (Bousman 2007).

Breeding and natural history

During the atlas project, the Great-tailed Grackle was noted only at McNabney Marsh near Martinez. Our lone nest confirmation involved a female building a nest 8 June. In San Diego County, where grackles are far more common, the following chronology was constructed: Nest building started as early as 29 March. Egg laying likely began to take place earlier than 25 April and continued to at least 1 July. A nest with nestlings was detected 28 July. Dependent fledglings were noted as late as 28 August (Unitt 2004). It is likely that, in general, the entire breeding process takes place slightly later in the season in Contra Costa County than it does in San Diego County.

Conservation

Because the Great-tailed Grackle in Northern California has tended to nest in freshwater marshes, the protection of remaining marshes would benefit this species as well as a whole host of others.

Brown-headed Cowbird • *Molothrus ater*

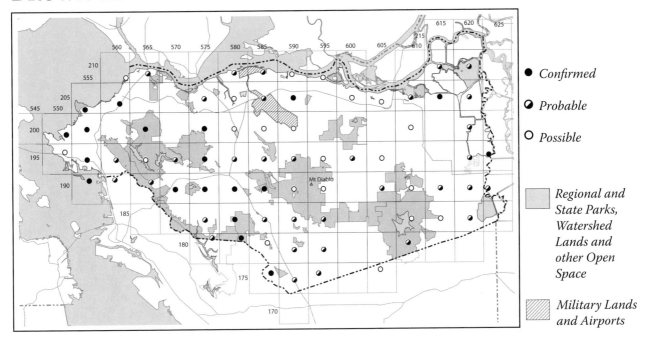

● *Confirmed*

◗ *Probable*

○ *Possible*

▨ *Regional and State Parks, Watershed Lands and other Open Space*

▨ *Military Lands and Airports*

Dawson, apparently filled with a virulent hatred for the cowbird, referred to the female Brown-headed Cowbird as "the unchaste mother of a race gone wrong" and an "avian marplot (that) lives only by stealth and by the secret practice of violence (Dawson 1923)." They don't write like that anymore and, in one of the few places in Dawson's otherwise monumental masterpiece, it is perhaps for the best.

Current status and distribution

The Brown-headed Cowbird is found throughout the county. The map indicates an increased presence in the western portion of the county but this is likely an artifact of coverage; the species was probably present in nearly every block, with the possible exception of some of the grassland blocks south and southeast of Mt. Diablo.

The cowbird lifestyle, uncluttered by any attachment to a specific nest site or the burden of feeding young, is unique. Mornings are spent in a wide variety of open habitats, the females searching for suitable targets and the males displaying and courting. In the afternoons, compact flocks go off in search of food. Favored habitats for foraging, often miles from morning sites, very often involve cattle pens or horse corrals, but may also include lawns and bird feeders.

Historical occurrence

The story of the spread of the Brown-headed Cowbird throughout the west in the 20th century is well documented, particularly in the East Bay. The invasion began in California at the Colorado River in about 1900, already reaching the Bay Area by 1922! The first record is believed to be the discovery of ten eggs in nests in Irvington (Fremont) in 1922. The species was not noted at Berkeley until 1934 (Rothstein 1994). The date of the first confirmed breeding in Contra Costa County is unknown.

The reasons for the spread are several. The creation of preferred foraging areas, namely areas of short grass or bare ground amongst large grazing animals, allowed the species to forage away from breeding areas. High fecundity of females (30–40 eggs per season) provided enormous growth potential. Finally, the pathway provided by man allowed this parasitic species to come into contact with host populations not previously sympatric with any species of brood parasite (Rothstein 1994).

Breeding and natural history

Apparent pairs of cowbirds were noted as early as the second week of March. Nests with young and adults feeding young were recorded on eleven occasions spanning 25 April–17 July. Fledglings were tallied another eight times between 16 May and 16 August. The high number of probable observations, as compared to the relatively low number of confirmations, suggests that the presence of young cowbirds either still on the nest or already fledged was often overlooked by observers concentrating on the identity of adult birds.

The Brown-headed Cowbird has been recorded parasitizing the nests of over 220 species and at least 144 species are known to have raised cowbird young. Hosts have ranged in size from creepers and kinglets to birds as large as meadowlarks (Lowther 1993). Because cowbirds may parasitize the nests of a certain species in one part of its range but not in another, it is difficult to generalize about host species although, as pointed out by Shuford (1993), any passerine within its breeding range is susceptible except for the larger corvids. Some frequent hosts in coastal Northern California include the Pacific-slope Flycatcher, Warbling Vireo, Common Yellowthroat and White-crowned Sparrow (Shuford 1993).

Conservation

In the case of the Brown-headed Cowbird, the traditional use of the term conservation is turned on its head, for current management efforts are aimed at culling cowbird populations rather than protecting them. This most often involves the trapping of cowbirds on the breeding grounds of sensitive species such as Bell's Vireos.

HOODED ORIOLE

HOODED ORIOLE • *Icterus cucullatus*

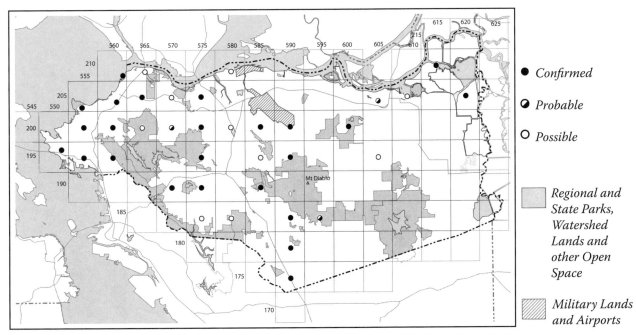

This recent colonist to Contra Costa County is a nice addition to residential neighborhoods with the coincidental foresight to plant the palm trees that this stunning oriole utilizes for nest sites.

Current status and distribution

The range of Hooded Oriole in the county is similar to that of the Rock Pigeon and House Sparrow, in that it is virtually never found away from populated areas and is thus absent from the extensive parklands and watershed areas of the Coast Range. The species seems to be rather uniformly distributed throughout the suburban areas of the county although, perhaps because of an abundance of feeders and exotic plantings, it may be most common along the Interstate 680 corridor.

The one constant factor in the presence or absence of breeding Hooded Orioles appears to be the presence of palm plantings, which the species inevitably uses for nesting. Most nests are found in *Washingtonia filifera* though in Marin, where the species has been closely studied, it has also been found to occasionally use *W. robusta* and the Canary Island date palm (Shuford 1993). Nesting birds in Marin may also nest in numerous other introduced trees such as eucalyptus but in all cases they utilize the filaments of *W. filifera* for nest construction.

It seems likely that suitable habitats in the county have already been colonized and that further expansion awaits additional palm plantings and the maturation of other exotic plantings. Such increases are most likely to occur in recently developed areas around Dougherty Valley east of San Ramon and in East County, where development in recent years has been explosive.

Historical occurrence

The Hooded Oriole had yet to arrive in Contra Costa County in 1927 (Grinnell and Wythe 1927). It is unclear when the first Hooded was detected in the East Bay but it was apparently about May 1930 at Oakland, Alameda County, and in Reliez Valley near Lafayette, Contra Costa County (Bousman 2007). The first confirmed nest for the Bay Area was at San Leandro, Alameda County in 1939 (Sibley 1952). The first probable nest for Contra Costa County was in Wildcat Canyon in 1937 (Grinnell and Miller 1944), although the next known nest was as late as 1954 (AFN 8: no. 5). See Shuford (1993) for a fine summary of the Hooded Oriole's colonization of California.

Breeding and natural history

The earliest Hooded Oriole to arrive during the atlas project was 10 March; the earliest pair was 25 March. Nest building was recorded on just two occasions: 16 April and 16 May. Seven occupied nests (contents unknown) were detected 8 April–21 July; a nest with young was tallied 31 May. Adults were found carrying food five times between 27 May and 3 July. Fledglings were detected on thirteen occasions between 5 May and 17 August.

Conservation

The Hooded Oriole has readily adapted to suburban settings with attendant palms for nesting and exotic plants and feeders for nectar, a habitat type likely only to increase in coming decades as suburban sprawl continues in East County.

229

BULLOCK'S ORIOLE • *Icterus bullockii*

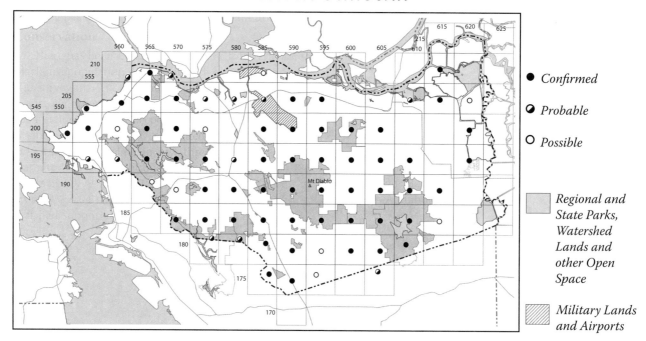

● *Confirmed*

◑ *Probable*

○ *Possible*

▨ *Regional and State Parks, Watershed Lands and other Open Space*

▨ *Military Lands and Airports*

The more common of our two orioles and the only one normally found in native habitats, the Bullock's Oriole adds a rare splash of orange to the woodlands of Contra Costa County. Its chatty calls are a sure sign that spring has returned.

Current status and distribution

The atlas map shows an even distribution across the county but the species is undoubtedly less common in the wetter western one-third of the county where it is often relegated to areas featuring introduced stands of eucalyptus—including suburban neighborhoods. Around Briones and Las Trampas Regional Parks, on the eastern side of the Berkeley Hills, the habitat begins to open up, the oaks become more widely spaced and, on cue, the chatter of the oriole becomes almost constant. The Bullock's Oriole is found throughout the wooded portions of Central County, particularly in oak woodlands but also in riparian situations where there is generally grasslands or agricultural areas nearby for foragaing. A particularly favored niche is in and around eucalyptus planted around defunct homesteads in savannah situations. The Bullock's Oriole is present in small numbers in suburban Central County, although usually in more established neighborhoods and often in smaller numbers than the Hooded Oriole. The species is found in East County where riparian habitats have survived the bulldozer but since this has only rarely been the case, it is relegated to planted eucalyptus windbreaks.

Historical occurrence

Except for the added opportunity afforded by eucalyptus plantings in the western portion of the county, it would appear that the status of the Bullock's Oriole has changed little in the past century.

Breeding and natural history

The Bullock's Oriole arrives fairly early in spring. During the atlas project the first returnee was noted 12 March and the first pair was detected 28 March. Adults carrying nest material or nest building were found eighteen times between 5 April and 27 May with additional reports from 7 June and 11 July. Because the Bullock's Oriole is generally thought to be single-brooded (Rising and Williams 1999), the June and July records probably represent re-nesting. Occupied nests (contents unknown) were detected seven times 11 May–8 July; nests with young were tallied three times from 20 May–12 June. Adults were found carrying food on seventeen occasions 11 May–8 July. Twenty-eight records of fledglings, many being fed, recorded 13 May–18 July.

Conservation

Development of former savannah habitats throughout the county has almost certainly affected local populations though urban feeders and exotic plantings, most notably eucalyptus, have probably made up for much of these losses.

PURPLE FINCH • *Carpodacus purpureus*

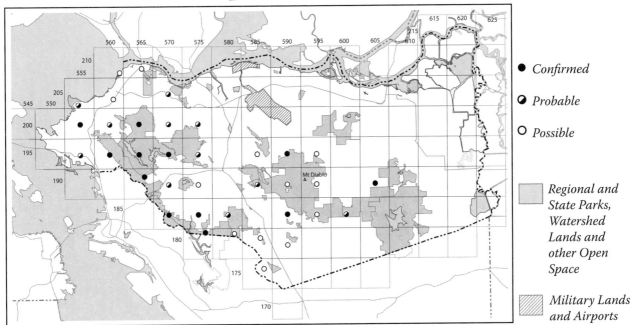

The Purple Finch, with its burgundy cast and pretty churring song, might be thought of as a replacement in native woodland habitats to the similar but generally more urban House Finch.

Current status and distribution

Like many of the county's breeding passerines, the Purple Finch is found most commonly in various forest and woodland types in the rain-soaked Berkeley Hills. Although present in the Diablo Range, the species is notably scarce and local, with breeding stations only in the shadier, forested canyons, most notably in Pine and Mitchell Canyons on Mt. Diablo and along the shady portions of Morgan Territory Rd. Breeding on the Bay plain around Richmond is extremely localized. There are no breeding birds even in the more wooded neighborhoods along the Interstate 680 corridor. The entirety of the Central Valley portion of the county lacks sufficient habitat for this forest-dwelling finch and the species has never been recorded there.

Purple Finches in the Berkeley Hills nest in moist coastal oak woodlands and stands of Monterey pine, as well as in riparian settings featuring alders. In the Diablo Range the species is primarily confined to coastal oak woodlands in shaded canyon bottoms but may also be found in blue oak gray pine woodlands.

Historical occurrence

Grinnell and Wythe (1927) considered the Purple Finch to be "a common resident of the more humid portion of the San Francisco Bay Area." Although this is likely a little overstated for Contra Costa County, it doesn't appear that its status has changed much in the ensuing eight decades.

Breeding and natural history

Though winter populations of the Purple Finch may be augmented by birds representing northern populations, the local breeding birds are assumed to be permanent residents. Birds thought to be pairs were recorded as early as 17 March, although little atlasing was done earlier in the season. The earliest recorded carrying of nest material during the atlas was 18 April; the other six records were 26 May or earlier. The only two records of active nests were a nest with young 30 May and an occupied nest (contents unknown) 8 June. Six records of fledglings, four being fed by adults, were detected between 9 May and 12 July. Some of these dates lend further credence to the idea that Purple Finches in the west have two broods and correlate well with findings from Monterey County (Roberson and Tenney 1993).

Conservation

No serious threats to the Purple Finch are currently known to exist in Contra Costa County.

HOUSE FINCH • *Carpodacus mexicanus*

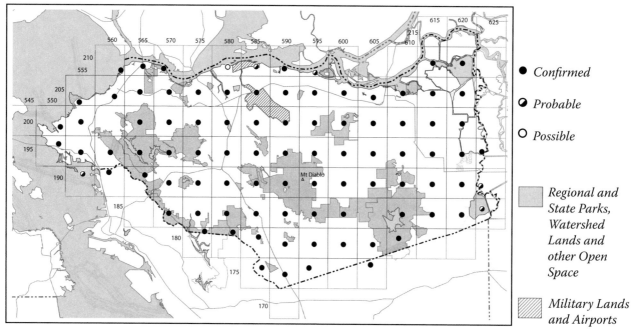

Confirmed

Probable

Possible

Regional and State Parks, Watershed Lands and other Open Space

Military Lands and Airports

Widespread and abundant, colorful and vocally talented, the House Finch is nevertheless an under-appreciated member of the county's avifauna, perhaps for just the reason suggested by William Leon Dawson in 1923: *"The bird is part and parcel of our California life, as much to be taken for granted as sunshine and dry weather."*

Current status and distribution

The House Finch breeds widely and often abundantly in open areas throughout the county. The species is found around the edges of all types of woodlands, in agricultural settings and in urban and suburban areas. Extensive open grasslands and marshes are shunned for nesting although they may be visited for foraging. Dense, closed-canopy forests are also unsuitable though the edges of such forests are widely used. Since these inappropriate habitats rarely encompass extensive areas, we were able to confirm the species in every complete block except for two and even in those cases it may well have been present and nesting in inaccessible areas.

Historical occurrence

The status and distribution of the "California Linnet" seems to have remained stable, as Grinnell and Wythe (1927) knew the House Finch as an abundant permanent resident.

Breeding and natural history

Adults carrying nest material or nest building were found on fifty-four occasions between 3 March and 24 June. Occupied nests were detected twenty-two times from 4 April to 31 May. Nests with young were tallied four times from 21 May–14 June. Fifty-five fledglings, thirty

of them being fed by adults, were recorded 12 April–16 August. Two sets of eggs at the MVZ were taken 31 July (#12079 and #12080).

It is assumed that local breeders are permanent residents. The population increases dramatically in winter, with large numbers of northerly breeders joining the locals to form flocks that may number in the hundreds.

Conservation

The status of the House Finch seems to be as secure as that of any of our breeding birds.

PINE SISKIN • *Carduelis pinus*

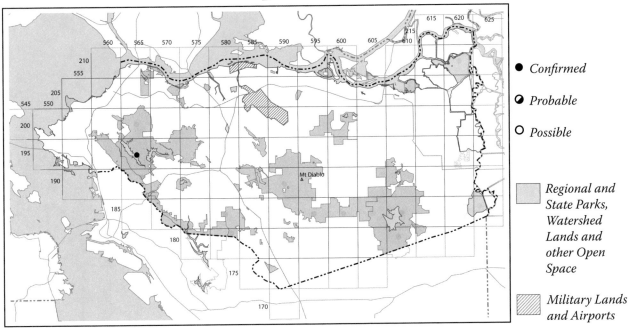

Confirmed

Probable

Possible

Regional and State Parks, Watershed Lands and other Open Space

Military Lands and Airports

The Pine Siskin, so abundant in the mountains and coastal forests of northern California, is one of Contra Costa County's rarest breeding bird species, with just one breeding record for the entire county. The siskin is, for the most part, an erratic winter resident in Contra Costa County, abundant some years but virtually absent in others.

Current status and distribution

A pair of Pine Siskins building a nest at San Pablo Res. on 23 May 1998 provided not only the only confirmation for the atlas project but the first for Contra Costa County. The species was detected nowhere else during the atlas, though two female-type birds were at Tilden Park on 28 July 2003, a date which suggests local breeding (county notebooks).

The scarcity of the Pine Siskin in Contra Costa County is somewhat surprising, considering it is a fairly common, widespread breeder in Marin and San Mateo counties (Shuford 1993, Sequoia Audubon Society 2001). The species is very rare, however, in Napa County (Napa-Solano Audubon Society 2003). Because the species breeds in Marin County in a wide variety of forest types, including isolated stands of Monterey pine or eucalyptus, it may be the relative lack of moistness in the forests of Contra Costa County which is the limiting factor.

Historical occurrence

Grinnell and Wythe (1927), without citing Contra Costa County, considered the Pine Siskin to be a common resident of the Bay Area, including at Berkeley. As of yet we have been unable to find any county nest records prior to the one during the atlas.

Breeding and natural history

In San Mateo County, adults were noted carrying nest material as early as 13 April, with a peak in mid-May. Records of adults feeding young spanned 6 June–27 July, with fledglings out and about as early as 18 June.

Conservation

Breeding bird survey data for California shows an annual decline of 6.8% from 1966 to 2007 (Sauer and others 2008). It is difficult to determine marked changes in Bay region populations but neither Shuford (1993) nor Roberson and Tenney (1993) noted any obvious declines. Bousman (2007) however, states that the species had disappeared from most of the areas occupied during 1987 to 1993 in Santa Clara County.

LESSER GOLDFINCH • *Carduelis psaltria*

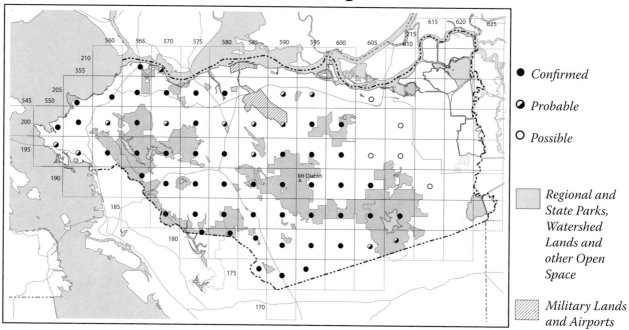

Confirmed
Probable
Possible

Regional and State Parks, Watershed Lands and other Open Space

Military Lands and Airports

Known rather non-poetically to Grinnell and Wythe (1927) as the Green-backed Arkansas Goldfinch, the chattering, often mimicking songs of the Lesser Goldfinch is a common sound in natural and residential settings of Central County. In the latter the species is often mistaken for a canary by the uninitiated. In Contra Costa County, as elsewhere, the species fills an ecological niche between the moisture-loving American Goldfinch and heat-seeking Lawrence's Goldfinch.

Current status and distribution

The Lesser Goldfinch, with the aid of its conspicuous mournful calls, is readily detected in open areas throughout the county with the exception of the Central Valley where the American Goldfinch holds sway. In fact, the species was confirmed or found to be probable in every block east to the western edge of the Central Valley with the exception of block 585-205 (where access was difficult) and three adjacent blocks composed almost exclusively of marshlands.

Because the Lesser Goldfinch prefers open, sunny habitats, it reaches maximum abundance in open oak and riparian woodlands, chaparral and weedy areas in the Diablo Range and indeed is usually among the most common of all species in such situations. In addition, the species has adapted well to suburban situations and attendant ornamental plantings.

Historical occurrence

The status of the Lesser Goldfinch in Contra Costa County seems to have changed little in the past century as Grinnell and Wythe (1927) considered them an abundant resident throughout the Bay Area.

Breeding and natural history

The Lesser Goldfinch was found carrying nest material or nest building on twenty-nine occasions between 11 April and 27 June. Earlier nest construction was likely missed, however, as the Monterey atlas detected dependent fledged young as early as 11 April (Roberson and Tenney 1993). Occupied nests (contents unknown) were detected 6 times 17 April–15 July. Thirty-seven records of fledglings (twenty-one of them being fed by adults) were recorded 4 May–23 August. Watt and Willoughby (1999) state that it is unknown if late nestings refer to renesting or multiple broods. Grinnell and Wythe (1927) reported an extremely late nesting from 2 November in nearby Berkeley, Alameda County, suggesting that the nesting season may occasionally extend much deeper into the year.

Conservation

There seems to be little reason for concern about local Lesser Goldfinch populations.

LAWRENCE'S GOLDFINCH • *Carduelis lawrencei*

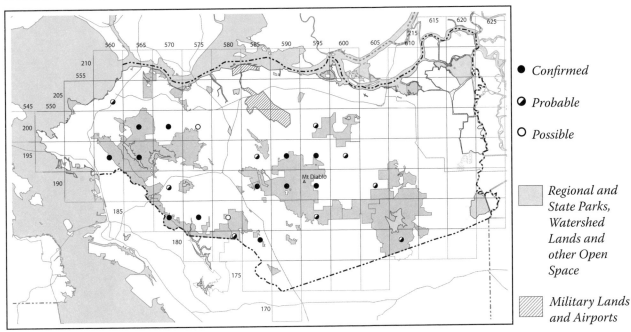

● *Confirmed*

◐ *Probable*

○ *Possible*

▨ *Regional and State Parks, Watershed Lands and other Open Space*

▨ *Military Lands and Airports*

With eye-pleasing plumage and tinkling songs, the Lawrence's Goldfinch is a favorite amongst local birders but it is its scarcity and unpredictability that makes it particularly prized. One of the true surprises of the atlas project wasn't that the species was found, but rather where.

Current status and distribution

The Lawrence's Goldfinch in Contra Costa County has long been sought, and even found with some regularity, in the drier portions of the county, especially at Mt. Diablo State Park, where it inhabits open blue oak and valley oak woodlands interspersed with the grasslands on which it depends for seeds and thistles. Other regular locations include Black Diamond Mines Regional Park near Antioch and Morgan Territory Regional Preserve southeast of Mt. Diablo.

During the atlas project the species was indeed found at these locations but it was unexpectedly more common in wetter, more fog-prone areas further west in the Berkeley Hills, particularly around Tilden Regional Park, San Pablo Res. and the Briones Valley area, areas in which it has always been considered rare.

A likely explanation for the species presence in the Berkeley Hills has been offered by Jeff Davis (pers. comm.). Nesting Lawrence's Goldfinches require access to fresh water and an abundance of favored seed plants (most often fiddleneck). In both wet and dry years, the species is drawn to extralimital breeding sites, in wet years because both water and food are widespread and in dry years because water and food are localized. In years of average rainfall it is more likely to be restricted to traditional sites.

Historical occurrence

Grinnell and Wythe (1927) described the Lawrence's Goldfinch as irregular and local but make no mention of Contra Costa County. There were at least two certain nestings prior to that: a set of eggs taken at Pinole 21 May 1900 (WFVZ #119258) and another set taken three miles east of Berkeley, Contra Costa County 14 Apr 1921 (MVZ #1845).

Breeding and natural history

Adults were found carrying nest material or nest building on four occasions between 5 April and 12 May, with an occupied nest being found 8 June. An adult carrying food was recorded 21 May. Fledglings, some being fed by adults, were detected on eight occasions 20 May–8 July.

The Lawrence's Goldfinch is virtually absent from Contra Costa County during the winter months and, in fact, has been found on the Contra Costa County CBC on just one occasion.

Conservation

Because a significant portion of the species' breeding range is threatened by encroaching human development, it was designated a Red List Species on Audubon's Watchlist 2002. Locally at least, most suitable habitat is tied up in parklands or reservoir watersheds.

AMERICAN GOLDFINCH • *Carduelis tristis*

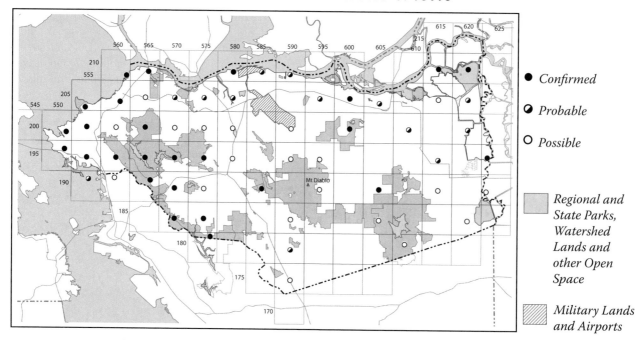

Confirmed

Probable

Possible

Regional and State Parks, Watershed Lands and other Open Space

Military Lands and Airports

The American Goldfinch is a familiar bird to feeder-watchers; the more observant of whom have the opportunity to watch the males slowly trade their modest brown winter plumage for a vivid costume of brilliant lemon-yellow, topped off with a dapper black cap.

Current status and distribution

The American Goldfinch is a common resident of the wetter, humid western portion of the county, including the Bay plain and the Berkeley Hills, as well as the eastern portion of the county. In all cases the species shows a decided tendency to nest near water, which goes a long way towards explaining its scarcity in the Diablo Range and around Las Trampas Regional Park.

The American Goldfinch is readily found during the breeding season around the edges of a wide variety of habitats including riparian settings, eucalyptus groves, marshes, weedy fields and, where most meet them for the first time, around backyard gardens, where it is a fixture at thistle feeders.

Historical occurrence

Although not mentioned specifically by Grinnell and Wythe (1927), they make it clear that the American Goldfinch was a common resident of the Bay Area and, indeed, a set of eggs was taken at Hercules 30 May 1902 (MVZ #3333).

Breeding and natural history

The earliest pair detected during the atlas project was 11 March with the first nest building observed 6 April. Such behavior likely occurs earlier in the county, however, as an adult was found carrying nest material in San Mateo County 10 March (Sequoia Audubon Society 2001). Observations of the carrying of nest material continued to 13 June, strongly indicating a second brood. Adults feeding young were tallied on twelve occasions between 17 May and the late date of 22 September.

Conservation

The degradation and destruction of riparian habitats has likely resulted in local declines. The widespread introduction of non-native thistles, the seeds of which are prized food items, has likely offset these losses, at least to some extent.

HOUSE SPARROW • *Passer domesticus*

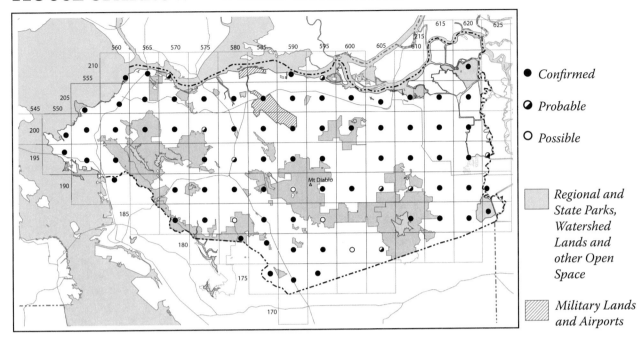

● *Confirmed*

◗ *Probable*

○ *Possible*

▨ *Regional and State Parks, Watershed Lands and other Open Space*

▨ *Military Lands and Airports*

This introduced old world sparrow is more closely tied to human presence than any other bird species found in the county, having filled brilliantly the shopping center niche left vacant by more discriminating native species.

Current status and distribution

The House Sparrow is currently found in virtually all of the urban, suburban and farming situations in the county. For all intents and purposes the species is completely absent from the parks and watershed lands of the Berkeley Hills and Diablo Range except where that habitat is open and where ranchette-style housing, often with attendant horses and stables, has been erected. Prime examples include Bear Creek Rd. near Orinda and Marsh Creek Rd. between Clayton and Brentwood. Its future spread is completely dependent upon further development of native habitats.

Historical occurrence

The House Sparrow was released in San Francisco in 1871–72 (Lowther and Cink 1992) and was already abundant in populated areas of the East Bay by the end of the 1880s (Belding 1890).

Breeding and natural history

Adults carrying nest material, or building nests, were recorded thirty-seven times between 14 March and 16 June. Occupied nests (contents unknown) were found on twenty-one occasions 29 March–4 July; nests with young were tallied five times from 11 April and 27 August. Adults carrying food were found twelve times between 29 April and 3 July, and fledglings, most being fed by adults, were recorded twenty-five times 27 April–27 June. Some of the latest confirmation dates during the atlas likely pertain to second or even third broods.

Conservation

Breeding Bird Survey data indicate a continent-wide population decline between 1966–2004 that is thought to primarily stem from changing farming practices, including the use of pesticides which reduces arthropod populations vital for feeding young; and increasing efficiency, which limits grain spillage and reduces weed seeds upon which adults feed.

APPENDIX A:
FORMER BREEDING SPECIES

The following species are known with certainty to have bred in Contra Costa County, though it is believed that neither of them currently does. Additional species may well have bred at some point in the distant past but were either never recorded or the records have never been found, the California Condor being the most prominent example.

Greater Roadrunner (*Geococcyx californianus*)

Tantalizing reports of this ground-dwelling cuckoo are occasionally received from Contra Costa County but most are second-hand and from unknown observers. Sadly, the last certain sighting for Contra Costa County was along Morgan Territory Rd. 22 May 1986, a date which suggests nesting (county notebooks). The atlas project was unable to detect even a single bird.

The Greater Roadrunner favors open, arid habitats, particularly combinations of chaparral, grassland and savannah. These habitats continue to exist in the Diablo Range but they do so in much reduced acreages.

Historically it is clear that the Greater Roadrunner was once a widespread nester in the county. The first nesting confirmation for the county involved a set of eggs collected from Mt. Diablo 2 May 1904 (California Academy of Sciences #4738). *The Condor* and *The Gull* list many sightings of roadrunners from the Berkeley Hills up to the late 1950s, including records from areas surprisingly far to the west such as Wildcat Canyon Rd., Grizzly Peak Blvd., Redwood Canyon and Tice Valley. These areas, it must be remembered, were once far more open than in mod-

ern times. Much of the Lafayette/Orinda/Moraga area has developed into heavily wooded neighborhoods with locally extensive plantings of Monterey Pine and other non-natives.

Yellow-headed Blackbird
(*Xanthocephalus xanthocephalus*)

The Yellow-headed Blackbird, with its strikingly colored head and grating, raucous song, is unfortunately not currently a breeder in Contra Costa County, and instead is relegated to being an unpredictable wintering bird in the far eastern portion of the county. The only tantalizing hint of breeding during the atlas project involved a singing male at the north end of McNabney Marsh near Martinez 8 Jun 2000. Alas, that bird was not seen again on subsequent visits.

The Yellow-headed Blackbird was not known to Grinnell and Wythe (1927) to have occurred in Contra Costa County, but Grinnell and Miller (1944) rectified this by citing an 1899 nest record from Pinole (eggs on 28 May; MVZ #3329). Primarily due to habitat loss, the Yellow-headed Blackbird has been designated as a Third Priority Bird Species of Special Concern (Jaramillo in Shuford and Gardali 2008).

APPENDIX B:
SPECIES CONFIRMED AFTER THE ATLAS

Bald Eagle (*Haliaeetus leucocephalus*)

The atlas project turned up no evidence whatsoever of Bald Eagles nesting in the county. Not a single bird was even seen during the breeding season, despite several large reservoirs with suitable breeding habitat and several birds present through the winter each year.

Grinnell and Miller (1927) knew of no records for either Contra Costa or Alameda counties and state that in the Bay Area the species was "very rare in late years", although they do state that the species was common in 1865 along the bay shore at Redwood City. Belding

(1890) documents that in 1854 Newberry found the species "not rare in California along the San Joaquin and Sacramento rivers." This hints that Bald Eagles likely occurred in the county in the mid-19th century.

In 2004 an adult and a subadult were discovered at San Pablo Res. on the summery date of 13 June (Ryan DiGuadio, pers. comm.). Neither bird was reported after that date, but they represented the first hint of possible nesting in the future.

On 8 Jun 2006, an adult Bald Eagle was reported carrying nest material over San Pablo Res. On 21

June an adult, a nest and a young bird just out of the nest were discovered, providing Contra Costa County with its first nesting confirmation. On the following day, a second fledgling was noted (Roger Hartwell, pers. comm.).

Black Skimmer (*Rynchops niger*)

The first California record of Black Skimmer was found in Orange County in 1962 (McCaskie and Suffel 1971). The first breeding record for California was at the Salton Sea in 1972 (McCaskie and others 1974). The first nest records for the Bay Area and Northern California came in 1994 at Hayward Regional Shoreline, Alameda County, and in the salt ponds of Santa Clara County. Nesting has occurred in each subsequent year (Bousman 2007). The first Contra Costa County record involved a single bird on Brooks Island near Richmond 9–14 May 1995 (county notebooks). There have been records during most years since, most often birds that are presumed to be post-breeding wanderers from South Bay colonies.

In an early draft of this account we opined that "the prospect of breeding, however, is slim unless the species decides to nest amongst the Caspian Tern colony on Brooks Island." Indeed, that is exactly what happened in 2007 when the species was noted throughout the summer in the Richmond area and confirmed by biologists with the EBRPD (*fide* Steve Bobzien; details to be published elsewhere).

It is impossible to say what the future will hold for the Black Skimmer in Contra Costa County but hopefully the species will maintain at least a toehold on Brooks Island. The Black Skimmer has been designated a Third Priority Species of Special Concern (Molina in Shuford and Gardali 2008). The chief reason for this designation is a shortage of suitable open nesting habitat and the continued loss of such habitats. Secondarily, "detrimental interactions" with other species due to limited habitat may result in limited reproductive success. For instance, in coastal southern California large aggregations of nesting Elegant Terns, a species with a very "cohesive" behavior, have been thought to interfere with skimmers' nest attendance (Molina in Shuford and Gardali 2008). It is unclear if the large Caspian Tern colony on Brooks Island could result in a similar problem.

Appendix C:
Potential Breeding Species

The following species have the potential to breed in Contra Costa County, although some are certainly much more likely than others. Each of the following has bred at least once in the Bay Area's nine counties. The data included here is far from exhaustive. For a more thorough treatment, the reader is urged to consult Bousman (2007), the source for much of the following.

Mute Swan (*Cygnus olor*)

The Mute Swan has been widely introduced in North America and is apparently now established in Sonoma and Marin counties (Bousman 2007). Not to be left out, the species has also begun to breed in Contra Costa County at the Concord Naval Weapons Station in recent years. This population appears to comprise about twenty birds and is growing slowly but steadily (pers. obs.). The species is known to be aggressive to other nesting waterfowl, but the extent of this is apparently not clear. A handful of states have attempted to control burgeoning Mute Swan populations, primarily through egg-addling and the removal of adults (Ciaranca and others 1997), but it is unclear if such methods will become necessary in the Bay Area.

American Wigeon (*Anas Americana*)

The American Wigeon is a very rare breeder in the Central Valley and is even rarer in the Bay Area, where there are just two nest records: Hayward Regional Shoreline, Alameda County, in 2000 and Guadalupe Slough, Santa Clara County, in 2005 (Bousman 2007). Although unlikely, breeding is conceivable at McNabney Marsh near Martinez, and would be even more likely in East County if suitable habitat was created and maintained at local sewage treatment plants.

Canvasback (*Aythya valisineria*)

The Canvasback has been confirmed breeding on only one occasion in the Bay Area, that being at Guadalupe Slough, Santa Clara County, in 1989 (Bousman 2007). There have also been sporadic breeding records from the Central Valley in the past 15 years, but there is very little suitable habitat currently available in eastern Contra Costa County.

Redhead *(Aythya americana)*

The Redhead historically nested as close to Contra Costa County as Alvarado and Irvington in the Union City/Fremont area, however Grinnell and Wythe (1927) do not cite a year. Grinnell and Miller (1944) list nesting in the Central Valley as close as Merced and Sacramento and even though Contra Costa County is not cited it is entirely possible that breeding took place in East County in historical times. It isn't believed to currently breed any closer in the Central Valley than Yolo County to the north and Merced County to the south. A couple of breeding records were recorded in Santa Clara County in the 1970s and 1980s but apparently there have been no confirmations there since 1984 (Bousman 2007). There is currently almost no suitable nesting habitat anywhere in the county and thus breeding is unlikely to take place in the near future.

Ring-necked Duck *(Aythya collaris)*

In California, the Ring-necked Duck breeds sparingly in the Sierra and Cascade Ranges, as well as in the Great Basin. The only known nest record for the Bay Area involves young at Calaveras Res., Santa Clara County, 8 Aug 1997 (FN 51:no. 5).

Lesser Scaup *(Aythya affinis)*

The Lesser Scaup is a very rare breeding bird in the Bay Area, known to nest regularly only in Santa Clara County. The species also bred as close as Hayward Regional Shoreline, Alameda County, in 1994 and 1995 (*fide* W. Bousman). Although the species could potentially breed in Contra Costa County, it doesn't seem terribly likely to occur anytime soon.

Common Merganser *(Mergus merganser)*

The Common Merganser has never been confirmed nesting in Contra Costa County, despite the presence of four watershed reservoirs where the species is found regularly during the winter months. In Alameda County the species is a very uncommon nester in the vicinity of Alameda Creek but no such large, permanent streams exist in Contra Costa County. The only hint of potential nesting was a single bird at San Pablo Res. 17 June 2000.

Neither Grinnell and Wythe (1927) nor Grinnell and Miller (1944) knew of nesting from anywhere in the vicinity of the Bay Area. The first confirmed nesting for the Bay Area involved flightless young in Sonoma County in 1979 (Bousman 2007). The species was confirmed breeding in 3 blocks during the Alameda County Breeding Bird Atlas, 1993–1997 (*fide* Robert J. Richmond), and presumably breeds annually around Sunol Regional Park and Calaveras Res.

Eared Grebe *(Podiceps nigricollis)*

The Eared Grebe is a very local nesting bird in the Central Valley and breeds only casually in the Bay Area. However, the species did nest successfully near Shadow Cliffs Regional Park, Alameda County, in 1983 and 1994, just a few miles south of Contra Costa County (*fide* W. Bousman). If nesting were to occur in Contra Costa County it would likely be at a sewage treatment plant in the eastern portion of the county.

Brandt's Cormorant *(Phalacrocorax penicillatus)*

The Brandt's Cormorant has never been confirmed nesting inside San Francisco Bay and, with very little seemingly suitable habitat available, is not likely to do so anytime soon. The species is seen in the Richmond area with some regularity, however, and there is a small amount of potential habitat on West Brother Island and on Red Rock, both offshore of Richmond, and those sites merit occasional attention during future breeding seasons.

Least Bittern *(Ixobrychus exilis)*

A record of fledged young at Olema Marsh, Marin County 25 July 1998 (FN 52: no. 4) is the only nest record for the Bay Area. In the Central Valley, recent breeding season records have been recorded at widely spaced locations, including as close as Yolo and Sacramento counties to the north and Merced County to the south. Also intriguing is a recent summer record from the Suisun Marsh, Solano County (Sterling in Shuford and Gardali 2008).

Because of the secretive nature of this species, and rather poor coverage of potentially suitable habitat in Contra Costa County, it is more than possible that this species is lurking undetected somewhere in north or East County.

Cattle Egret *(Bubulcus ibis)*

The Cattle Egret has never been found breeding in Contra Costa County, nor even found during the heart of the breeding season, but the possibility of future nesting appears somewhat likely. After invading North America earlier in the 20th century, this species first reached California in 1962 at Orange County and was first recorded breeding in Imperial County in 1970 (Small 1994). The species currently breeds in most of the Central Valley counties, although its distribution is quite patchy. There have also been sporadic nesting attempts in several Bay Area counties, including Hayward Regional Shoreline, Alameda County, in 2001 (NAB 55: no. 3).

In Contra Costa County this species is routinely found in modest numbers between November and April. The vast majority of records are from the Central Valley portion of the county, though birds have occasionally been found further west, including the first county record at Martinez 11–12 Jan 1975 (county notebooks).

White-faced Ibis (Plegadis chihi)

The White-faced Ibis was a common nester in the Central Valley in the early 20th Century but had declined by the time of Grinnell and Miller (1944), a trend which continued into the 1970s. By the 1980s this Ibis had begun to reclaim its former North American Range; due to improved management of federal and state refuges; the banning of DDT and other pesticides; and, in the western US, the widespread planting of alfalfa (Ryder and Manry 1994). This comeback has resulted in the establishment of numerous new colonies in the Central Valley during the past 15 years (Bousman 2007).

Ibis have always been considered rare in the Bay Area counties. Grinnell and Wythe (1927) were aware of just two records for the Bay Area, one of which was from Irvington, Alameda County 18 May 1923. The first record for Contra Costa County involved a flock of seven to nine birds at West Pittsburg (now Bay Point) 18 Dec 1982 through 26 Jan 1983 (county notebooks). Beginning in the mid-1990s, the species began to be noted with some regularity in the Central Valley portion of the county, particularly around Bethel Island and Holland Tract. This includes several breeding season records, suggesting that breeding may be taking place either in Contra Costa County or in an adjacent county (pers. obs.).

Sora (Porzana carolina)

Before the atlas project started, it seemed to be common knowledge that the Sora is a viable member of Contra Costa County's breeding avifauna. It came as a great surprise to discover that not only is the species not common, it may not breed at all. The atlas database contains just five records and none

later in the season than 11 April, far too early to rule out wintering birds. While it is admittedly true that the coverage of potential Sora breeding habitat was far from thorough, both Black and Virginia rails were recorded in multiple blocks during the breeding season. The habitat requirements for breeding Soras and Virginia Rails is quite similar, although Shuford (1993) felt that the Sora tends to be far more stringent in its choices of habitat.

Grinnell and Wythe (1927) knew the Sora to nest at Alvarado, Alameda County but not in Contra Costa County. In fact, it is possible that the Sora has never been confirmed breeding in the county.

Snowy Plover (Charadrius alexandrinus)

In California, the Snowy Plover is primarily a beach nester but inside the San Francisco Bay estuary it has adapted rather nicely to the construction of salt ponds. These ponds have been constructed in the shallow southern end of San Francisco Bay and northern edge of San Pablo Bay. The deep waters of Contra Costa County are unsuitable for salt pond construction, leaving the small section of beach on Brooks Island as the only conceivable potential nest site in the county.

Wilson's Phalarope (Phalaropus tricolor)

The Wilson's Phalarope typically breeds in eastern California from the Oregon border south to Inyo County but extralimital breeding has occasionally been noted, even as close as Sonoma County in 1982 (Burridge 1995) and Solano County in 2005 (fide William Bousman).

Heermann's Gull (Larus heermanni)

The likelihood of the Heerman's Gull breeding in Contra Costa County is admittedly quite small but it did attempt to nest on nearby Alcatraz Island, San Francisco County, during the breeding seasons of 1979, 1980 and 1981 (Bousman 2007).

Forster's Tern (Sterna forsteri)

Although the Forster's Tern has been known to nest along the southern shore of Alameda County since at least 1948 (Sibley 1953), and has also nested in Marin, Napa, San Mateo and Santa Clara counties (Bousman 2007), the species has never been found to do so in Contra Costa County and, due to a lack of appropriate habitat, is unlikely to do so anytime in the near future. This being said, several pairs have been noted in courtship behavior on tiny islands at McNabney Marsh near Martinez during recent seasons, although apparently nothing has come of it so far.

Arctic Tern (*Sterna paradisaea*)

Of all the species on the list of potential breeding birds, the Arctic Tern might be the least likely to ever occur. Still, a female summered at the Hayward Regional Shoreline, Alameda County for much of the 1990s and, with the cooperation of a male Forster's Tern, produced three hybrid young in 1999, one of which fledged and returned the next season. The adult female also attempted to nest in 2000 but the nest was abandoned (Bousman 2007).

Pigeon Guillemot (*Cepphus columba*)

Yet another species which would seem an unlikely candidate to nest in Contra Costa County, the Pigeon Guillemot has actually bred as close as Alcatraz Island, San Francisco County, where twenty-two nests were discovered in 1999 (www.ssfo.org). In Contra Costa County the species is best considered a very uncommon, but nearly annual, post-breeding migrant to deep water in the Richmond area.

Yellow-billed Cuckoo (*Coccyzus americanus*)

Yellow-billed Cuckoos have never been recorded breeding in Contra Costa County and, unfortunately, there is no existing habitat that appears suitable. The last known breeding record for the Bay Area was in Sonoma County in 1923 (Bousman 2007). In the Central Valley, the cuckoo population plummeted in the 20th century, a victim of widespread degradation and destruction of riparian woodlands. The current Central Valley population nests exclusively in the Sacramento Valley (NAB notebooks).

Spotted Owl (*Strix occidentalis*)

The beleaguered Spotted Owl has never been recorded in the East Bay, though it does nest as close as Napa County to the north (Napa-Solano Audubon Society 2003) and Marin County to the west (Shuford 1993). In Marin County, the Spotted Owl is resident in forests dominated by Douglas fir, Bishop pine and coast redwood, though it is locally found in mixed evergreen hardwood forests dominated by coast live oaks (Shuford 1993). Contra Costa County contains no Douglas fir or Bishop pine forests and but a fragment of remnant redwood forest. Coast live oak habitat is more common

but is either insufficient to support Spotted Owls or this generally sedentary species has simply never reached the East Bay.

Barred Owl (*Strix varia*)

The Barred Owl, once primarily confined to the southern and eastern United States, has in the past half century undergone a massive range expansion. The first documented records for California were from Del Norte and Trinity counties in 1981 and by 1998 it had been recorded in twelve counties as far south as Sonoma County in western California and Yuba County in the Sierra Nevada (Dark and others 1998). Since that time, the species has appeared as far south in the Coast Range as Marin and Napa counties (NAB notebooks).

Vaux's Swift (*Chaetura vauxi*)

In California the Vaux's Swift primarily breeds in a narrow strip along the coast from the Oregon border south to Santa Cruz County (Sterling and Paton 1996), although they are thought to probably breed in Monterey County in very small numbers (Roberson and Tenney 1993). Sterling and Paton (1996) cite two summer records from Contra Costa County as being indicative of breeding: Walnut Creek 12 June 1972 and Alamo 17 June 1981. Whether or not these birds were truly breeders, or even correctly identified, will never be known, but in any event the species has never been found in the ensuing years and is currently assumed to be absent as a breeding species.

Costa's Hummingbird (*Calypte costae*)

Although the habitat certainly appears suitable around Mt. Diablo, the lovely little Costa's Hummingbird is known only as a very uncommon migrant in Contra Costa County, found most often at backyard feeders. Intriguing, however, was a male in suitable breeding habitat along South Gate Rd. in Mt. Diablo State Park on the summery date of 11 June 2006 (*Quail* 51: no. 10).

Grinnell and Wythe (1927) were aware of just two records for the Bay Area. Grinnell and Miller (1944) considered the species to be sparsely represented as a breeding bird west of the San Joaquin Valley as far north as Merced County. This species is now known to breed annually as far north as Del Puerto Canyon, Stanislaus County (NAB notebooks), but much of the habitat north of there is remote and in private hands. Alameda County's first nest record, nest-building at Arroyo Valle 20 May 1995, came from an area where they may well prove to breed annually (FN 49: no. 3).

Lewis's Woodpecker *(Melanerpes lewis)*

This magnificent pink and green woodpecker is unfortunately only found as a rare migrant or wintering bird in Contra Costa County and has never been confirmed nesting. This is somewhat surprising considering the amount of suitable habitat along the eastern flank of the Diablo Range and the fact that it nests as close as the vicinity of the Carnegie State Vehicular Recreation Area in Alameda and San Joaquin counties. Sadly, the Lewis's Woodpecker has declined even in Alameda County in recent decades and there are only a handful of breeding pairs remaining, all on private property. Conventional wisdom has it that the European Starling has been the main culprit in this decline but the matter is likely more complicated than that.

The only sighting during the atlas project was a single bird at the north end of Los Vaqueros Res. near Byron on 7 June 2002. The date is certainly suggestive of nesting but the bird acted as if it was migrating and was not seen again. Still, hope springs eternal that Contra Costa County will one day be graced by breeding Lewis's Woodpeckers.

Red-breasted Sapsucker *(Sphyrapicus ruber)*

Neither Grinnell and Wythe (1927) nor Grinnell and Miller (1944) were aware of any breeding records for the Bay Area. The first known nest record for the Bay Area is now thought to have been from Sonoma County in 1979, followed closely by a confirmation in Marin County in 1980. There are now breeding records from as far south as San Mateo and Santa Cruz counties (Bousman 2007). Despite this recent range extension southward into the Santa Cruz Mountains, there are as of yet no records for the East Bay during the breeding season.

Willow Flycatcher *(Empidonax traillii)*

Grinnell and Wythe (1927) mention nesting as close as Pleasanton, Alameda County. They also note that the species was common at Antioch, Contra Costa County on 4 June but this is prime migration time for this late-arriving species so nesting can in no way be inferred. More recently, the species was thought to possibly be breeding at Arroyo Mocho, southeastern Alameda County in 1972 and 1973 (AB 26: no. 5; AB 27: no. 5). Its modern absence is part of a widespread decline for this species in California, where it has been victimized by destruction of riparian habitats and brood parasitism by the Brown-headed Cowbird.

Dusky Flycatcher *(Empidonax oberholseri)*

Unknown to Grinnell and Wythe (1927) as having occurred anywhere in the Bay Area, the Dusky Flycatcher is now thought to be very uncommon as a migrant, particularly in spring. To the south the species is known to nest as close as the San Benito Mountains, San Benito and Fresno counties, and to the north in the mountains of Lake County (Johnson and Cicero 1985).

San Benito Mountain, with an elevation of 5241 ft, is apparently high enough to support significant stands of mixed conifers. Johnson and Cicero (1985) found Dusky Flycatchers to be common among the yellow pines and incense-cedars, tree species absent from Contra Costa County.

Cassin's Kingbird *(Tyrannus vociferans)*

The northwest corner of the breeding range of the Cassin's Kingbird in California is roughly the southwest corner of San Joaquin County and the southeast corner of Alameda County (NAB notebooks) but there have been occasional instances of extralimital breeding, including near Bolinas, Marin County, in 1972 (Shuford 1993) and Vallejo, Solano County, in 2005 (NAB 59: no. 3).

Bell's Vireo *(Vireo bellii)*

The Bell's Vireo was never confirmed to have occurred in Contra Costa County but it was found nesting as close as Stockton, San Joaquin County and, as recently as 1932, at Corral Hollow in southwestern San Joaquin County. Grinnell and Miller (1944) include the Delta portion of the county in this vireo's range map although this was somewhat of an "educated guess" and was not backed up by sightings or specimens. By the 1970s the species was extirpated from northern and central California, apparently a victim of a combination of habitat destruction and cowbird parasitism (Bousman 2007).

In recent years there have been signs of recovery. Numerous records of migrants have been recorded in the Central Valley (NAB notebooks) and nesting was confirmed in Stanislaus County in 2005 (NAB 59: no. 4). Contra Costa County, however, has very little in the way of riparian forests, and possibly none suitable for this species.

Purple Martin *(Progne subis)*

The Purple Martin has never been confirmed nesting in Contra Costa County and migrants have very rarely been detected in recent decades, although Grinnell and Wythe (1927) state that the species had been reported from "parts of Contra Costa County." Belding (1890) says that the Purple Martin was a rare summer resident so perhaps the species did breed as late as the 19th century. Since the early 1950s the county has averaged a sighting about every 7–10 years, all in spring, except for an intriguing report of thirty immature birds over Lafayette Ridge 22 July 1979 (county notebooks). Of great surprise was a report of a male and a female or immature bird at Upper San Leandro Reservoir near Moraga 6 July 2008 (NAB notebooks). This mid-summer date is intriguing but subsequent searches failed to re-find the birds.

Bank Swallow *(Riparia riparia)*

Grinnell and Wythe (1927) cite the Bank Swallow as a "common summer resident locally" yet the Northern Rough-winged Swallow as a "Summer visitant; not common", quite a change from their current status. Grinnell and Wythe also state that the species had been reported from Contra Costa County. It is unknown where in the county it was reported and it is further unclear that it was ever confirmed nesting though perhaps this could be inferred from Grinnell and Wythe. Since East County began to be seriously birded in about 1980 there have been many sightings but nearly all have been spring or fall migrants with some mid-summer records likely pertaining to post-breeding dispersants. In truth there appears to be no truly suitable nesting habitat for this species in the county and it is not expected that the Bank Swallow will nest again in the future.

American Dipper *(Cinclus mexicanus)*

The American Dipper is found throughout its range on clear, cool rushing streams and as such is a very rare vagrant to Contra Costa County with approximately ten records, all from fall and/or winter. The species does nest locally in southeastern Alameda County in the vicinity of Alameda Creek but there is no such suitable habitat present in Contra Costa County and it should not be expected to nest in the future.

Golden-crowned Kinglet *(Regulus satrapa)*

The Golden-crowned Kinglet nests as close as the wet coniferous forests of Marin County (Shuford 1993), as well as in the Santa Cruz Mountains (NAB notebooks), but has never been recorded in the East Bay during the breeding season. In Marin County the species nests in moist, shaded Douglas fir and redwood forests (Shuford 1993) but Contra Costa County has no Douglas fir forests and only a tiny remnant of redwood forest that appears insufficient to meet the needs of this species.

Varied Thrush *(Ixoreus naevius)*

Grinnell and Miller (1944) were aware of Varied Thrushes breeding only in the northwest corner of California. Since that time there has been a significant range extension along the coast as far south as the Santa Cruz Mountains, San Mateo and Santa Cruz counties, where breeding was first confirmed in 1991 (Bousman 2007). Since Varied Thrushes find conditions lacking for breeding in the coniferous forests of Marin and Sonoma counties, habitat seemingly far better suited to this species than those of the East Bay, it would seem unlikely that the species will become established locally.

Northern Parula *(Parula americana)*

The Northern Parula is routinely recorded as a vagrant species in California during the late spring and fall months and has bred sporadically along the coast of northern California, including at least four times in Marin County and twice in San Mateo County (Bousman 2007). Singing males have been found in late spring at Jewel Lake in Tilden Park (county notebooks) but no hints of nesting have ever been uncovered.

Yellow-rumped Warbler *(Dendroica coronata)*

The Yellow-rumped Warbler, so abundant in higher altitudinal mountainous areas throughout California and resident in modest numbers in the better developed coastal forests of the Bay Area, has never been found nesting in Contra Costa County. It has, however, been confirmed nesting twice in Alameda County. On 1 June, 1941 a pair was seen feeding two bob-tailed juveniles near Sequoia Park east of Oakland in Monterey pines (Seibert 1942), just ¼ mile west of the Contra Costa County line. The birds were noted. More surprising still was breeding in a knobcone pine forest at Lookout Point in arid southeastern Alameda County 16 July, 1994 (FN 48: no. 5).

Hermit Warbler (*Dendroica occidentalis*)

Grinnell and Wythe (1927) knew of absolutely no summer records for the Bay Area. Grinnell and Miller (1944) state that birds had been taken in the Santa Cruz Mountains during the breeding season. The first nest record for the Bay Area was recorded in 1954 at Castle Rock State Park on the border of San Mateo and Santa Cruz counties (Bousman 2007). The species also breeds in relatively closed canopy Douglas fir and redwood forests of Marin (Shuford 1993) and Sonoma (Burridge 1995) counties.

Recent July records from Tilden Park, including immature birds, are intriguing but for now are best considered post-breeding wanderers as there are no known breeding season records for the East Bay.

Hooded Warbler (*Wilsonia citrina*)

The handsome Hooded Warbler breeds widely in deciduous thickets of eastern North America, particularly in the southeast. In California the species is generally considered a scarce vagrant, although occasional "flight years" bring this species in greater numbers, as in 1992. During that year breeding was actually confirmed in Kern and Los Angeles counties (Small 1994). A somewhat more modest invasion in 2005 resulted in a breeding confirmation from Butano State Park, San Mateo County, the first and only nest record for the Bay Area (NAB 59: no. 4).

Despite a dearth of records of "vagrant" warblers in Contra Costa County, there have been at least five spring/summer records of singing males at Tilden Park, at least three of which lingered into July (county notebooks). It would appear that when vagrant birds reach Jewel Lake they find a spot that bears more than a passing resemblance to habitats occupied within their normal range.

Rose-breasted Grosbeak (*Pheucticus ludovicianus*)

Although the Rose-breasted Grosbeak is generally considered to be an "eastern" bird that doesn't normally nest west of the Rocky Mountains, Contra Costa County is occasionally brightened by the presence of this dapper congener of our own Black-headed Grosbeak. The species is most often detected in California as a spring or fall "vagrant" but in recent years there have been numerous mid-summer sightings, most often from feeders, in Contra Costa County. During the atlas, males at feeders were found 1 July 1999, 15 July 1999, July 2000, and 27 June–1 July 2002 (county notebooks). It is likely that at least some females of this species are passing through undetected.

Stunningly, in 1992 a male Rose-breasted nested with a female Black-headed and fledged two young at Tilden Regional Park, Contra Costa County (AB 46:1176 1992)!

Red Crossbill (*Loxia curvirostra*)

Grinnell and Wythe (1927) knew only of sporadic winter records for the Bay Area. The first Bay Area nest record is thought to be from Inverness Ridge, Marin County 23 April 1960 (Bousman 2007). The Red Crossbill has never been found nesting anywhere in the East Bay but it would not be terribly surprising if it were to do so.

The Red Crossbill is an enigmatic bird, constantly in search of unpredictable cone crops and prepared to travel great distances at any time of year to find them. This dependence forces this obligate wanderer to nest at any time of year, complicating efforts to confirm breeding. Since the vast majority of local records are from fall and winter it is generally assumed that these birds represent northerly populations pushed south in search of food sources. If breeding were to take place here it would likely be in the vicinity of Redwood or Tilden Regional Parks where there are extensive plantings of Monterey pines.

APPENDIX D:
SCIENTIFIC NAMES OF PLANTS MENTIONED IN THE TEXT

Based upon the Jepson Online Interchange for California Floristics.

COMMON NAME   SCIENTIFIC NAME

TREES

Kangaroothorn	*Acacia paradoxa*
Alder, White	*Alnus rhombifolia*
Bay, California	*Umbellularia californica*
Cedar, Incense	*Calocedrus decurrens*
Cottonwood, Fremont	*Populus fremontii*
Eucalyptus	*Eucalyptus* spp.
Eucalyptus, Blue Gum	*Eucalyptus globulus*
Fir, Douglas	*Pseudotsuga menziesii*
Madrone, Pacific	*Arbutus menziesii*
Maple, Big-leaf	*Acer macrophyllum*
Oak, Black	*Quercus kelloggii*
Oak, Blue	*Quercus douglasii*
Oak, Canyon Live	*Quercus chrysolepis*
Oak, Coast Live	*Quercus agrifolia*
Oak, Interior Live	*Quercus wislizeni*
Oak, Tanbark	*Lithocarpus densiflorus*
Oak, Valley	*Quercus lobata*
Palm, Canary Island Date	*Phoenix canariensis*
Palm, Fan	*Washingtonia* spp.
Pine, Bishop	*Pinus muricata*
Pine, Gray	*Pinus sabiniana*
Pine, Monterey	*Pinus radiata*
Redwood	*Sequoia sempervirens*
Sycamore, Western	*Platanus racemosa*
Walnut, California Black	*Juglans californica*
Willow	*Salix* spp.

SHRUBS

Blackberry, Himalayan	*Rubus discolor*
Buckwheat, California	*Eriogonum fasciculatum*
Ceanothus	*Ceanothus* spp.
Chamise	*Adenostoma fasciculatum*
Coffeeberry, California	*Rhamnus Californica*
Coyote Brush	*Baccharis pilularis*
Cream Bush	*Holodiscus discolor*
Elderberry, Blue	*Sambucus mexicana*
Grape, California	*Vitis californica*
Hemlock, Poison	*Conium maculatum*
Hop Tree	*Ptelea crenulata*
Huckleberry, California	*Vaccinium ovatum*
Manzanita	*Arctostaphylos* spp.
Poison Oak, Western	*Toxicodendron diversilobum*
Sage, Black	*Salvia mellifera*
Sagebrush, California	*Artemisia californica*
Common Snowberry	*Symphoricarpos albus*
Thimbleberry	*Rubus parviflorus*
Toyon	*Heteromeles arbutifolia*

FORBS AND GRASSES

Arrow-grass, Seaside	*Triglochin maritima*
Bluegrass, One-sided	*Poa secunda*
Bulrush	*Scirpus* spp.
Cattail	*Typha* spp.
Clover, Strawberry	*Trifolium fragiferum*
Clover, White	*Trifolium repens*
Cord Grass	*Spartina* spp.
Fern, Sword	*Polystichum* spp.
Fescue, Tall	*Festuca arundinacea*
Fiddleneck	*Amsinckia* spp.
Grass, Dallis	*Paspalum diliatatum*
Gumplant	*Grindelia* spp.
Melic, California	*Melica californica*
Mustard	*Brassica* spp.
Needlegrass, Purple	*Nassella pulchra*
Pickleweed	*Salicornia* spp.
Reed, Common	*Phragmites australis*
Rushes	*Juncus* spp.
Ryegrass	*Lolium* spp.
Saltgrass	*Distichlis spicata*
Scirpus	*Scirpus* spp.
Squirreltail, Big	*Elymus multisetus*
Trefoil	*Lotus* spp.
Tule	*Scirpus acutus*
Marsh Jaumea	*Jaumea carnosa*
Alkali Heath	*Frankenia salina*
Dwarf Mistletoe	*Arceuthobium* spp.

APPENDIX E:
COMPREHENSIVE CHART OF BLOCKS,
NUMBERS OF SPECIES, HOURS, OBSERVERS

The following chart includes the following: 1) the numeric code for each block in sequential order; 2) whether a block is completely composed of Contra Costa County (Full or "F") or partially composed of a neighboring county (Partial or "P"); 3–5) the number of species found to be either confirmed, probable or possible; 6) the total number of species for which evidence of breeding was obtained; 7) the percentage of species for which evidence of confirmation was obtained; 8) the hours spent atlasing in the block, and 9) the name of the observers who atlased the block (no attempt has been made to determine which of the atlasers listed contributed the most hours).

Block #	P/F	Confirmed	Probable	Possible	Total	%	Hours	Observers
545-200	P	2	0	0	2	100	1	Glover
550-195	P	37	9	6	52	71.15	42.53	Daniel/ B. Lewis/ Scalf/ Spight
550-200	P	48	6	8	62	77.41	89.6	Daniel/ B. Lewis/ Scalf/ Spight
555-190	P	9	11	4	24	37.5	18.8	Daniel/ Spight/ Walters
555-195	P	29	15	8	52	55.76	30	Schmoldt/ Fujii/ Hayashi
555-200	P	42	12	9	63	66.66	44.3	Daniel/ B. Lewis/ Scalf
555-205	P	43	8	11	62	69.35	61	Swenson/ Blustein
560-190	P	15	6	7	28	53.57	10.75	Green
560-195	F	54	22	6	82	65.85	102	Kaplan/ K. Koundakjian, T. Koundakjian
560-200	F	35	15	10	60	58.33	49	Green
560-205	P	51	8	18	77	66.23	150.5	Loughman, Foley, Lucken
560-210	P	22	10	6	38	57.89	27.5	Diernisse/ Blake/ Gibbs
565-190	P	60	8	18	86	69.76	250.25	Strauss
565-195	F	71	14	14	99	71.71	124.75	B. Brandriff/ B. Brandriff
565-200	F	66	6	9	81	81.48	226.75	Fujii/Hayashi/Furseth
565-205	F	49	10	14	73	67.12	82	Loughman, Fujii, Hayashi
565-210	P	45	12	28	85	52.94	187.83	Leong/ Loughman/ Lucken/ White/ Foley/ Williams/ Strangberg/ Fujii/ Hayashi
570-185	P	68	6	7	81	83.95	369	Larkin/ Methvin/ Schnitzen/ Vaughn
570-190	F	64	9	5	78	82.05	373.75	Morrow, Mathews
570-195	F	46	14	23	83	55.42	74.5	Rice
570-200	F	42	18	9	69	60.86	48.25	Wills/ Glover
570-205	P	40	20	19	79	50.63	67.25	Leong/ White/ Williams/ Strangberg, Glover
570-210	P	10	11	17	38	26.31	24.25	Leong/ White
575-180	P	39	33	8	80	48.75	103.3	D. Lewis/ Herr
575-185	F	63	29	10	102	61.7	204.9	D. Lewis/ Herr/ Methvin
575-190	F	55	14	13	82	67.07	141.45	Stern/ Methvin

Block #	P/F	Confirmed	Probable	Possible	Total	%	Hours	Observers
575-195	F	75	4	5	84	92.2	469.5	Wenninger/ Schnitzen
575-200	F	43	15	21	79	54.43	111.5	Abel/ Kirshen/ Wight/ Willa
575-205	P	52	16	16	84	61.9	61.75	Abel, Glover
580-180	P	48	15	11	74	64.86	31.5	Richmond
580-185	F	57	11	14	82	69.51	45.25	Richmond/ Methvin
580-190	F	29	7	18	54	53.7	25.5	Luther/ Hedgecock
580-195	F	35	8	8	51	68.62	43.5	Safier
580-200	F	25	13	12	50	50	18.75	Jamerson, Wight
580-205	F	35	4	5	44	79.54	11	Glover
580-210	P	18	11	13	42	42.85	8	Rottenborn, Wight, Glover
585-175	P	42	15	9	66	63.63	14.5	Luther/ Glover
585-180	P	41	16	17	74	55.4	19	Luther/ Glover
585-185	F	36	12	3	51	70.58	27	Safier
585-190	F	72	7	4	83	86.74	297.5	MacEachern
585-195	F	37	23	21	81	45.67	54	Herr
585-200	F	28	14	6	48	58.33	30.5	Fernandez/ Herr, Glover
585-205	F	27	11	7	45	60	25.75	Hedgecock/ Glover
585-210	P	17	14	7	38	44.73	7.5	Rottenborn/ Hedgecock
590-175	P	51	10	7	68	75	22.45	Glover
590-180	F	36	8	7	51	70.58	12.5	Glover
590-185	F	61	15	10	86	70.93	99.5	Diernisse/ Gibbs/ Glover
590-190	F	59	6	8	73	80.82	126	Finger/ Plant
590-195	F	62	4	8	74	83.78	175	Finger/ Plant/ Leong
590-200	F	24	11	7	42	57.14	13.25	Glover
590-205	F	27	8	4	39	69.23	5.75	Glover
590-210	P	18	7	9	34	52.94	4.75	Glover
595-175	P	19	8	8	35	54.28	8	Glover
595-180	F	32	8	7	47	68.08	18.5	Glover
595-185	F	52	19	17	88	59.09	223	Sproul
595-190	F	43	9	26	78	55.12	64.25	Brandriff/ Glover
595-195	F	35	15	21	71	49.25	21.5	Glover
595-200	F	36	13	15	64	56.25	42	Blandin/ Glover
595-205	F	26	6	1	33	78.78	143.5	Scruggs/ Glover
595-210	P	2	7	5	14	14.28	1.25	Glover
600-175	P	2	1	0	3	66.66	0.5	Glover
600-180	F	35	10	10	55	63.63	22.25	Glover
600-185	F	44	15	13	72	61.11	32.55	Glover
600-190	F	46	8	9	63	73.01	17.75	Glover
600-195	F	33	13	6	52	63.46	20	Glover/ Blandin
600-200	F	43	9	5	57	75.43	126.5	Summerhill/ Cannon/ Glover
600-205	P	28	12	10	50	56	28	Bonner/ Scruggs/ Glover
605-175	P	6	2	3	11	54.54	5	Glover

Block #	P/F	Confirmed	Probable	Possible	Total	%	Hours	Observers
605-180	F	23	10	8	41	56.09	9	Glover
605-185	F	31	14	18	63	49.2	28.25	S. Hein/ C. Hein, Wenninger, Glover
605-190	F	46	19	13	78	58.97	52	S. Hein/ C. Hein, Stern, Glover
605-195	F	20	8	13	41	48.78	19.5	Bonner, Glover
605-200	F	24	6	7	37	64.86	6.25	Glover
605-205	P	30	4	7	41	73.17	29.25	Glover/ Wallace
610-180	P	22	20	7	49	44.89	13.75	Glover
610-185	F	34	8	18	60	56.66	20	Gibbs/ Diernisse/ Glover
610-190	F	32	14	21	67	47.76	20.75	Glover
610-195	F	19	8	13	40	47.5	8.5	Glover
610-200	F	22	3	9	34	64.7	9	Glover
610-205	F	34	21	18	73	46.57	44.75	Bettencourt/ Glover
615-185	F	14	8	5	27	51.85	5	Glover
615-190	F	21	10	6	37	56.75	13	Glover
615-195	F	23	4	6	33	69.69	4.5	Glover
615-200	F	24	6	4	34	70.58	4.75	Glover
615-205	F	37	10	24	71	52.11	103.5	Griffeth/ Glover
615-210	P	37	12	12	61	60.65	55	Carver/ Glover
620-185	F	25	7	9	41	60.97	11.35	Carratello/ Glover
620-190	F	35	6	5	46	76.08	11.5	Glover
620-195	F	26	12	8	46	56.21	9.5	Glover
620-200	F	32	8	6	46	69.56	8	Glover
620-205	F	20	12	11	43	46.51	7.75	Glover
620-210	P	14	6	6	26	53.84	2.5	Glover
625-185	P	7	14	2	23	30.43	4.75	Glover
625-190	P	7	9	8	24	29.16	2.5	Roberson
625-195	P	23	6	9	38	60.52	9	Glover
625-200	P	2	0	0	2	100	1	Glover

REFERENCES CITED

Allen AS. 1917. Western Robin and Sierra Junco Nesting in Alameda Co., California. The Condor 19(6):185.

Allen AS. 1943. Additional Notes on the Birds of a Berkeley Hillside. The Condor 45(4):149–57.

Altman B, Sallabanks R. 2000. Olive-sided Flycatcher (*Contopus cooperi*), The Birds of North America Online (A. Poole, Ed.). Ithaca: Cornell Lab of Ornithology; Retrieved from the Birds of North America Online: http://bna.birds.cornell.edu/bna/species/502doi:10.2173/bna.502

Ammon EM, Gilbert WM. 1999. Wilson's Warbler (*Wilsonia pusilla*), The Birds of North America Online (A. Poole, Ed.). Ithaca: Cornell Lab of Ornithology; Retrieved from the Birds of North America Online: http://bna.birds.cornell.edu/bna/species/478doi:10.2173/bna.478

Arcese P, Sogge MK, Marr AB, Patten MA. 2002. Song Sparrow (*Melospiza melodia*), The Birds of North America Online (A. Poole, Ed.). Ithaca: Cornell Lab of Ornithology; Retrieved from the Birds of North America Online: http://bna.birds.cornell.edu/bna/species/704doi:10.2173/bna.704

Arnold JR. 1935. The Changing Distribution of the Northern Mockingbird in California. The Condor 37(4):193–9.

Arnold JR. 1980. Distribution of the Mockingbird in California. Western Birds 11(2).

Austin JE, Miller MR. 1995. Northern Pintail (*Anas acuta*), The Birds of North America Online (A. Poole, Ed.). Ithaca: Cornell Lab of Ornithology; Retrieved from the Birds of North America Online: http://bna.birds.cornell.edu/bna/species/163doi:10.2173/bna.163

Baltosser WH, Russell SM. 2000. Black-chinned Hummingbird (*Archilochus alexandri*), The Birds of North America Online (A. Poole, Ed.). Ithaca: Cornell Lab of Ornithology; Retrieved from the Birds of North America Online: http://bna.birds.cornell.edu/bna/species/495

Banks RC, Springer PF. 1994. A century of population trends of waterfowl in western North America. In: Jehl JR, Johnson NK editors. A Century of Avifaunal Change in Western North America: Proceedings of an International Symposium at the Centennial Meeting of the Cooper Ornithological Society, Sacramento, California, April 17, 1993. Studies in Avian Biology No. 15:134–146.

Beason RC. 1995. Horned Lark (*Eremophila alpestris*), The Birds of North America Online (A. Poole, Ed.). Ithaca: Cornell Lab of Ornithology; Retrieved from the Birds of North America Online: http://bna.birds.cornell.edu/bna/species/195doi:10.2173/bna.195

Beedy EC. 2008. In: Shuford, WD, Gardali T, editors. California Bird Species of Special Concern 2008: a ranked assessment of species, subspecies, and distinct populations of birds of immediate conservation concern in California. Studies of Western Birds 1.

Beedy EC, Granholm SL. 1985. Discovering Sierra Birds. Yosemite Natural History Association and Sequoia Natural History Association. 229 p.

Beedy EC, Hamilton III WJ. 1999. Tricolored Blackbird (*Agelaius tricolor*), The Birds of North America Online (A. Poole, Ed.). Ithaca: Cornell Lab of Ornithology; Retrieved from the Birds of North America Online: http://bna.birds.cornell.edu/bna/species/423doi:10.2173/bna.423

Belding L. 1890. Land birds of the Pacific District. San Francisco, CA: California Academy of Science. 274 p.

Bent AC. 1948. Life histories of North American nuthatches, wrens, thrashers, and their allies No. 195. Washington DC: US Nat'l Museum Bulletin. 475 p.

Boarman WI, Heinrich B. 1999. Common Raven (*Corvus corax*), The Birds of North America Online (A. Poole, Ed.). Ithaca: Cornell Lab of Ornithology; Retrieved from the Birds of North America Online: http://bna.birds.cornell.edu/bna/species/476doi:10.2173/bna.476

Bousman WG. 2007. Breeding avifaunal changes in the San Francisco Bay Area 1927–2005. Western Birds 38:102–136.

Bousman WG. 2007. Breeding Bird Atlas of Santa Clara County, California. Cupertino, CA: Santa Clara Valley Audubon Society. 547 p.

Brisbin Jr. IL, Pratt HD, Mowbray TB. 2002 American Coot (*Fulica americana*) and Hawaiian Coot (*Fulica alai*). In: Poole A, Gill F, editors. The Birds of North America No. 697. Academy of National Science and American Ornithologists' Union, Philadelphia and Washington DC. USA.

Brown CR, Brown MB. 1995. Cliff Swallow (*Petrochelidon pyrrhonota*), The Birds of North America Online (A. Poole, Ed.). Ithaca: Cornell Lab of Ornithology; Retrieved from the Birds of North America Online: http://bna.birds.cornell.edu/bna/species/149doi:10.2173/bna.149

Brown CR, Brown MB. 1999. Barn Swallow (*Hirundo rustica*), The Birds of North America Online (A. Poole, Ed.). Ithaca: Cornell Lab of Ornithology; Retrieved from the Birds of North America Online: http://bna.birds.cornell.edu/bna/species/452doi:10.2173/bna.452

Brown CR, Knott AM, Damrose EJ. 1992. Violet-green Swallow (*Tachycineta thalassina*), The Birds of North America Online (A. Poole, Ed.). Ithaca: Cornell Lab of Ornithology; Retrieved from the Birds of North America Online: http://bna.birds.cornell.edu/bna/species/014doi:10.2173/bna.14

Burridge B, editor. 1995. Sonoma County Breeding Bird Atlas. Santa Rosa, CA: Madrone Audubon Society. 216 p.

Cabe PR. 1993. European Starling (*Sturnus vulgaris*), The Birds of North America Online (A. Poole, Ed.). Ithaca: Cornell Lab of Ornithology; Retrieved from the Birds of North America Online: http://bna.birds.cornell.edu/bna/species/048doi:10.2173/bna.48

Cannings RJ, Angell T. 2001. Western Screech-Owl (*Megascops kennicottii*), The Birds of North America Online (A. Poole, Ed.). Ithaca: Cornell Lab of Ornithology; Retrieved from the Birds of North America Online: http://bna.birds.cornell.edu/bna/species/597

Chan Y, Spautz H. 2008. In: Shuford WD, Gardali T, editors. California Bird Species of Special Concern 2008: a ranked assessment of species, subspecies, and distinct populations of birds of immediate conservation concern in California. Studies of Western Birds 1.

Ciaranca MA, Allin CC, Jones GS. 1997. Mute Swan (*Cygnus olor*), The Birds of North America Online (A. Poole, Ed.). Ithaca: Cornell Lab of Ornithology; Retrieved from the Birds of North America Online: http://bna.birds.cornell.edu/bna/species/273doi:10.2173/bna.273

Cicero C. 2000. Oak Titmouse (*Baeolophus inornatus*), The Birds of North America Online (A. Poole, Ed.). Ithaca: Cornell Lab of Ornithology; Retrieved from the Birds of North America Online: http://bna.birds.cornell.edu/bna/species/485adoi:10.2173/bna.485

Chu M, Walsberg G. 1999. Phainopepla (*Phainopepla nitens*), The Birds of North America Online (A. Poole, Ed.). Ithaca: Cornell Lab of Ornithology; Retrieved from the Birds of North America Online: http://bna.birds.cornell.edu/bna/species/415doi:10.2173/bna.415

Clabaugh ED. 1924. Western Bluebird Nesting in Berkeley. The Condor 26(6):228.

Contra Costa County Watershed Atlas. [Internet]. Contra Costa County: Contra Costa County Community Development Department and the Contra Costa Watershed Forum.; c2003 [cited.]. Available from http://cocowaterweb.org/resources/ccwf-publications/watershed-atlas.

Conway CJ. 1995 Virginia Rail (*Rallus limicola*), The Birds of North America Online (A. Poole, Ed.). Ithaca: Cornell Lab of Ornithology; Retrieved from the Birds of North America Online: http://bna.birds.cornell.edu/bna/species/173doi:10.2173/bna.173

Curl AL. 1956. March Trip to Tilden Park. The Gull 38:20.

Curl AL. 1957. March Trip to Tilden Park and Bear Creek Rd. The Gull 39:27.

Curry RL, Peterson AT, Langen TA. 2002. Western Scrub-Jay (*Aphelocoma californica*), The Birds of North America Online (A. Poole, Ed.). Ithaca: Cornell Lab of Ornithology; Retrieved from the Birds of North America Online: http://bna.birds.cornell.edu/bna/species/712doi:10.2173/bna.712

Cuthbert FJ, Wires LR. 1999. Caspian Tern (*Sterna caspia*), The Birds of North America Online (A. Poole, Ed.). Ithaca: Cornell Lab of Ornithology; Retrieved from the Birds of North America Online: http://bna.birds.cornell.edu/bna/species/403doi:10.2173/bna.403

Dahlsten DL, Brennan LA, Mccallum DA, Gaunt SL. 2002. Chestnut-backed Chickadee (*Poecile rufescens*), The Birds of North America Online (A. Poole, Ed.). Ithaca: Cornell Lab of Ornithology; Retrieved from the Birds of North America Online: http://bna.birds.cornell.edu/bna/species/689doi:10.2173/bna.689

Dark SJ, Gutierrez RJ, Gould Jr. GI. 1998. The Barred Owl (*Strix varia*) Invasion in California. The Auk 115(1):50–6.

Dawson WL. 1923. The Birds of California Vol. 1–4. San Diego: South Moulton Co. 2400 p.

Derrickson KC, Breitwisch R. 1992. Northern Mockingbird (*Mimus polyglottos*), The Birds of North America Online (A. Poole, Ed.). Ithaca: Cornell Lab of Ornithology; Retrieved from the Birds of North America Online: http://bna.birds.cornell.edu/bna/species/007doi:10.2173/bna.7

DeSante DF, George TL. 1994. Population Trends in the Landbirds of Western North America. In: Jehl JR, Johnson NK editors. A Century of Avifaunal Change in Western North America: Proceedings of an International Symposium at the Centennial Meeting of the Cooper Ornithological Society, Sacramento, California, April 17, 1993. Studies in Avian Biology 15:173-190.

Dixon J. 1920. Nesting of the Olive-sided Flycatcher in Berkeley, California. The Condor 22(6):200–2.

Dixon KL. 1954. Some Ecological Relations of Chickadees and Titmice in Central California. The Condor 56(3):113–24.

Drilling N, Titman R, Mckinney Frank. 2002. Mallard (*Anas platyrhynchos*), The Birds of North America Online (A. Poole, Ed.). Ithaca: Cornell Lab of Ornithology; Retrieved from the Birds of North America Online: http://bna.birds.cornell.edu/bna/species/658doi:10.2173/bna.658

Eckert AW. 1973. The Owls of North America. Doubleday, New York. 287 p.

Eddleman WR, Flores RE, Legare ML. 1994. Black Rail (*Laterallus jamaicensis*), The Birds of North America Online (A. Poole, Ed.). Ithaca: Cornell Lab of Ornithology; Retrieved from the Birds of North America Online: http://bna.birds.cornell.edu/bna/species/123doi:10.2173/bna.123

Ellison WG. 1992. Blue-gray Gnatcatcher (*Polioptila caerulea*), The Birds of North America Online (A. Poole, Ed.). Ithaca: Cornell Lab of Ornithology; Retrieved from the Birds of North America Online: http://bna.birds.cornell.edu/bna/species/023doi:10.2173/bna.23

Emerson WO. 1900. Notes from Haywards, California. The Condor 2(1):19.

England AS, Bechard MJ, Houston CS. 1997. Swainson's Hawk (*Buteo swainsoni*), The Birds of North America Online (A. Poole, Ed.). Ithaca: Cornell Lab of Ornithology; Retrieved from the Birds of North America Online: http://bna.birds.cornell.edu/bna/species/265doi:10.2173/bna.265

Erickson MM. 1938. Territory, annual cycle, and numbers in a population of wren-tits (*Chamaea fasciata*). University of California Publications in Zoology. 42:247–334.

Erickson RA. 1989. Checklist of the Birds of the East Bay Region. Golden Gate Audubon Society:San Francisco, CA.

Ertter B, Bowerman ML. 2002. The Flowering Plants and Ferns of Mt. Diablo, California. 2002. Grass Valley, CA: California Native Plant Society. 424 p.

Evens JG, Page GW, Laymon SA, Stallcup RW. 1991. Distribution, relative abundance, and status of the California Black Rail in western North America. The Condor 93(4):952–66.

Fitton SD. 2008. In: Shuford WD, Gardali T, editors. California Bird Species of Special Concern 2008: a ranked assessment of species, subspecies, and distinct populations of birds of immediate conservation concern in California. Studies of Western Birds 1.

Gallagher S . 1997. Atlas of Breeding Birds, Orange County, California. Irvine, California: Sea and Sage Audubon Press. 223 p.

Gammonley JH.1996. Cinnamon Teal (*Anas cyanoptera*), The Birds of North America Online (A. Poole, Ed.). Ithaca: Cornell Lab of Ornithology; Retrieved from the Birds of North America Online: http://bna.birds.cornell.edu/bna/species/209doi:10.2173/bna.209

Gardali T. 2008 In: Shuford WD, Gardali T, editors. California Bird Species of Special Concern 2008: a ranked assessment of species, subspecies, and distinct populations of birds of immediate conservation concern in California. Studies of Western Birds 1.

Geupel GR, Ballard G. 2002. Wrentit (*Chamaea fasciata*), The Birds of North America Online (A. Poole, Ed.). Ithaca: Cornell Lab of Ornithology; Retrieved from the Birds of North America Online: http://bna.birds.cornell.edu/bna/species/654doi:10.2173/bna.654

Gibbs JP, Melvin S, Reid FA. 1992. American Bittern (*Botaurus lentiginosus*), The Birds of North America Online (A. Poole, Ed.). Ithaca: Cornell Lab of Ornithology; Retrieved from the Birds of North America Online: http://bna.birds.cornell.edu/bna/species/018doi:10.2173/bna.18

Gill Jr. R. 1977. Breeding Avifauna of the South San Francisco Bay Estuary. Western Birds 8(1):1–12.

Gilliam H . 2002. Weather of the San Francisco Bay Region. Berkeley, California: University of California Press. 115 p.

Guillion GW. 1954. The reproductive cycle of American Coots in California. The Auk 71:366–412.

Green M, Edson L. 2004. 2004 Tricolored Blackbird April Survey. Central Valley Bird Club Bulletin 7(2):23–31.

Greene E, Davison W, Muehter VR. 1998. Steller's Jay (*Cyanocitta stelleri*), The Birds of North America Online (A. Poole, Ed.). Ithaca: Cornell Lab of Ornithology; Retrieved from the Birds of North America Online: http://bna.birds.cornell.edu/bna/species/343doi:10.2173/bna.343

Grinnell H. 1935. Minutes of the Cooper Club Meetings Northern Division. The Condor 37(2):92.

Grinnell J. 1911. Distribution of the Mockingbird in California. The Auk 28(3).

Grinnell J. 1914. A Second List of the Birds of the Berkeley Campus. The Condor 16(1):28–40.

Grinnell J, Linsdale JM. 1936. Vertebrate Animals of Point Lobos Reserve 1934–1935. Washington DC: Carnegie Institute of Washington. 160 p.

Grinnell J, Miller AH. 1944. The distribution of the birds of California. Pacific Coast Avifauna (27).

Grinnell J, Wythe MW. 1927. Directory to the bird-life of the San Francisco Bay Region. Pacific Coast Avifauna (18).

Grubb Jr. TC, Pravosudov VV. 2008. White-breasted Nuthatch (*Sitta carolinensis*), The Birds of North America Online (A. Poole, Ed.). Ithaca: Cornell Lab of Ornithology; Retrieved from the Birds of North America Online: http://bna.birds.cornell.edu/bna/species/054doi:10.2173/bna.54

Guinan JA, Gowaty PA, Eltzroth EK. 2008. Western Bluebird (*Sialia mexicana*), The Birds of North America Online (A. Poole, Ed.). Ithaca: Cornell Lab of Ornithology; Retrieved from the Birds of North America Online: http://bna.birds.cornell.edu/bna/species/510doi:10.2173/bna.510

Guzy MJ, Ritchison G. 1999. Common Yellowthroat (*Geothlypis trichas*), The Birds of North America Online (A. Poole, Ed.). Ithaca: Cornell Lab of Ornithology; Retrieved from the Birds of North America Online: http://bna.birds.cornell.edu/bna/species/448doi:10.2173/bna.448

Guzy MJ, Lowther PE. 1997. Black-throated Gray Warbler (*Dendroica nigrescens*), The Birds of North America Online (A. Poole, Ed.). Ithaca: Cornell Lab of Ornithology; Retrieved from the Birds of North America Online: http://bna.birds.cornell.edu/bna/species/319

Hejl SJ, Newlon KR, Mcfadzen ME, Young JS, Ghalambor CK. 2002. Brown Creeper (*Certhia americana*), The Birds of North America Online (A. Poole, Ed.). Ithaca: Cornell Lab of Ornithology; Retrieved from the Birds of North America Online: http://bna.birds.cornell.edu/bna/species/669doi:10.2173/bna.669

Hepp GR, Bellrose FC. 1995. Wood Duck (*Aix sponsa*), The Birds of North America Online (A. Poole, Ed.). Ithaca: Cornell Lab of Ornithology; Retrieved from the Birds of North America Online: http://bna.birds.cornell.edu/bna/species/169doi:10.2173/bna.169

Herman SG, Kirven MN, Risebrough RW. 1970. The Peregrine Falcon Decline in California: A Preliminary Review. Audubon Field Notes 24:609–13.

Hertz PE, Remsen JV, Zones SI. 1976. Ecological Complementarity of Three Sympatric Parids in a California Oak Woodland. The Condor 78(3):307–16.

Hill GE. 1995. Black-headed Grosbeak (*Pheucticus melanocephalus*), The Birds of North America Online (A. Poole, Ed.). Ithaca: Cornell Lab of Ornithology; Retrieved from the Birds of North America Online: http://bna.birds.cornell.edu/bna/species/143doi:10.2173/bna.143

Hobson KA. 1997. Pelagic Cormorant (*Phalacrocorax pelagicus*), The Birds of North America Online (A. Poole, Ed.). Ithaca: Cornell Lab of Ornithology; Retrieved from the Birds of North America Online: http://bna.birds.cornell.edu/bna/species/282doi:10.2173/bna.282

Hutchings JM. 1872. Scenes of Wonder and Curiosity in California: A Tourist's Guide to the Yo-semite Valley. New York, NY: Roman. 292 p.

Hunter JE, Fix D, Schmidt GA, Power JC. 2005. Atlas of Breeding Birds of Humboldt County, California. Eureka, California: Redwood Region Audubon Society. 440.

Jaramillo, A. 2008. In: Shuford WD, Gardali T, editors. California Bird Species of Special Concern 2008: A ranked assessment of species, subspecies, and distinct populations of birds of immediate conservation concern in California. Studies of Western Birds 1.

Jepson Online Interchange for California Floristics. [Internet]. UC Berkeley: Jepson Flora Project.; ©2008 [cited 2008 Dec]. Available from http://ucjeps.berkeley.edu/interchange.html

Jewett SG. 1942. The European Starling in California. The Condor 44(2):79.

Johnson K. 1995. Green-winged Teal (*Anas crecca*), The Birds of North America Online (A. Poole, Ed.). Ithaca: Cornell Lab of Ornithology; Retrieved from the Birds of North America Online: http://bna.birds.cornell.edu/bna/species/193doi:10.2173/bna.193

Johnson NK, Cicero C. 1985. The Breeding Avifauna of San Benito Mountain, California: Evidence for Change Over One-Half Century. Western Birds 16(1):1–23.

Johnston DW. 1952. Western Gull Breeding in San Francisco Bay. The Gull 34: 36.

Kellogg M. 1924. Western Tanagers in Berkeley in Midsummer. The Condor 26 (6): 227–8.

Kelly JP, Etienne K, Strong, C, McCaustland M, Parkes ML. Annotated atlas and implications for the conservation of heron and egret nesting colonies in the San Francisco Bay area. [Internet]. Stinson Beach, CA.; ©2006 [cited 2008 Oct.]. Available from http://www.egret.org/atlas

Kennedy ED, White DW. 1997. Bewick's Wren (*Thryomanes bewickii*), The Birds of North America Online (A. Poole, Ed.). Ithaca: Cornell Lab of Ornithology; Retrieved from the Birds of North America Online: http://bna.birds.cornell.edu/bna/species/315doi:10.2173/bna.315

Keppie DM, Braun CE. 2000. Band-tailed Pigeon (*Patagioenas fasciata*), The Birds of North America Online (A. Poole, Ed.). Ithaca: Cornell Lab of Ornithology; Retrieved from the Birds of North America Online: http://bna.birds.cornell.edu/bna/species/530

Kessel B. 1953. Distribution and migration of the European starling in North America. The Condor 55(2):49–67.

Kingery HE, Ghalambor CK. 2001. Pygmy Nuthatch (*Sitta pygmaea*), The Birds of North America Online (A. Poole, Ed.). Ithaca: Cornell Lab of Ornithology; Retrieved from the Birds of North America Online: http://bna.birds.cornell.edu/bna/species/567doi:10.2173/bna.567

Kirk DA, Mossman MJ. 1998. Turkey Vulture (*Cathartes aura*), The Birds of North America Online (A. Poole, Ed.). Ithaca: Cornell Lab of Ornithology; Retrieved from the Birds of North America Online: http://bna.birds.cornell.edu/bna/species/339doi:10.2173/bna.339

Kochert MN, Steenhof K, McIntyre CL, Craig EH. 2002. Golden Eagle (*Aquila chrysaetos*), The Birds of North America Online (A. Poole, Ed.). Ithaca: Cornell Lab of Ornithology; Retrieved from the Birds of North America Online: http://bna.birds.cornell.edu/bna/species/684doi:10.2173/bna.684

Koenig WD, Stacey PB, Stanback MT, Mumme RL. 1995. Acorn Woodpecker (*Melanerpes formicivorus*), The Birds of North America Online (A. Poole, Ed.). Ithaca: Cornell Lab of Ornithology; Retrieved from the Birds of North America Online: http://bna.birds.cornell.edu/bna/species/194doi:10.2173/bna.194

Kunzmann MR, Ellison K, Purcell KL,. Johnson RR, Haight LT. 2002. California Towhee (*Pipilo crissalis*), The Birds of North America Online (A. Poole, Ed.). Ithaca: Cornell Lab of Ornithology; Retrieved from the Birds of North America Online: http://bna.birds.cornell.edu/bna/species/632doi:10.2173/bna.632

Lidicker WZ, McCollum FC. 1979. Canada Goose Established as a Breeding Species in San Francisco Bay. Western Birds 10(3):159–62.

Lowther PE. 1993. Brown-headed Cowbird (*Molothrus ater*), The Birds of North America Online (A. Poole, Ed.). Ithaca: Cornell Lab of Ornithology; Retrieved from the Birds of North America Online: http://bna.birds.cornell.edu/bna/species/047doi:10.2173/bna.47

Lowther PE, Cink CL. 2006. House Sparrow (*Passer domesticus*), The Birds of North America Online (A. Poole, Ed.). Ithaca: Cornell Lab of Ornithology; Retrieved from the Birds of North America Online: http://bna.birds.cornell.edu/bna/species/012

Mack DE, Yong W. 2000. Swainson's Thrush (*Catharus ustulatus*), The Birds of North America Online (A. Poole, Ed.). Ithaca: Cornell Lab of Ornithology; Retrieved from the Birds of North America Online: http://bna.birds.cornell.edu/bna/species/540doi:10.2173/bna.540

Manolis T. 1978. Status of the Black Rail in central California. Western Birds 9: 151–158.

Marschner J. 2001. California 1850: A Snapshot in Time. Sacramento, CA: Coleman Ranch Press. 280 p.

Marshall JT. 1948. Ecologic Races of Song Sparrows in the San Francisco Bay Region: Part I. Habitat and Abundance. The Condor 50(5):193–215.

Marshall JT, Dedrick KG. 1994. Endemic Song Sparrows and Yellowthroats of San Francisco Bay. In: Jehl JR, Johnson NK editors. A Century of Avifaunal Change in Western North America: Proceedings of an International Symposium at the Centennial Meeting of the Cooper Ornithological Society, Sacramento, California, April 17, 1993. Studies in Avian Biology 15:316–327.

Martin SG. 2002. Brewer's Blackbird (*Euphagus cyanocephalus*), The Birds of North America Online (A. Poole, Ed.). Ithaca: Cornell Lab of Ornithology; Retrieved from the Birds of North America Online: http://bna.birds.cornell.edu/bna/species/616doi:10.2173/bna.616

McCain. 1932. Minutes of the Cooper Club Meetings. The Condor 34(5):234

McCaskie G, Liston S, Rapley WA. 1974. First Nesting of Black Skimmer in California. The Condor 76(3):337–8.

McCaskie G, Stallcup R, DeBenedictis P. 1966. Notes on the Distribution of Certain Icterids and Tanagers in California. The Condor 68(6):595–7.

McCaskie G, Suffell S. 1971. Black Skimmers at the Salton Sea, California. Western Birds 2(2):69–71.

McPhee J. 1994. Assembling California. New York, NY:Farrar, Straus and Giroux. 224 p.

Miller AH. 1929. A New Race of Black-Chinned Sparrow from the San Francisco Bay District. The Condor 31(5):205–7.

Miller EV. 1941. Behavior of the Bewick Wren. The Condor 43(2):81–99.

Molina KC. 2008. In: Shuford, WD, Gardali T, editors. California Bird Species of Special Concern 2008: a ranked assessment of species, subspecies, and distinct populations of birds of immediate conservation concern in California. Studies of Western Birds 1.

Napa-Solano Audubon Society. 2003. Breeding Birds of Napa County, California: an illustrated atlas of nesting birds. Vallejo, CA: Napa-Solano Audubon Society. 204 p.

National Audubon Society 2005 Audubon WatchList. [Internet]. New York, NY: National Audubon Society; ©2005 [cited 2008]. Available from http://audubon2.org/webapp/watchlist/viewWatchlist.jsp

National Audubon Society Christmas Bird Count Historical Results. [Internet]. New York, NY: National Audubon Society.; ©2002 [cited 2008]. Available from http://www.audubon.org/bird/cbc/hr/index.html

Palmer TS. 1921. Notes on Some Birds of the Berkeley Campus. The Condor 23(5):163–4.

Parsons KC, Master TL. 2000. Snowy Egret (*Egretta thula*), The Birds of North America Online (A. Poole, Ed.). Ithaca: Cornell Lab of Ornithology; Retrieved from the Birds of North America Online: http://bna.birds.cornell.edu/bna/species/489doi:10.2173/bna.489

Patten MA. 2001. The roles of habitat and signaling in speciation: Evidence from a contact zone of two Song Sparrow (*Melospiza melodia*) subspecies. Ph.D. dissertation, Univ. Calif., Riverside.

Phillips AR. 1975. The Migrations of Allen's and other Hummingbirds. The Condor 77(2): 196-205.

Pickwell G, Smith E. 1938. The Texas Nighthawk in its Summer Home. The Condor 40(5):193-215.

Pitelka FA. 1951. Breeding seasons of hummingbirds near Santa Barbara, California. The Condor 53(4):198–201.

Poole A, Bierregaard RO, Martell MS. 2002. Osprey (*Pandion haliaetus*), The Birds of North America Online (A. Poole, Ed.). Ithaca: Cornell Lab of Ornithology; Retrieved from the Birds of North America Online: http://bna.birds.cornell.edu/bna/species/683doi:10.2173/bna.683

Predatory Bird Research Center. 1997. A population study of Golden Eagles in the Altamont Pass Wind Resource Area; second-year progress report. Santa Cruz, CA: University of CA Santa Cruz. 99 p.

Purcell KL, Verner J. 1998. Density and reproductive success of California Towhees. Conservation Biology 12(2):442–50.

Remsen Jr JV. 1978. Bird Species of Special Concern in California: An annotated list of declining or vulnerable bird species. Wildlife Management Branch Administration. Report 78-1. California Department of Fish and Game, Sacramento. Available from http://www.prbo.org/cms/docs/ecol/Remsenlist1978.pdf

Reynolds MD. 1995. Yellow-billed Magpie (*Pica nuttalli*), The Birds of North America Online (A. Poole, Ed.). Ithaca: Cornell Lab of Ornithology; Retrieved from the Birds of North America Online: http://bna.birds.cornell.edu/bna/species/180doi:10.2173/bna.180

Ridgeway R. 1889. Bewick's Wren (*Thryothorus bewickii*). Ornithology of Illinois 1(1):92–3.

Rising JD, Williams PL. 1999. Bullock's Oriole (*Icterus bullockii*), The Birds of North America Online (A. Poole, Ed.). Ithaca: Cornell Lab of Ornithology; Retrieved from the Birds of North America Online: http://bna.birds.cornell.edu/bna/species/416

Roberson D, Tenney C, editors. 1993. Atlas of the Breeding Birds of Monterey County, California. Carmel, CA: Monterey Peninsula Audubon Society. 438 p.

Robertson RJ, Stutchbury BJ, Cohen RR. 1992. Tree Swallow (*Tachycineta bicolor*), The Birds of North America Online (A. Poole, Ed.). Ithaca: Cornell Lab of Ornithology; Retrieved from the Birds of North America Online: http://bna.birds.cornell.edu/bna/species/011doi:10.2173/bna.11

Rothstein SI. 1994. The cowbird's invasion of the Far West: history, causes and consequences experienced by host species. In: Jehl JR, Johnson NK editors. A Century of Avifaunal Change in Western North America:

Proceedings of an International Symposium at the Centennial Meeting of the Cooper Ornithological Society, Sacramento, California, April 17, 1993. Studies in Avian Biology 15:301–315.

Root RB. 1964. Ecological Interactions of the Chestnut-Backed Chickadee Following a Range Extension. The Condor 66(3):229–38

Root RB. 1969. The Behavior and Reproductive Success of the Blue-Gray Gnatcatcher. The Condor 71(1):16–31.

Ryder RA, Manry DE. 1994. White-faced Ibis (*Plegadis chihi*), The Birds of North America Online (A. Poole, Ed.). Ithaca: Cornell Lab of Ornithology; Retrieved from the Birds of North America Online: http://bna.birds.cornell.edu/bna/species/130.

Sauer JR, Hines JE, Fallon J. 2008. The North American Breeding Bird Survey, Results and Analysis 1966–2007. Version 5.15.2008. USGS Patuxent Wildlife Research Center, Laurel, MD Available from http://www.mbr-pwrc.usgs.gov/bbs/bbs.html.

Seibert ML. 1942. Occurrence and Nesting of Some Birds in the San Francisco Bay Region. The Condor 44(2):68–72.

Sequoia Audubon Society. 2001. San Mateo County Breeding Bird Atlas. Millbrae, CA: Sequoia Audubon Society. 223 p.

Shuford WD, Gardali T, editors. 2008. California Bird Species of Special Concern: A ranked assessment of species, subspecies, and distinct populations of birds of immediate conservation concern in California. Studies of Western Birds 1. Western Field Ornithologists, Camarillo, California, and California Department of Fish and Game, Sacramento.

Shuford WD. 1993. The Marin County Breeding Bird Atlas: a distributional and natural history of coastal California birds. Bolinas, CA: Bushtit Books. 479 p.

Sibley CG. 1952. The Birds of the South San Francisco Bay Region. Unpublished mimeograph. San Jose State University, San Jose, CA.

Sibley CG. 1953. Forster Terns Breeding on San Francisco Bay, California. The Condor 55(5):278–9.

Sloan D. 2006. Geology of the San Francisco Bay Region. Berkeley, California: University of California Press. 360 p.

Sloane SA. 2001. Bushtit (*Psaltriparus minimus*), The Birds of North America Online (A. Poole, Ed.). Ithaca: Cornell Lab of Ornithology; Retrieved from the Birds of North America Online: http://bna.birds.cornell.edu/bna/species/598doi:10.2173/bna.598

Small A. 1994. California Birds: Their Status and Distribution. San Diego California: San Diego Natural History Museum. 360 p.

Sogge MK, Gilbert WM, Van Riper III C. 1994. Orange-crowned Warbler (*Vermivora celata*), The Birds of North America Online (A. Poole, Ed.). Ithaca: Cornell Lab of Ornithology; Retrieved from the Birds of North America Online: http://bna.birds.cornell.edu/bna/species/101doi:10.2173/bna.101

Spautz H, Nur N. 2008. In: Shuford WD, Gardali T, editors. California Bird Species of Special Concern 2008: a ranked assessment of species, subspecies, and distinct populations of birds of immediate conservation concern in California. Studies of Western Birds 1.

State and Federally Listed Endangered and Threatened Animals of California. [Internet]. Sacramento, CA: California Department of Fish and Game; ©2009 [cited 2009]. Available from http://www.dfg.ca.gov/biogeodata/cnddb/pdfs/TEAnimals.pdf

State of California Resources Board. 1988. A Guide to Wildlife Habitats of California. (K. Mayer, W. Laudenslayer Jr Eds.) Department of Fish and Game: Sacramento, CA. 166 p.

Sterling J. 2008. In: Shuford WD, Gardali T, editors. California Bird Species of Special Concern 2008: a ranked assessment of species, subspecies, and distinct populations of birds of immediate conservation concern in California. Studies of Western Birds 1.

Sterling J, Paton P. 1996. Breeding Distribution of Vaux's Swift in California. Western Birds 27(1):30–40.

Sterling J. Welcome to the California County Birding Page [Internet]: c27 March 2009 [cited 2008]. Available from http://www.sterlingbirds.com/california_county_birding.htm

Stoner EA. 1934. Recent Occurrence of the American Egret in the San Francisco Bay Region. The Condor 36(2):57–9.

Storer T. 1926. Range Extensions by the Western Robin in California. The Condor 28(6):264–7.

Storer RW, Nuechterlein GL. 1992. Western Grebe (*Aechmophorus occidentalis*), The Birds of North America Online (A. Poole, Ed.). Ithaca: Cornell Lab of Ornithology; Retrieved from the Birds of North America Online: http://bna.birds.cornell.edu/bna/species/026adoi:10.2173/bna.26a

Tenney CR. 1997. Black-chinned Sparrow (*Spizella atrogularis*), The Birds of North America Online (A. Poole, Ed.). Ithaca: Cornell Lab of Ornithology; Retrieved from the Birds of North America Online: http://bna.birds.cornell.edu/bna/species/270doi:10.2173/bna.270

Unglish WE. 1929. The Texas Nighthawk in Santa Clara County, California. The Condor 31(5):223.

Unitt P. 2004. The San Diego County Bird Atlas. San Diego, CA: San Diego Natural History Museum. 645 p.

U.S. Fish and Wildlife Service (USFWS). 13 June 2002. Review of species that are candidates or proposed for listing as endangered or threatened; annual notice of findings on recycled petitions; annual description of progress on listing actions. Federal Register 67(114):40657–40679.

Verbeek NA. 1973. The exploitation system of the yellow-billed magpie. Berkeley, CA: University California Press Berkeley. 58 p.

Watt DJ, Willoughby EJ. 1999. Lesser Goldfinch (*Carduelis psaltria*), The Birds of North America Online (A. Poole, Ed.). Ithaca: Cornell Lab of Ornithology; Retrieved from the Birds of North America Online: http://bna.birds.cornell.edu/bna/species/392

White CM, Clum NJ, Cade TJ, Hunt WG. 2002. Peregrine Falcon (*Falco peregrinus*), The Birds of North America Online (A. Poole, Ed.). Ithaca: Cornell Lab of Ornithology; Retrieved from the Birds of North America Online: http://bna.birds.cornell.edu/bna/species/660doi:10.2173/bna.660

Winkler DW. 1996. California Gull (*Larus californicus*), The Birds of North America Online (A. Poole, Ed.). Ithaca: Cornell Lab of Ornithology; Retrieved from the Birds of North America Online: http://bna.birds.cornell.edu/bna/species/259

Witmer MC, Mountjoy DJ, Elliot L. 1997. Cedar Waxwing (*Bombycilla cedrorum*), The Birds of North America Online (A. Poole, Ed.). Ithaca: Cornell Lab of Ornithology; Retrieved from the Birds of North America Online: http://bna.birds.cornell.edu/bna/species/309doi:10.2173/bna.309

HOUSE WREN

Index of Bird Names

Species accounts are indicated by bold face; illustrations are indicated by italics.

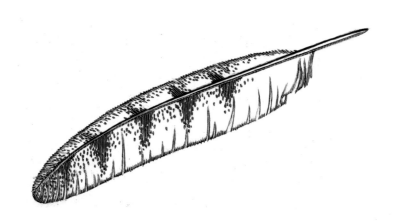